therapeutic recreation:
a helping profession

second edition

therapeutic recreation:
a helping profession

second edition

gerald s. o'morrow
university of georgia

reston publishing company, inc.
a prentice-hall company
reston, virginia

dedicated to the prospective
therapeutic recreation specialist
and the grassroot professional

Library of Congress Cataloging in Publication Data

O'Morrow, Gerald S.
   Therapeutic recreation, **second edition**
   Includes bibliographic references and index.
   I. Recreational therapy. I. Title.
RM736.7.046   1980   615.8'5153   80-10376
ISBN 0-8359-7659-9

© 1980 by Reston Publishing Company, Inc.
A Prentice-Hall Company
Reston, Virginia

10 9 8 7 6 5 4 3 2

Printed in the United States of America

contents

foreword   ix

foreword to the second edition   xv

preface   xiii

chapter one: introduction   1
The Value of Recreation, 2   The Challenge of Therapeutic
Recreation, 6

chapter two: special populations   8
Prevalence of Special Populations, 9   Attitude of Society, 14
Concepts: Health-Disease and Rehabilitation-Punishment, 19
Conditions or Disorders, 25

**chapter three: agencies and institutions providing service
  to special populations**   55
Organizations, 55   Services, 64   Personnel, 66   Facilities, 72
Accreditation, Licensure, Certification, and Registration, 79

chapter four: the historical development of rehabilitation and therapeutic recreation   **83**
Historical Development, 84   Twentieth Century, 95

chapter five: therapeutic recreation   **116**
Therapeutic Recreation, 116   Therapeutic Recreation Process, 122
Therapeutic Recreation Service, 124

chapter six: therapeutic recreation activities and leadership   **138**
Human Needs, 139   Activities, 142   Leadership, 156

chapter seven: therapeutic recreation and human service models   **168**
Medical-Clinical Model, 169   Custodial Model, 171
Therapeutic Community or Therapeutic Milieu Model, 173
Education and Training Model, 176   Community Model, 178

chapter eight: the therapeutic recreation process   **186**
Process Models, 186   Process Rationale, 188   Process Goals, 191
Components of the Therapeutic Recreation Process, 192
Relationship: Process and Models, 217

chapter nine: the therapeutic recreation specialist   **220**
Leadership Roles, 221   Personal and Professional Relationships, 229   Occupational Opportunities, 233
Selection of a Position, 238

chapter ten: personal professional development in therapeutic recreation   **243**
Professional Education, 244   Professional Organizations, 249
Therapeutic Recreation Organizations, 254
Personal Philosophy, 258

chapter eleven: the future of therapeutic recreation   **261**

appendix a: medical terminology   **266**

appendix b: drug therapy   **275**

appendix c: progress note terminology guide   **284**

appendix d: voluntary registration program standards   **290**
  of the national therapeutic recreation society

appendix e: therapeutic recreation resources   **293**
  National Professional and Voluntary Organizations
  and Agencies Serving Special Populations, 293
  Recreation and Competitive Sport Organizations
Serving Special   Populations, 297   Periodicals, 298

footnotes   **300**

index   **323**

foreword

In 1971 the following quotation was published in an issue of the *Thera-peutic Recreation Journal.*

> The therapeutic recreation specialist will become a fully accepted member of the rehabilitation team and will gain true professional status with other disciplines. His interaction with patients will be respected to a greater degree; his value to the community recreation program will be more fully real-ized. The extent to which these three assumptions become valid, and the time it will take to occur, is dependent upon when therapeutic recreation specialists begin to understand themselves and explain to others why they offer recrea-tion activities in conjunction with care and treatment programs.

This statement was made by Dr. Gerald O'Morrow in an article con-cerning the rationale for recreation in rehabilitation and in his discussions on the professional development of the therapeutic recreation field. The statement reflects, first of all, the author's belief in the significant role that recreation can play in the therapeutic process; and secondly, his belief that whether or not the profession reaches its potential depends largely upon the dedication and commitment of its present members and the students who will become its future members.

Over the past several years tremendous strides have been made by the therapeutic recreation field in its growth as a recognized profession. As is indicated in this text, we have come from a profession that has been split by terminology and semantics to a united profession called therapeutic recreation. We have developed, in the past few years, specific training programs and currently have over 80 colleges and universities providing training opportunities. We are a profession that is recognized by several federal agencies concerned with services to the ill and disabled. And we are a field that increasingly is being given the opportunity to make significant contributions to individuals who are called special populations. This progress has been made because many talented professionals have dedicated themselves to that end and have demonstrated the type of commitment that breeds success.

Over the past several years there has been a significant increase in professional literature and specifically in texts concerning therapeutic recreation. Each of these texts has made a unique contribution to the profession and presents a specific approach to experience in services to disabled or disadvantaged individuals. This text, *Therapeutic Recreation: A Helping Profession,* adds immeasurably to the profession due to the special qualifications and expertise of the author.

My first professional exposure to the work of Dr. O'Morrow was in 1960, when as a neophyte to the therapeutic recreation field, I attended a workshop on activity leadership for state hospital employees that he conducted. In more recent years I have had the privilege of working with him on numerous projects dealing with the high-level philosophical development of the profession. It is precisely this wide scope of experience and talent that makes this text so valuable to students and practitioners in therapeutic recreation. Dr. O'Morrow has personally experienced and lived what he is writing about, from very basic face-to-face activity leadership and programming with patients and clients to the high-level theoretical and philosophical development and all of the dimensions in between. When he discusses recreation programming and activity adaptation with the various disability groups, he does so from personal experiences, and when he discusses philosophical frameworks and the future of the field, he speaks with authority because he has been an integral part of the development of that philosophy and has been one of the architects of the future. He has distinguished himself as a practitioner, as a researcher, as an educator, and as a writer, all culminating in making this book factual, scholarly, and extremely readable for the new student coming into the field.

Finally, the text incorporates from start to finish the basic ingredient that makes the profession what it is today: the concern for providing opportunities for physically, emotionally, socially, and intellectually handicapped individuals to lead more productive and more satisfying lives—not out of sympathy but out of a firm conviction that all individuals, regardless of race, creed, or condition of life, should have the same opportunities for life, liberty, and the pursuit of happiness. The dedication and commitment to the therapeutic recreation field demonstrated by Dr. O'Morrow in his professional life permeates the pages of the text and will, I believe, have a great influence on the reader who ultimately chooses therapeutic recreation as a profession.

david c. park, m.t.r.s.
department of human kinetics
and leisure services
george washington university
formerly executive secretary
national therapeutic
recreation society

foreword
to the second edition

As has been reflected in this text, the therapeutic recreation field is a vibrant, dynamic profession. As such, it is involved in constant self evaluation in an effort to insure that the services provided are relevant to the needs of the individual being served and are of the highest quality possible.

Since the first edition of this book, many changes have occurred in the entire human services field which have required the therapeutic recreation profession to even more stringently scrutinize its programs and services. For instance, national economic concerns have forced all health care practitioners to become more accountable for the services they provide and the impact of these services on clients. This has caused the therapeutic recreation field to seriously evaluate its basic goals and objectives and to push for more definitive approaches to curriculum development, credentialing and program standards.

The Education for All Handicapped Children Act has called attention to the total education of children and has specifically included the need for recreation and leisure education. This has caused the profession to reevaluate its programs and services in order to relate more effectively with the established educational community. Section 504 of the 1973

Rehabilitation Act has served as a civil rights bill, mandating non-discrimination in federally funded programs. This has caused the field to increase its efforts to advocate for and assist public recreation agencies in providing services for handicapped populations.

Finally, the 1978 Amendments to the Rehabilitation Act have called attention to the need for comprehensive rehabilitation services for all handicapped individuals and specifically promote increased recreation opportunities.

Thus, this revision to this textbook is very necessary and very timely. Dr. O'Morrow, as a continuing national leader in the field of therapeutic recreation, has provided direction to the profession and has appropriately and adequately reflected those changes in the text.

david c. park, m.t.r.s.
president, national
therapeutic recreation
society

preface

Since the first edition of this book, the profession of therapeutic recreation has continued to grow and mature as an important field of service within the park and recreation profession. This is undoubtedly the result of the continued expression of a social concern on the part of society and park and recreation personnel for those individuals who are considered to be special populations—i.e., limited physically, emotionally, socially, and intellectually in their ability to participate in leisure experiences and to contribute to society.

As in the first edition, *Therapeutic Recreation: A Helping Profession* is written primarily for the student who is considering and preparing for a professional career in therapeutic recreation. For practical purposes, it is to inform all those who are interested in knowing about therapeutic recreation. The book is an introductory text for use by students in colleges and universities offering an introductory course in therapeutic recreation. In addition, parts of it could be adapted for use in an in-service training program within health and correctional agencies and institutions.

In general, the book explores with the student the profession of therapeutic recreation, what demands the profession will make of him, and whether he possesses the talents and abilities to meet those demands. Most important, it is hoped that the student will learn that a professional career in therapeutic recreation can be exciting and challenging, stimulating and satisfying.

Faculty who use a specific textbook are rarely consulted to any great extent by an author in the matter of a second edition. However, in preparation for this edition colleagues whom I knew were using the original text in their introductory therapeutic recreation course as well as college and university departments of part and recreation which were previous and current adopters of the book were invited to suggest proposed changes.

The response was most gratifying, and, while the organization of the text remains the same, a considerable amount of suggested changes were incorporated. I hope that some responders, as they read this edition, will understand that not all suggestions could be incorporated, otherwise the concept of an introductory text would have been lost. In the main, the book considers the historical, professional and personal aspects of therapeutic recreation. It is neither a program development, leadership or administrative text since these elements of therapeutic recreation are discussed in other texts. However, aspects of these elements are briefly considered so as to familiarize the student with them as they relate to professional development and therapeutic recreation as a service.

Some chapters including suggested readings have been revised considerably and new materials added while other chapters have been only updated and limited changes made. Also, in some instances I have purposely avoided discussing possible implications of specific events and statements so as to encourage debate and discussion among the readers, and perhaps among the readers and instructor. Generally speaking, this edition contains the latest facts and reflects present day concepts in therapeutic recreation although the reader will note that differences and divergent thinking among quoted authors exist. This is healthy and should exist within a human service field. To those who have flattered me about the last edition I would like to say that I have tried in this edition to preserve its spirit and general characteristics.

The book has been organized into 11 chapters and can be arbitrarily divided into three units, each designed to help the student to understand the profession of therapeutic recreation from various perspectives.

Chapter 1 offers a brief overview of the importance of recreation opportunities to meet one's leisure needs and satisfy basic growth and development needs. The next three chapters address the student on such vitally important subjects as (1) the prevalence and characteristics of special populations, the attitude of society toward special populations, and the concept of health—illness and rehabilitation—punishment; (2) the agencies and institutions that offer rehabilitation and special services to special populations; and (3) the historical base of rehabilitation and therapeutic recreation.

Chapters 5 through 8, which form the second unit, consider the general philosophical orientation toward therapeutic recreation and the major views held toward therapeutic recreation as a process and as a service, the contribution of activities to successful adjustment for special populations, and the leadership roles in therapeutic recreation, as well as briefly discussing basic human needs. This unit also discusses the various human service models found in rehabilitation and community settings and the role of therapeutic recreation in these models, and the use of therapeutic recreative experiences in the assessing, planning, implementing, and evaluating process.

The third unit, Chapters 9 and 10, explores the competencies necessary to be a successful therapeutic recreation specialist, including career opportunities, and makes recommendations for personal and professional improvement along with considering the many ways the student can serve the profession and benefit from it. Chapter 11 considers the future of therapeutic recreation.

At the end of each chapter is a list of suggested readings that will help the student increase his understanding of the topics discussed within the chapter. These reference lists are not intended to be complete, and outside reading should not be limited to the books and articles listed.

The appendixes that conclude the book are intended to expand the dimensions of this introductory text and include medical terminology, drug therapy, progress note guidelines, therapeutic recreation professional standards, and a listing of voluntary and professional organizations involved in rehabilitation as well as special population sport organizations.

For an introductory course in therapeutic recreation, the author suggests that the instructor use outside speakers to discuss specific matters; likewise, panel discussions of issues, visits to health and correctional agencies, interviews, and films should augment this text. In other words, I suggest that this book be used as a springboard to other courses and experiences in therapeutic recreation.

Also, I intended to provide therapeutic recreation job descriptions, but they are so varied that when one considers the various types of hospitals/institutions and agencies that employ therapeutic recreation specialists, a decision was made to leave them out. However, the students and the instructor are encouraged to obtain such job descriptions and to review them relative to position responsibilities and requirements.

As the number of therapeutic recreation specialists who publish ideas about and concepts of their profession increases, so does agreement about what therapeutic recreation is and what the goals of therapeutic recreation are. In many instances, it is impossible for me to cite original ideas, for mine are molded and developed by the thoughts and ideas of many. Many therapeutic recreation educators and some practitioners will read their own ideas and convictions into those presented. To me, this is healthy; it reflects increasing evidence that therapeutic recreation specialists are beginning to agree about our mission.

acknowledgements

Were it not for the challenge and stimulation given by colleagues with whom I have been associated for many years, this book would not have been possible. Thus, I would like to express my appreciation to a number of them by acknowledging them here; educationally, to Lee Helsel, Dr. Fred M. Chapman, and Dr. Elliott M. Avedon and to those whom I have been associated with professionally as a practitioner and as an educator — Albert L. Meuli, Dr. Martin W. Meyer, Dr. Virginia Frye, Dr. Fred Humphrey, Dr. Doris L. Berryman, and David C. Park.

Although the help and ideas of many individuals have gone into the first and second editions of the book, the author is especially appreciative and grateful to Dr. Fred Humphrey who reviewed the original manuscript and made invaluable suggestions for improvement. Likewise, my thanks to Dr. Stephen Anderson and Ms. Lee-Lanz Stewart for their extensive input relative to the second edition. I would be remiss not to acknowledge David C. Park, President of the National Therapeutic Recreation Society, for accepting my invitation to write a postscript to his original Foreword. While only concerned with the first edition, it is equally important to express my appreciation to the National Therapeutic Recreation Society and Dr. Doris L. Berryman and her committee for permitting me to incorporate materials from the NTRS 750-Hour Training Program and to Jerome Kern, M.D. for his advice and suggestions relative to Chapter 2 and Appendix A & B respectively.

Because a book is dependent on authors', editors', and publishers' permission to reprint materials, I wish to express my gratitude to all those who have given permission to quote materials, especially the National Recreation and Park Association, Stackpole Books, and Prentice-Hall, Inc. The author wishes to extend his appreciation to those agencies and individuals who responded to my request for pictures which are associated with each chapter. These agencies and individuals include Glen Van Andel, Director of Recreational Therapy, North Carolina Memorial Hospital, Chapel Hill; David Christian, Director, Valdosta Parks and Recreation Department, Valdosta,

Georgia; University of Georgia Wheelchair Intramural Sports Unit; Mr. and Mrs. Alex Boatwright; and Mr. and Mrs. Al Queen. The author is also indebted to Ruby Pfleging and Penelope Little who gave in all goodwill their time and assistance in typing the endless drafts and the final manuscript of the first edition and to Stephanie L. Kelley for typing revisions incorporated in the second edition. A special thanks to Mary Lu McFall for her sympathetic understanding and editorial assistance in bringing greater unity of style to these pages in the former edition and to Lynn Bryant in the present edition; likewise, to the Production Editor of Reston Publishing Company, Inc., for her editing. Lastly, I am especially grateful to Mrs. Marion N. Hormachea, Consulting Editor, Public Service Series, Reston Publishing Company, Inc., for inviting me to do this book initially.

gerald s. o'morrow

chapter 1
introduction

The purposes of this book are to introduce you to a professional field of service to mankind and to help you to evaluate it as a career for yourself. I feel that it is a great profession and one in which you will find deep satisfaction as well as a challenge to the best that is in you.

An intelligent approach to any subject is to explore it. It has been my experience over the years that most beginning students do not have a very clear understanding of what therapeutic recreation service is or what its basic purposes are. This book, therefore, has been prepared to help you obtain a clear idea of the career that you are considering. It may not be long before some of you decide that a career in therapeutic recreation is not what you thought it was; and you may choose to explore other professional opportunities. But I hope that before reading far in this book and going far in your introductory course, you will encounter the spirit of excitement that permeates the field and discover the sources of enthusiasm that members of the profession enjoy. Most important, I hope that you will learn that the profession offers unlimited opportunities and challenges to men and women with an adventurous spirit and an ability to discover new areas in therapeutic recreation service that require the energies, abilities, and viewpoints of young, imaginative, dynamic persons.

the value of recreation

Before our exploration of the nature and the scope of therapeutic recreation, let us briefly consider the contribution that leisure, recreation, and play make to our normal daily living experience.

While wholesome recreation cannot substitute for the basic necessities of sustaining life, it does have the potential for therapeutic benefits for all people. A person who has acquired a fund of recreational interest, knowledge, appreciation, and skills will include in daily living activities that are creative, stimulating, or relaxing. Recreation contributes to physical, mental, and emotional fitness and to social stability. Thus, the participation in such activities can be considered therapeutic.

satisfaction of personal needs

It is essential to recognize first of all that humans are social beings with needs, interests, and desires that are biological, physical, and social in nature. These needs, interests, and desires are conditioned by the environment in which each individual lives, by the scientific and technological advances that constantly modify the social scene, and by the level of each individual's physical, emotional, social, intellectual, and economic development. Furthermore, although different writers in the recreation profession have described leisure and recreation in different ways and have placed greater emphasis upon some objectives than others, there is strong agreement among them that individuals through their choice of leisure activities and their participation in recreative experiences can find partial satisfaction of their needs, interests, and desires.

Underlying all of the objectives stated for recreation, there is the basic idea that recreation contributes to good living and has value as a philosophy of life. The ancient Greeks believed that the purpose of all education should be to teach people how to live well. To philosophers such as Socrates, the only worthwhile objective of living was to live "the Good Life." Thus, choice of and participation in leisure interest activities can help people to live a better life; and this means, in part, having fun as they live.

personality development

As indicated above, recreation can be considered as an area of living related to other life activities—a part of living in which certain human needs and interests are satisfied. Indeed, if you read the work of the writers in the park and recreation field, you will discover that they look upon recreation as a means for providing experiences that benefit the "whole person." That is to say, recreation has objectives that apply to the "total personalities" of those who participate in it.

Although there is much debate and controversy as to what the human personality is and why people behave as they do, for our purposes I will define *total personality* or *whole person* simply as the sum total of all physical, mental, emotional, and social aspects of any individual. These aspects are of equal importance to the balance and health of the personality; the personality as a whole can be considered to be healthy only if all four aspects are healthy. The condition of any one aspect affects the health of each other aspect and of the personality as a whole. It is unrealistic to think of one aspect without also considering all aspects. A fine automobile is fine because of the excellence of its individual parts and because of the excellence of the way in which the parts fit and work together. So it is with the human being.

physical well-being

To begin with, it may be stated generally that recreation can contribute to the physical aspects of the personality. Physiologists and cardiac specialists agree that active participation in activities and exercise is essential if the individual is to develop and maintain maximum physical efficiency and total fitness for living. Efficient use of the body requires endurance, strength, agility, balance, and coordination. One is only reminded of the large number of youths between 16 and 25 years of age who were below the rather meager fitness levels required for military service in the two World Wars and the Korean and Vietnam Wars.

Moreover, if the body is maintained at a reasonable level of efficiency, it is more likely to be able to meet the demands made on it without undue stress or fatigue. The individual who must use all of his muscular strength in performing his daily physical tasks is operating at a low level of efficiency and has little or no energy left at the end of the day for recreational and leisure pursuits. As one specialist puts it:

> A healthy person with optimal (not necessarily maximum) physical fitness can carry out his usual everyday tasks without undue fatigue and have enough reserve energy left over to enjoy his leisure; and to engage in activities requiring reasonably prolonged, vigorous physical effort when necessary or desired.[1]

Adults are not the only ones who benefit from physical activity. Children also need physical activity; thus, play is an absolute physiological need. Pediatricians have repeatedly pointed out that the vigorous play of children is necessary for the satisfactory growth of various organs and systems of the body. This usually can be obtained in the normal manner—

by free play and the exercise obtained in the daily life of children. As they grow, boys and girls need an adequate amount of muscular strength and cardiovascular endurance to participate without undue fatigue in strenuous physical activities, to do their required work at home and school, and to take part in the social activities that they enjoy, with a reserve amount of strength to meet unexpected emergencies.

emotional well-being

It is of basic importance in our culture that people learn to cooperate with others, to work in groups, and to maintain their poise under the pressures of modern living. There is widespread political and economic unrest in the world today—a basic insecurity. Confusion, fear, distrust, and pressure cause terrific physical and mental strain. According to some physicians, at least 50 percent of all office visits are the result of various kinds of stress. Moreover, there is reason to believe that many of the restraints necessary for social living—submitting to the authority of bosses and teachers, holding back impulses to fight and/or cry out—build up in individuals a need to "let go": to strike, to lash out, to kick, to yell, and perhaps to smash. Of course, one would find himself in jail in a hurry if he did these things in most places and under most circumstances. But involvement in leisure pursuits does provide just such opportunities for release under controlled conditions, and no one is the worse for it.

The late Dr. William C. Menninger, a world-famous authority on mental health, expressed some years ago this thought in these terms:

> Mentally healthy people participate in some form of volitional activity to supplement their required daily work. . . . Their satisfaction from these activities meets deep seated psychological demands, quite beyond the superficial rationalism of enjoyment.[2]

A great many adults who are mentally and emotionally disturbed simply cannot "let go," and some psychiatrists have wondered whether a lack of opportunities to let off steam in the joyful and free atmosphere that leisure activities provide might not be a factor in bringing about some cases of mental illness.

The same principle of "letting go" applies to children as well as adults. Activities of a recreational nature serve an important purpose as a refreshing relief from the confinement and routine of the classroom. On the other hand, participation in such activities by youngsters provides meaningful and natural opportunities to experience the joy of winning, the disappointment of defeat, the fun of accomplishment, and the frustration of failure. Participation in activities provides one of the finest training grounds for the development of emotional stability. Here the participant acquires a feeling of belonging to a group, has an opportunity to develop an independent personality, and realizes a reasonable amount of satisfaction and happiness. Thus, leisure activities, especially of a group nature, offer individuals an opportunity to increase their capacity to handle and control their emotions.

social interaction

It was mentioned earlier that all aspects of an individual's personality are profoundly influenced by the personalities of others. If one is to be happy and have a healthy personality, it is essential that one's relationships with other people be of a certain quality. If reasonably good quality relationships are to exist, it is necessary that one possess many social skills. Recreational activities offer some of the very best means for individuals to learn and develop vital social skills. As people learn to play together, a basis is provided for helping to promote a profound sense of social awareness upon which the idea of the brotherhood of man rests.

To be an accepted group member, one must have social skills or social know-how. We know that most children acquire a great deal of their social skill through group play; the more fortunate ones have had the benefit of parents and others who did not leave this matter to chance. Individuals who fail to develop social skills are, of course, socially awkward and handicapped. That is, they do not know how to deal with other people, to adjust to them, or to enjoy them. Every recreative experience has some contribution to make to the social development and adjustment of adults and children—for, you see, play brings people together in happy activity. Getting along with and working with others are essential parts of play. Neither adults nor children just get together to do nothing in their leisure. They get together to do things, and the social interaction that goes along with play is one of the reasons for playing.

Social behavior is learned through practice. Leisure pursuits offer opportunities for experiencing both objectionable and desirable forms of behaving. These experiences will enable the individual to learn which forms are desirable. Behavior that is rewarded is apt to be repeated and learned. However, behavior is not learned with one correct response. In social learning, just as in motor learning, practice is essential. Thus, the positive rewards of participation in leisure activities help individuals to gain friends, respect, and prestige and to make a more satisfactory social adjustment. Social adjustment is a prerequisite for optimum success on the job, in family living, and in social and community activities.

It would appear, therefore, that the individual in a democratic society has responsibilities as well as rights. One of these duties is to use his leisure so that it contributes to expanding his personality to the end that he is a more competent member of society. Beyond this, however, there are the concomitant effects which Frye and Peters speak of in their publication *Therapeutic Recreation: Its Theory, Philosophy and Practices.* These include refreshing both the mind and the body by releasing and rechannelling aggression and tension, reaffirming a sense of personal dignity, providing opportunity for association with and acceptance of other people, expanding one's interests and self-awareness, providing an opportunity for creative expression, and affording a meaning to life, a *raison d'être.*[3]

the challenge of therapeutic recreation

Unfortunately, there are individuals who, because of a variety of circumstances, are unable at times to fulfill their social responsibilities or benefit from the concomitant effects of recreative experiences. These individuals do not have the key that unlocks the door to self-discovery, or to self-respect, or to the joy of sharing interests and experiences with others. This segment of our population includes those who are affected by some form of physically and/or mentally incapacitating disease or disability, old age, poverty, socially deviant behavior, institutionalization, and the like.

However, students should recognize that this segment has the same needs and interests that everyone else in society has—self-expression, social involvement, and creative experience. To deny these individuals the opportunity to participate in the recreational life of the Nation, even though participation may be extremely limited, is to deny an important experience. As pointed out by the delegates to the National Forum on Meeting the Recreation and Park Needs of Handicapped People, handicapped people are being denied opportunity to develop through recreation.[4] As Joseph H. Margalis, a National Recreation and Park Association Board of Trustee member commented in testimony before the House Subcommittee on Labor, Health, Education and Welfare on supporting an appropriation of $10 million to expand recreation services for the handicapped as authorized by the Rehabilitation Act Amendments of 1978:

> Recreation experiences provide an excellent opportunity for the handicapped to associate informally with society as a whole. . . . Those experiences can contribute to the rehabilitation of handicapped individuals and their inclusion in education, employment and other individual social functions.[5]

Just as public hygiene is concerned with the health of people who are well as much as with the illness of those who are sick, so recreation has implications for everyone. In its broadest sense, the aim of leisure and recreation service is to help all people achieve fuller, happier, and more harmonious and effective lives. A constructive attitude toward life is important to each individual, and recreative experiences can contribute to such an attitude.

Students, therefore, should realize that they are in a position to help this segment of our population progress toward better physical, emotional, social, and intellectual adjustment through recreation. If we accept the concept that was stated above—that recreative experiences have values that promote the growth of the whole person—then it follows that the value and significance of leisure and recreation service increase when related to this special segment of our population. This is so because society, to a greater or lesser degree, has denied this segment the opportunity to participate and thereby has denied growth and development experiences. Herein lies the challenge of therapeutic recreation as a helping profession.

suggested references

Brightbill, Charles K., and Tony A. Mobley. *Educating for Leisure-Centered Living.* New York: John Wiley and Sons, 1977.

Carlson, Reynold E., Janet R. MacLean, Theodore R. Deppe, and James A. Peterson. *Recreation and Leisure: The Changing Scene* (3rd ed.). Belmont, Calif.: Wadsworth Publishing Company, Inc. 1979.

Craig, Timothy, ed. *The Humanistic and Mental Health Aspects of Sports Exercise and Recreation.* Chicago: American Medical Association, 1976.

Ellis, Michael J. *Why People Play.* Englewood Cliffs, N.J.: Prentice-Hall, Inc., 1973.

Gray, David, and Donald A. Pelegrino, eds. *Reflections on the Recreation and Park Movement.* Dubuque, Iowa: Wm. C. Brown Co. Publishers, 1973.

"How Americans Pursue Happiness," Special Section, *U.S. News and World Report* (May 23, 1977), pp. 60–76.

Kaplan, Max, and Phillip Bosserman, eds. *Technology, Human Values and Leisure.* Nashville, Tenn.: Abingdon Press, 1971.

Kraus, Richard G. *Recreation Today* (2nd ed.). Santa Monica, Ca.: Goodyear Publishing Company, Inc., 1977.

Levy, Joseph. *Play Behavior.* New York: John Wiley and Sons, 1978.

Martin, Alexander Reid, "Leisure and Our Inner Resources," *Parks and Recreation,* 3:3 (1975).

Murphy, James F., ed. *Concepts of Leisure: Philosophical Implications.* Englewood Cliffs, N.J.: Prentice-Hall, Inc., 1974.

Veblen, Thorstein. *The Theory of the Leisure Class.* Boston: Houghton Mifflin Company, 1973.

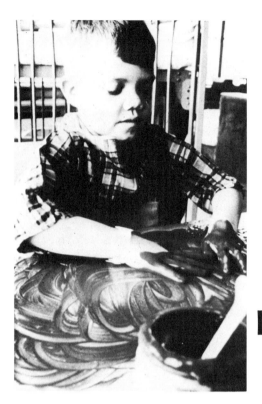

chapter 2
special
populations

In the preceding chapter we noted that the various disabling conditions and social problems of some individuals affect their ability to engage in leisure and recreative activities. Frequently, these individuals are termed special populations. The term *special populations* hereafter is used to describe those individuals who, because of a variety of circumstances, differ from the average in their physical, emotional, social, and intellectual behavior.

If these individuals are to achieve and participate in recreative activities at a level commensurate with their respective abilities, it is important for the student to have a knowledge and understanding about those health conditions and social problems that prevent and limit participation.

To achieve this goal, however, it is well for us to briefly consider three factors relative to special populations—namely, the prevalence of special populations, the attitude of society toward special populations, and the concepts of health-disease and rehabilitation-punishment in our society.

prevalence of special populations

Whether individuals or groups want to admit it or not, every community, large or small, has its special populations. However, research on the extent of such groups suggests that the numbers vary from community to community.

difficulties in gathering data

Various attempts to determine the prevalence of physical, emotional, social, and intellectual problems in the population have yielded such diverse results that investigators hesitate to give a definite figure for each problem. Thus, words of caution are needed concerning the figures presented herein.

Much of the difficulty in determining the prevalence of special populations stems from the fact that the line of demarcation between the "normal" or "average" and the individuals most often considered to be special population members cannot always be agreed upon.

A second difficulty exists due to the fact that the law and the definition change; what is defined as criminal or delinquent behavior, for example, also changes from time to time and from place to place. Consequently, increases in the figures shown in reports may reflect legislative addition, modification, or even elimination of offenses rather than any changes in the habits and activities of the people. The same is true for physical, emotional, and intellectual impairments and disabling conditions.

A third difficulty arises because there appears to be no uniform reporting procedure used by all agencies, nor is there a single governmental agency responsible for collecting information. The 1970 census did attempt to make possible the cumulation of more nearly accurate census data concerning special populations. Voluntary organizations report those illnesses or disabilities in which they are directly involved. Secondary problems associated with the primary problem may be unreported.

Another difficulty is the labeling of figures as national estimates. While such figures may well apply to a state or a geographical district, they will be found lacking in specific instances, especially when applied to certain local communities. For example, the number of mentally retarded children will be much greater in the slum areas than in the wealthy suburbs of a city. Certain states and parts of states, such as Florida and southern California, attract individuals who are chronically ill.

A fifth difficulty exists because many times additional information is needed if a clear picture of the problem is to be obtained. For years it has been reported that 3 percent of the population of the United States is mentally retarded. This figure is now being questioned in relation to customs, traditions, and environments.

All of these factors, therefore, caution against overdependency on prevalent figures. Those figures should be used only as an index.

Despite the difficulties in determining the prevalence of special populations, investigators have been able to hazard guesses based on different studies. These guesses have provided us with valuable information that can be used as baseline data for the planning, administration, and evaluation of programs as well as for action by legislative bodies.

disabled persons

Dependable statistics of the total number of individuals who fall within the special population category are still lacking, although it has been estimated by some investigators that as much as 35 percent of the population may have some form of physical, emotional, social, or intellectual problem. This estimate does not include social offenders.

Not until the 1970 Census of the Population was there any attempt to identify the numbers of disabled persons in the United States. Studies conducted by the U.S. Public Health Service (PHS) and the Social Security Administration (SSA) between 1963 and 1966 estimated that there were at least 22.6 million, and probably over 30 million individuals unable to participate in activities normal for their age group.[1,2] The 1970 Census showed a total adult population in America of 121 million (excluding those in institutions and in military service) in the typical accepted employable age-range of 16 to 64 years of age. Of this total, there were nearly 11.3 million persons with disabilities which had existed for six months or longer and which affected their ability to work. The Census, therefore, concluded that one in every 11 people in the United States—over nine percent of the population—has a disability. The Census also showed, as might be expected, that the disability rate between 16 and 64 years of age increases by age and is true for both men and women, but with one exception. There is a very slight decrease in the disability rate of men from the 16–24 age bracket to the 25–34 age bracket. The Census also revealed a sharp increase in the disability rate after age 44 with little difference between men and women.[3]

It is assumed that the reader has already recognized the limitations of the 1970 Census findings. The Census was seriously limited in that the questions asked were solely concerned with whether or not a person had a health or physical condition which affected the ability to work. Many disabled persons do work; hence, their condition is not an impediment to employment. These persons were not counted. Another limitation is the stigma society attaches to disability; many disabled people undoubtedly did not identify themselves. Finally, the Census did not include disabled persons under 16 and over 64 years of age or those in various types of institutions.

The American Coalition of Citizens with Disabilities estimates that 36 million people in this country—one in six—have physical and/or developmental disabilities.[4] This does not include an additional 10 million alcoholics and 1.5 million drug addicts.[5] Citing statistics provided by the National Arts Foundation, the National Handicapped Information Service, and the National Center for Health Statistics, the *New York Times* indicated there are 68 million persons in the United States with limiting conditions and disabilities.[6] The U.S. Bureau of the Education of the Handicapped reports there are 8 million handicapped children, aged 1 to 21.[7] *The Statistical Abstracts of the United States* indicates admissions to institutions for the mentally ill and outpatient psychiatric centers at over 5 million in a given year.[8] Between 20 and 32 million Americans require some kind of mental health care according to the President's Commission on Mental Health.[9] There are more than 10 million disabled elderly Americans, and nine million have major activity limitations states Dr. Lois Schwab, a pioneer in the field of rehabilitation and the elderly.[10] Lastly, disabling work injuries in this country totaled approximately 2.5 million in 1973. About 90,000 of these results in permanent disability according to the U.S. Department of Labor.[11] Regardless of the number of limiting and disabling conditions, it is important to note, that most of these individuals live in the community.[12]

social offenders

To ascertain the exact dimensions of socially deviant behavior is extremely difficult as a result of the distinctions made between adult and juvenile offenders and between crime and delinquency, and also as a result of the disparities in criminal codes and in sentencing and release policies from jurisdiction to jurisdiction.

Statistics obtained from the 1967 President's Commission on Law Enforcement and Administration of Justice projected that the average daily population in the correctional system would be over 1.8 million (felons and misdemeanants) by 1975. Of these, approximately one-third would be in some type of institution (juvenile or adult) and the remaining two-thirds would be under supervision in the community (parole, probation, and aftercare).[13] In 1976, according to *Corrections Magazine,* prison population was at an all-time high. The magazine reported 250,000 in federal and state prisons.[14]

A recent study of the juvenile justice system prepared for the Ford

Foundation indicates that most violent delinquents are minority-group males living in lower-class or slum neighborhoods of large urban centers, having come from broken homes where there was a poor relationship with the only parent. In addition, they were most likely to be school failures, have learning disabilities, and show psychological problems. Rage, low self-esteem, lack of empathy and limited frustration tolerance are typical characteristics of violent youths, the study said.[15]

The profile of the individuals found in our prisons is also an interesting one. The Association of State Correctional Administrators reports that 85 percent of the average state adult prison inmates are school dropouts and 65 percent come from broken homes; the average educational attainment is between the fifth and sixth grade levels with the average I.Q. being 85. In addition, 20 percent are mentally retarded, of which 5 percent are severely retarded; 50 percent are under the age of 25, 18 percent are illiterate, and 40 percent are without previous sustained work experience. The association concludes their report by stating that approximately 96 percent of those incarcerated will be on the "streets" after an average stay of two years.[16]

These statistics only describe part of the picture. According to Muth, the national recidivism rate of those who have been incarcerated is estimated at 65 percent for adults and 75 percent for youth. Further, nearly 80 percent of the crimes are committed by those adults and youth who have previously been through the criminal justice system. Lastly, nearly 75 percent of the prison population is made up of individuals who are economically deprived and who belong to a minority group.[17]

disadvantaged persons

Turning our attention to those who are unable to participate fully in American society because of educational, economic, or social barriers, we note that by the federal government's income criteria, in 1973 there were about 23 million people living at the poverty level. Approximately one out of every seven Americans is thus considered socially and economically disadvantaged. Who are these people? They include the families of black southern sharecroppers who moved North expecting to find work. They also include members of other ethnic minority groups: Puerto Ricans and other Spanish-speaking Americans, citizens of Oriental extraction, and almost all American Indians. They also include the residents of Appalachia and other economic disaster areas, and the unskilled workers everywhere. Perhaps the most disadvantaged of this latter group are the migrant farm workers.[18,19]

Report after report by federal agencies reflects the by-product of poverty. The President's Committee on Mental Retardation notes in its 1976 report:

Mental retardation, especially in mild forms, tends to be more prevalent and more devastating among disadvantaged social groups. In perhaps 85 to 90 per cent of cases, mild retardation, not involving identifiable organic or physical cause, is associated with conditions arising from the environment, poverty, racial, and ethnic discrimination, and family distress.

The quality of life represented in the kind of nurturant care and stimulation which the child experiences in the very early years may substantially and perhaps permanently influence his or her cognitive functions as well as physical health.

Poverty in itself produces magnified hazards to life, health and human development, but when it is accompanied by racial and ethnic discrimination, cultural deprivation and family disintegration, the consequent disadvantage is multiplied many times over. This is the case on the American scene most frequently among Blacks, Spanish-speaking, Native Americans, Asiatic groups, and multiple disadvantaged urban and rural whites. Members of these groups appear among those identified as mentally retarded in numbers far out of proportion to their presence in the total population. This cannot be ascribed to inherent racial, ethnic, or familial defect, but to social, economic, and educational disadvantages to which these groups are subjected. The problems we refer to are not limited solely to ethnic groups nor do they characterize all members of such groups. They haunt the scene of poverty, however, in Appalachia as well as on the Rosebud Reservation, in Harlem, and in the San Joaquin Valley.[20]

Since good care early in life is the best protection against subsequent disability and illness, adequate health care for children is basic to the improvement of the nation's health. However, the health needs of poor children are less well met than those of other children for a variety of reasons: lack of facilities and manpower, especially in impoverished rural areas; limited available funds for both tax-supported and voluntary programs; and restrictive eligibility requirements for free or low cost care. The result is that few poor children receive regular medical supervision, preventive services, and early diagnosis and treatment. They tend to receive medical attention only when their health problems are very serious.[21]

Over 20 million Americans suffer from malnutrition which, if severe, can lower IQ, impair physical functions, cause brain alteration and damage, produce memory deficiency, impair neurological function, reduce learning ability, cause irritability and impaired judgment, and produce irreversible mental retardation.[22] As a result of substandard housing many poor children have died of lead poisoning. Up to 600,000 children each year are afflicted with high blood lead levels and lead poisoning. Of these children, 6,000 will be permanently handicapped by physical and mental impairments.[23]

Other disconcerting facts regarding disadvantaged handicapped are as follows:

- Fifteen percent of the population 16 to 64 years of age with work disability of six months or more had earnings below $2000 a year while 23 percent had no earnings during 1970.[24]

- The incidence of disability is three times higher in disadvantaged households than in other households of the nation—17 percent compared with 5 percent.
- Handicapped people from low income areas are less likely to receive rehabilitation services than those from other income levels.
- Lower-income families do not know where to go for rehabilitation—only 11 percent knew, compared to 38 percent of other income levels.
- A higher proportion of low-income handicapped people were "nonfunctioning" than handicapped people of other income levels.[25]
- In 1976, eight billion dollars was paid out in Social Security benefits to over 2.6 million disabled and nearly 3.5 billion dollars more was paid to over 2.1 million blind and disabled in Supplemental Security Income.[26]

attitude of society

While significant changes have taken place in society's attitudes toward special populations during the past century, the myths, superstitions, and guilt feelings still exist today. These stigmas are reflected in the day-to-day contact with the disabled, the disadvantaged, and the social offender. Many challenges lie ahead in helping society to accept the values of the individual and the philosophy that each individual has the right to the pursuit of his best self-realization.

Generally speaking, nobody is against those considered to be special population members. Yet, attitudes, actions, and our institutions show a clear pattern of considering special population members as those surplus members of our society who are to be hidden out of sight or isolated. Prejudice toward these persons, with open or hidden rejection by the non-disabled, occurs at all social and economic levels and in all regions of our country. It is evident in the social, educational, and vocational discriminations that hamper special population members. It is reflected through the very existence of some legislations to assist special populations to have the same opportunities as nonspecial population members. And lastly, it is clearly manifest in the self-depreciation of the disabled.

Until 1973, no federal law specifically prohibited discrimination against disabled persons. Under pressure from 800 various groups concerned with the rights of disabled, and after a much publicized sit-in by disabled people at the Lincoln Memorial, the United States Congress passed the Rehabilitation Act of 1973. Section 504 of the Act prohibits any federally funded institution from excluding disabled persons from programs or facilities on the basis of their disability. However, the regulations to implement the new law were not signed until April 28, 1977 — and then only after nationwide protest demonstrations.

In a society where people's marketability depends largely on physical appearance, disabled persons — particularly women — are often excluded from the job market. The U.S. Department of Labor estimates that 58 percent of disabled people are unemployed. They cite a New York City advocacy organization estimate that 64 percent of those disabled New Yorkers who have a skill and can work are unemployed, that former mental patients hide their illness when seeking jobs because they cannot afford to tell potential employers for fear of not being hired, that only about one in ten of the people trained in sheltered workshops find work after training.[27]

Despite the national commitment to improve the social and economic lives of special population members, language and thought still confirm the antiquated attitude toward persons who are "different" from the normal. Reference to the disabled as "paraplegics," "epileptics," or "mentally retarded," or better yet as "cripples," "deformed," or "abnormal" reinforce the distinction between the disabled and the nondisabled. They are seen as overly sensitive, easily hurt, weak, shy, nonsexual or sexually perverse. As pointed out in a recent *New York Times* article, societal attitudes do not reflect the reality of disabled people's capabilities. "Our bodies make us disabled, but society makes us handicapped."[28]

Attitudes toward the disabled are expressed in the form of consistently negative prejudgments and behavior. It appears to be a stereotyped reaction, acquired during development, that emphasizes devaluation and rejection of the disabled. The roots of these negative attitudes are found in our social customs and norms, our child-rearing practices that stress normalcy, our personal insecurities, and the discriminating — provoking behavior of the disabled.

Society, conceived of as a pattern of institutions, customs, and interpersonal relations designed to routinize social living, provides preestablished social roles and expectations regarding behavior appropriate to these roles. One such role is that of the disabled. Cues learned in childhood serve as a guide for distinguishing and differentiating various types of disabilities in accordance with socially accepted norms. Society furnishes, in addition to roles and language, a historical attitude toward the disabled: the Greek belief that the physically impaired were inferior; the preprophetic Hebraic idea that the sick were being punished by God; the early Christian concept that disabled persons acquired more virtue because of the disabling condition; the Darwinian theory of the survival of the fittest; the faith in the progress of mankind through science; and lastly, the concern for human rights that is evidenced in the social and economic legislation enacted by the U.S. Congress during the last quarter century aimed at restoring the physically or mentally disabled individual to a responsible, contributing role in society.

This mixture of attitudes results in a marked ambivalence toward disability. A continuous barrage of advertising that emphasizes health and well-being inculcates the belief that physical or emotional disability or injury results from inadequacy, misfortune, or lack of care. Studies show that the nicknames most commonly used by children refer to physique, such as "Four-Eyes," "Fatty," "Slim," and "Freckles." Our comics, our films, and our ads on television, on billboards, and in newspapers have long utilized physical attributes of individuals for comedy effect. As Meyerson has pointed out, if normal variations in physique, such as being strong or weak, tall or short, handsome or ugly, are important factors in personality development, clearly the pathological variations known as physical disability are likely to be even more potent.[29]

Social attitudes toward the disabled are reflected in the family, which teaches discrimination by example, by custom, and by institutionalized values. Child-rearing practices tend to predetermine adult behavior toward the disabled. Psychologists tell us that parents, as a group, live in constant anxiety lest a child of theirs become disabled. The fear of impairment is evident when a parent examines a newborn child. Seeing a physically whole child brings an instantaneous feeling of relief. An impaired child evokes a sense of guilt.

Similar feelings are evident in the reluctance of many parents to permit a close relationship between nondisabled and disabled children. In a recreation setting, it is easy to imagine the reactions of parents who bring their children to a playground program and encounter a mentally retarded youth when they were not expecting it. Or, the reaction of individuals who attend a public pool and encounter several amputees or a cerebral palsied individual. What reactions do they emit and what types of questions are raised? How many readers can recall instances where even passing contact with a physically disabled person was avoided. Why? Because you had undoubtedly learned that the attributes or behaviors of such a person were so bizarre as to be annoying, embarrassing, dangerous, or sufficiently distasteful to warrant avoidance. The barrier that is raised by society's emphasis on conformity and reinforced by the peer group leads both parents and children to avoid physically and mentally impaired children.

The existence of a prejudicial climate conditions disabled persons or former mental patients to accept the role of the disabled. As they assume the pattern of behavior and value deemed appropriate, they prepare themselves to become an object of prejudice. Their appraisal of themselves as inferior reflects the attitudes of those about them. As Mariann Soulek, a recreator with a physical impairment states:

> To a degree we are what people think of us. If we are constantly reminded both in words and in actions that we are dependent, we will be dependent. Society has placed the physically impaired in a minority role by its attitudes toward physical impairment; a well-developed stigma has resulted in prejudice and discrimination. We have reacted and, in many cases, performed according to what society has expected.[30]

The physically disabled child at any early age, for example, requires an unusual amount of help and attention, and thus receives social status and self-esteem. However, as he becomes older, his reactions to his disability change. He is more expensive in terms of both time and money. His parents may reject the child because of feelings of resentment or guilt. This rejection may then be transferred to the child who, in turn, resents the parents. But being dependent upon the parents, the child is forced to suppress his blame, which produces self-hostility, guilt, and anxiety. On the other hand, the parents, either from genuine sympathy or from guilt reactions, may tend to overprotect the child, with equally harmful results. In either instance, the child's ego and social status needs are frustrated.

The forces that make for a differentiated and segregated social life for the disabled child follow him through all phases of his development. During adolescence perceptible differences in appearance, gait, mannerisms, or speech make dating difficult. As he grows into adulthood, he becomes categorized as a member of a minority group. In many instances, he is socially ostracized and rejected by normal persons. He is discriminated against in employment, even for jobs that he is physically and mentally able to perform. The disabled person is a marginal person—physically, socially, and economically; the fact that many avenues of normal relationships are blocked for him—whether actually by his disability, by his attitude toward his disability, or by social pressures—then tends to produce more frustration and conflict.

Many disabled, of necessity, seek the companionship of other disabled persons in social clubs or at centers for various disability groups. Here the person sees himself as not being different, and, therefore, groups composed of persons with similar disabilities tend to become self-perpetuating subcultures. Within them, the person becomes acclimated to the role of a disabled person. He learns the pattern of behavior prescribed for his disability group and adopts feelings and attitudes consonant with society's perception of the role of the disabled person.

Because of the value society places on the "body-whole" and "body beautiful," emotional stability, mental alertness, and other like positive concepts, the role the individual must assume carries with it a sense of devaluation. He may feel shame, inferiority, even worthlessness. Not only is he often considered inferior, but also it is felt that he "ought" to feel inferior, that he "ought to know his place" much in the manner of some minority group members. The assumption seems to be that the disabled are not only perceived as being different, but that this difference is "bad." Thus, we observe that the disabled are confronted with a serious situation because two basic psychological needs are the need for self esteem—i.e., for high self-evaluation—and the need for social status—i.e., for high evaluation by others. For optimal adjustment these needs must be satisfied in some way and to some degree. At the same time the disabled expect and become dependent upon preferential treatment and assistance from the nondisabled.

Distinguishable differences, therefore, in behavior and social perception accentuate the impact of the disability. The characteristics ascribed to and accepted by disabled persons exercise a reciprocal influence upon the behavior and attitudes of the nondisabled. However, in the final analysis, it is the individual who exhibits prejudice and rejects disabled persons. It is the "I" rather than the "he" who commits discriminatory actions. The roots of prejudice come to fruition in the attitudes and behavior of a nondisabled John Doe toward a disabled Richard Roe. According to behavioral scientists, these prejudices appear to be rooted in the prior life experiences of the nondisabled. Whatever the reasons or lack of them, it is undeniable that such attitudes exist and are a deterrent to successful participation in activities of daily living by the disabled.[31]

In summary, there appears to be no question but that American people harbor mixed feelings about special population members and that these members sense the resistance to their reentry into any functionally useful roles. While the attitudes of the American people cannot easily be changed, it is suggested by Hamilton and others ". . . that positive, informal interaction, away from institutional settings, is effective in producing accepting attitudes." He continues by suggesting ". . . that integrated leisure activities would provide a conducive environment for attitude change."[32]

Regardless of the attitude that is reflected by society toward special population members, it is important for you, as a potential therapeutic recreation specialist, to consider the following values and concepts regarding special population members:

- Special population individuals are a normal part of today's society and do not exist as a group apart with separate lives. Their needs and rights are the same as those of any other person; their problems are the problems of all people and should be considered as a part of the whole society.

- The special population person should be regarded as a whole person, physically, mentally, socially, and emotionally, rather than within the narrow confines of his/her limiting condition.

- Leisure program designs should be made with and for special population persons on the basis of abilities, not disabilities, and capabilities, not limitations, to most fully develop their assets.
- If these program designs are to be reflected in care and treatment services, teamwork of the highest order is required in association with other professional personnel (and such teamwork includes the patient).

concepts: health-disease and rehabilitation-punishment

Basic to the practice of all the health and allied health professionals is the *health-disease concept*. A second basic concept, relating to the field of corrections, is the *rehabilitation-punishment concept*.

health-disease

In an earlier period of time the term *health* was generally accepted to mean the normal, harmonious function of the body—in other words, the absence of organ disease. Thus, the person who was an alcoholic, mentally ill, or a criminal was considered to be in a state of perfect health if there was no physical cause for his behavior. Over the years this narrow concept changed as the result both of a generally broader and better integrated view of the individual and of advances in the physical and social sciences. Today, the concept incorporates the wide diversity of individual capacities (physical, mental, emotional, and social), goals and values, and life-styles. Further, the relationship between these factors will differ from person to person. And still further, these factors are constantly being modified or changed as a result of human and natural forces. Health, therefore, is a multidimensional variable.

Definitions of illness vary greatly because the standards of normality and dysfunctioning held by lay persons in diverse social groups vary widely; they may also differ between physicians and patients and even among physicians.[33] The concept of disease, which at times is used synonymously with illness, usually refers to some deviation from normal functioning that has undesirable effects because it produces personal discomfort or adversely affects the individual's future health status. However, one must keep in mind that this concept has various meanings. In its most narrow meaning it refers to a medical hypothesis that implies particular pathological processes underlying a specific clinical syndrome. More generally, the concept is used to refer to physical or behavioral deviations that pose social problems for individuals or the community. Finally, there are occasions in which particular personal problems may be defined as diseases although they neither imply underlying pathology nor pose serious problems for the community.

If we take into consideration those concepts associated with health and disease, a model as suggested by Hoyman (Table 2.1) can be quite useful in understanding the factors which are health producing and disease producing.[34] However, one must be reminded that these factors are ever-

TABLE 2.1 HEALTH-PRODUCING AND DISEASE-PRODUCING FACTORS

Health-Producing	Disease-Producing
Good hereditary endowment	Poor hereditary endowment
Healthful, safe environment	Unhealthy, unsafe environment
Adequate service and education	Personal experiences and behavior
Resistance to communicable and non-communicable diseases	Psychogenic factors
Optimum nutrition, growth, and development	Inadequate standard of living
Organic soundness and functional vigor	Inadequate medical and dental care, public health, and education
Optimum dynamic motor fitness and suitable exercise throughout life	Health fads and fallacies and self-diagnosis and self-treatment
Refreshing rest, relaxation, and sleep	Sociocultural isolation and deprivation
Resistance to stress, fatigue, frustration, and boredom	Abnormal growth and development and pathologic conditions, including neoplasmas
Homeostasis and optimum metabolism	Poor health practices
Healing, repair, and recovery from injury or illness	Endogenous factors related to homeostasis and metabolic disorders
Resistance to premature aging and death	Defects, disabilities, pain, and decay
Healthy mature personality and healthful living	Aging and senescence
A will to live	Stressors and stress
Healthful attitudes, beliefs, and practices	Excesses of deficiencies and deprivations
Freedom for personal-social fulfillment through significant commitments to ultimate concerns	Pathogenic organisms
Useful, satisfying work and creative achievement	Noxious agents and allergens
Love and affectionate sharing and belonging	Radiation hazards
Heterosexual adjustment	Accident hazards and traumatic injuries
Enjoyable constructive recreation and use of leisure	Motion, noise, vibration, and pressure changes
Enjoyable esthetic experiences including those with nature	Existential "human predicament"[35]
Opportunities for risk, challenges, adventure, and new experiences	
Spiritual faith, ideals, values, and a search for meaning	

changing. René Dubos, an eminent microbiologist and medical historian, has made this point most elegantly:

> (Man's) self-imposed striving for ever-new distant goals makes his fate even more unpredictable than that of other living things. For this reason health and happiness cannot be absolute and permanent values, however careful the social and medical planning. Biological success in all of its manifestations is a measure of fitness, and fitness requires never-ending efforts of adaptation to the total environment, which is ever changing.[36]

One cannot discuss the concepts of health and disease however briefly without mentioning how people react to a health need or problem for which assistance is desired. The ability to cope with one's problem—whether physical, emotional, or social—depends on the way one defines the problem, the causes one identified as having brought the problem about, the alternatives one sees for reversing the problem, and one's resources for making use of various alternatives to the problem. While personal experiences, family composition, peer pressures, age-sex role learning, and knowledge acquired about health and disease in the course of one's life are determining factors in the ability to cope with a problem as well as influencing attitudes toward the problem, cultural and social conditioning play a major role though not an exclusive role.[37]

Many studies in the interdisciplinary field of medical sociology dealing with illness behavior reflect the importance of developmental and cultural experiences in determining reactions to illness. Baumann, in a study of differences in people's attitudes toward illness, identified three distinct ways by which people tend to determine whether or not they are ill. One is related to the presence or absence of pain. If a person has pain of a severe nature, he usually considers himself ill. However, pain is relative; a person may live with a backache for years and not consider this an abnormal condition. The second method is related to how they feel: they feel good, or they feel sick. The third way relates to the individual's ability to carry out daily activities. A person is in good health because he works all day and still has energy to play a round of golf in the evening, while another person doing the same work cannot play golf because he feels exhausted and should perhaps have a physical examination. Baumann concludes that whether a person determines the state of his health on the basis of symptoms, feelings, or performance tends to vary with age, education, socioeconomic status, cultural background, and value system.[38]

The subject of health, disease or illness cannot be left without some discussion of illness and disability. The term *disability* generally evokes thoughts of the permanent paralysis which sometimes results from traumatic injuries or the deteriorating effects of some of the dramatic conditions such as multiple sclerosis; it seldom calls to mind such mundane afflictions as the "common cold" or the Monday morning "hangover," which are undoubtedly among the leaders in terms of the total days of disability they cause. The habit of stereotyping illness according to its most dramatic effect often leads to some poor judgments. People many times think of coronary heart disease as something that causes a quick form of death; however, a heart attack disables more often than it kills.

Illnesses vary widely in the degree of disability they necessitate, and the same illness may produce considerable variation in disability among persons so afflicted. Although the "illness condition" itself may be an important contributor to disability, many other factors not associated with the illness may influence the extent to which the person feels unable to undertake a variety of activities. Illness is frequently regarded as disabling when the person's physical or physiological condition makes it impossible for him to perform his usual role obligations. As noted earlier, this is as dependent on the nature of his role obligations and his attitude toward them as it is on his physical condition. It is also dependent on the attitudes and reactions of family members, employers, and society in general.

In considering the social aspects of disability, we must note that the disabled individual's willingness or motivation for retraining plays a crucial role. Individuals who have a keen attitude toward rehabilitation appear to overcome vast difficulties, while others who seem handicapped by medical criteria only to a minimal extent are greatly hampered in their rehabilitation by attitudes that encourage their disability. The attitude of family and colleagues can have a similarly substantial impact on the course a pattern of disability takes. To the extent that the family and others value the person, they are more likely to try to impose their own definition of the situation on him.[39]

In sum, we must recognize that while the social and culture of a group affects aspects of growth and development, the acquisition of goals and aspirations, and the modes of response and adaptation to health, disease, and illness behavior, other factors such as heredity, physical condition, emotional adjustment, environment, and life-style play their part.

rehabilitation-punishment

Since the beginning of time, punishment has been the penalty inflicted by society on those who have violated the laws of society. Its intention is to produce some kind of pain in retribution for breaking a law or harming someone. This concept of retributive punishment is deeply rooted in the minds and emotions of man. Today, most forms of punishment are mental—when there is a loss of freedom, reputation, and personal property—as opposed to physical. The degree of punishment varies with the circumstances surrounding the violation and the personality of the offender. Associated with this pain, the idea of paying a debt to society helps support the moral code and unify society against crime and criminals. However, it is argued today that while retributive punishment does help unify society, there are other ways in which social solidarity can be achieved against crime and criminals. The present social movement designed to prevent crime is one such example. But the student should realize, as pointed out by one group of investigators, that "To underpunish, or not to punish at all, belies the purposes of deterrence and fails at least partially, in the broad objective of public protection."[40]

Since almost all offenders are reabsorbed into society after imprisonment, there has been in recent years an increasing emphasis on the rehabilitation of the offender although the slowness with which this movement has taken place is related to many factors, some economic, others philosophical, and still others political and administrative.

The concept of rehabilitation is interwoven with cultural changes in general and the attitudes of society toward the offender. (However, as early as 1870, the American Prison Association adopted the concept of rehabilitation.) In surveying these changes and attitudes, the history of treatment of the offender has moved through three periods and is presently in a fourth period. These periods include *retaliatory, exploitative, humanitarian,* and the present one, *reeducational-therapeutic* (treatment). However, there is no clear division between one and another, and all four exist in various forms and degrees today.[41]

The reeducational-therapeutic concept appeared during the late eighteenth century as a result of a rise in democratic thought and the development of the behavioral sciences which initiated investigations into the cause of crime and the nature of the offender and his treatment. However, it was not until 1916 at the Auburn Prison in New York, and later in other state prisons and within the federal prison system, that the concept of individual treatment began to be realized.

While giant steps have been taken over the years to implement more thoroughly the reeducational-therapeutic model, authorities in the field consider that the present penal philosophy is in a transition state that contains much of both old and new ideas. Today, we have two conflicting philosophies about inmate treatment. One philosophy—the "custodial prison" in which security is the primary purpose and the idea of treatment is tolerated—reflects the past. The second is the "progressive prison" or treatment type that superimposes on the discipline philosophy programs of classification, medical care and service, vocational and academic training, religion, counseling, recreation, and involvement in the outside world. This form of treatment is found not only within adult correctional institutions, but also within juvenile institutions. While it is the most attractive form of treatment today, it is not the ultimate answer according to the people in the field. One reason given is that the recidivism rates have changed little since its inception. Another reason is that punishment (imprisonment) is so disconnected from the time when the offense was committed that the offense is no longer in the mind of the offender. But by and large, most correctional administrators subscribe to the concept of rehabilitation within the limitations of funds and personnel.[42]

According to Caldwell, rehabilitation, to be successful, must "contain both negative and positive elements, both pleasure and pain, and both persuasion and authority; and to be most effective it must be based upon an intensive study of the individual."[43] It has been said by many in the correctional field that rehabilitation takes place only with inmates' cooperation. What is meant here is that rehabilitation must not be so pleasant as to encourage further criminal activity, but it should be designed to produce changes in the personality of the individual. If the cooperation needed for successful rehabilitation is to be achieved, resentment must be dissolved and support secured.

Since the first edition, the concept of rehabilitation seems to have regressed some. Unfortunately, in some geographical regions it appears that theory and practice have yet to catch up if a recent ABC-TV *20/20* production portrayed the Texas prison system correctly. Prisons were overcrowded, vocational training programs were directed toward production rather than training for potential jobs in the community following release, and recreation services were limited.[44] Likewise, many Southern states still use a version of the "Chain Gang." Although modern in that the inmates are unchained, they still maintain highways as their primary responsibility; they also operate heavy equipment and assist in the construction of government buildings. According to one county official in Georgia, inmate labor saved the taxpayers one-million dollars in working man-hours in his county in 1978.[45] In the juvenile justice system study cited earlier it was found that juvenile training schools had little impact on subsequent criminal behavior. Although 70 percent of all funds spent on juvenile corrections now goes toward supporting juvenile institutions rather than juvenile probation, these institutions are still inadequate.[46]

Two forms of correctional rehabilitation associated with the modern philosophy of rehabilitation—probation and parole—have also felt a setback. As a result of never receiving adequate funds for the number of offenders under supervision, their full cost/benefit potential is yet to be achieved even though when properly implemented has been effective.[47]

There is growing evidence, on the other hand, that new rehabilitation programs making use of community approaches are gathering momentum. Community-based corrections recognizes the failure of massive, impersonal institutions far removed from population centers. It recognizes the importance of working with the offender in his home community, or near it where his ties with family and friends can be used to advantage in his

rehabilitation. Among the types of community and transitional release programs are: pretrial intervention, modified probation and parole programs,
halfway houses, work-release programs, and prerelease centers.[48]

conditions or disorders

As we begin this section it should be reemphasized that acute and chronic
conditions may be physical, emotional, social, or intellectual or any combination thereof in nature. Furthermore, whatever the nature of the condition may be, individual differences exist. The following two examples will
give you some idea of what is meant by individual differences. Cerebral
palsy, for example, may require one child to walk only with a cane, a second to walk with the aid of leg braces and a Canadian crutch, and leave a
third child helpless. Dianne, whose IQ is 85, manages to struggle along in
the regular grades, though her marks are usually poor; but her sister,
Sharon, whose IQ is 60, attends an educable class for the mentally retarded, and Marie, a neighbor's child with an IQ of 20, has to be sent to a
state institution for the mentally retarded.

There is another important characteristic that must be taken into consideration, and that is the time factor. How long has the condition existed?
What was the individual's age at the time the disorder originated? What
can be inferred with respect to its probable duration? The child who
becomes blind at the age of 10 is in a very different position from the one
who has been blind from birth. That which can be accomplished with
relative ease at one age may become difficult at another, for growth proceeds inexorably and ceases when maturity is reached. Correction of a
physically disabling condition or behavior deviation often depends on the
stage that the difficulty has already reached. Thus, it may be concluded
that the nature of the deviation may require services and/or devices
anywhere from a short period of time to a lifetime.

The potential therapeutic recreation specialist should also become
aware, if not already, that all diseases are not detected early in life. Some
are unmistakable as soon as the child is born. *Cleft lip* and *palate, clubfoot,
spina bifida,* and *Down's Syndrome* are among them. Other conditions
which are invisible to the layman are readily recognized by the physician.
Within a minute of birth a physician usually calculates an infant's "Apgar
score," based on heart rate, respiratory effort, muscle tone, reflexes, and
color. A low Apgar score and extremely low birth weight are considered immediate danger signals of a possible internal defect. Some defects are not
apparent until 30 days after birth or later during the first year of the child's
life. Others do not appear until adolescence or adulthood. A child may be
in his teens before he shows symptoms of *Wilson's disease,* a metabolic

malfunction which results in a deficiency of copper and consequent brain damage—although the condition can now be detected and corrected at three months with a family history of the disease. *Huntington's chorea,* a degenerative nervous system disease, strikes in the victim's late 30s and 40s. The inborn tendency to *diabetes mellitus* may not cause disease until the victim is 50 or older.

The following pages present some of the major types of acute and chronic conditions found in special populations. The problem of organizing the various disease and behavior conditions into logical subcategories leads to many complex and somewhat tedious considerations. Nevertheless, it has been prepared primarily to assist potential therapeutic recreation specialists in developing an awareness of those conditions that affect people's ability to engage in recreative activities, likewise, those kinds of conditions which therapeutic recreation specialists are more likely to encounter in offering recreation services to special populations. It presupposes some knowledge of medical terminology. However, for those lacking such knowledge, a brief introduction to medical terminology and definitions is provided in Appendix A.

mental retardation

Mental retardation is a condition, a description of behavior, not a disease. It is estimated that the number of retarded people in the United States numbers nearly six million as of 1976 although this number is open to question.[49] Of this six million, over one-half are adults. Approximately 176,000 of the six million live in public institutions.[50] This later figure represents a decline of nearly 25,000 since 1971.[51]

According to the President's Committee on Mental Retardation there is no method currently available to determine either the true incidence or the true prevalence of mental retardation. Some factors, for example, that contribute to difficulty in determining the incidence of mental retardation include: (1) the inability to identify in every case the cause of mental retardation; (2) in only a small percentage of cases can it be determined at birth that a person is, or ever will be, mentally retarded; and (3) most mentally retarded persons are not identified until five or six years of age when they enter school.[52]

A recent analysis of epidemiological studies that were conducted in the United States concluded that the overall prevalence of mental retardation is very close to three percent.[53] However, this prevalence figure is affected by the recent changes in the definition of mental retardation and interpretations of other definitions by governing bodies, courts, educators, psychologists, and welfare workers. While there appears to be general statistical agreement relative to those considered to be "moderately" "severely" and "profoundly" retarded since the diagnosis for these so classified individuals can be confirmed medically, psychometrically, and through adaptive behavior, consensus completely breaks down when "mild" mental retardation is added.[54]

While problems exist concerning the incidence and prevalence of mental retardation as it relates to the way the term is defined, it is well to note the current estimated distribution of the mentally retarded in the United States by age and degree of retardation. Table 2.2 shows this distribution from data collected by the National Association of Retarded Citizens (NARC). It should be noted that variations exist between what the President's Committee is reporting and the NARC.

A vast range of conditions and diseases can cause or contribute to retarded intellectual development. There are more than 250 known causes of mental retardation, or diseases and conditions so associated with the later development of retardation as to be considered probable causes. The causes cover the range of hereditary, biological, psychological, and sociological determinants of life conditions and development. They include chromosomal-genetic influences derived from heredity or physiology. They include diseases, infections, accidents, and the physical neglect and mistreatment of children. And they include the slow, sometimes subtle, influences of the physical, psychological, and social environment which may influence the development of mental retardation through deprivation.

In addition to cause and probable cause of mental retardation, the reader should also be aware that mental retardation is frequently associated with other types of problems. In 1971, a nationwide survey of persons labeled mentally retarded found that a very large percentage had significant speech and language problems which restricted them from engaging in effective communication with others. Other problems which

TABLE 2.2 ESTIMATED DISTRIBUTION OF RETARDED PERSONS IN THE UNITED STATES BY AGE AND DEGREE OF RETARDATION

| Degree | All Ages | | Age By Years | | | |
	No.	%	Under 20	%	20 & Over	%
Total	6,152,050	100.0	2,507,970	40.8	3,644,080	59.2
Mild	5,332,050	86.7	2,132,820	40.0	3,199,230	60.0
Moderate	615,000	10.0	264,450	43.0	350,550	57.0
Severe and Profound	205,000	3.3	110,700	54.0	94,300	46.0

Source: National Association of Retarded Citizens as cited in President's Committee on Mental Retardation, *Mental Retardation: Century of Decision* (Washington, D.C.: U.S. Government Printing Office, March 1976), 7.

occurred with high frequency included impaired hearing and vision, seizures, ambulation, and perceptual motor disorders.[55]

Over the years, the term *mental retardation* has defied a definition. In fact, even the term itself has been altered many times. For example, terminology has shifted among *idiocy, amentia, oligophrenia, feeblemindedness, mental deficiency, mental subnormality* and *slow learner.*

The problem of defining mental retardation is made difficult because so many types of specialists are interested in the totality of its psycho-socio-medical implications. Obviously, each type of specialist focuses on the specific dimensions in which he is trained and interested. Representatives of the medical profession, for example, view mental retardation in terms of pathology, or sickness, which differentiates individuals in their physical make-up and function from the characteristics of the "normal" individual. Educators, on the other hand, become concerned when the mentally retarded individual does not respond to the usually successful methods of instruction in use in the schools. This has led to the statistical focus, which attempts to classify individuals according to intellectual potential and thereby predict the limits of future success or achievement.

As important as scientific concerns are, societal attitudes have been just as important in recent years in the development of any definition about mental retardation. As evidence mounted that more retarded persons were "found" in certain ethnic or income groups and in certain geographical areas, pressure was exerted to reexamine definitions of retardation to determine whether the consequences of deprivation were being confused with constitutional disability.

Definitions of mental retardation have included reference to such variables as causation, curability, age of onset, intelligence quotient, mental age, educability, and social adequacy. In 1959, the American Association on Mental Deficiency (AAMD) recognizing that only a broad description would encompass the diversity of the field, the many disciplines involved, and all ages of retardates, arrived at a definition which placed emphasis on the broad aspects of functional behavior as well as measured intelligence. The definition, which was prepared by Rick Heber and revised in 1961, received wide use and reads as follows: "Mental retardation refers to subaverage general intellectual functioning which originates during the developmental period and is associated with impairment of adaptive behavior."[56] Subaverage functioning is defined in the language of statisticians to mean more than one standard deviation below the normal (IQ approximately 84 and below). The developmental period extends from birth to approximately 16 years of age. And impaired adaptive behavior is associated with maturation, learning, and social adjustments. With the support of the AAMD, Heber also suggested a system of classification relating degree of retardation to measured intelligence. It included a group called "borderline retarded," and labeled successive degrees of impairment as mild, moderate, severe, and profound mental retardation.[57]

In 1973, the AAMD on advice of its Task Force on Classification and Terminology headed by Herbert Grossman adopted the following definition: "Mental retardation refers to significantly subaverage general intellectual functioning existing concurrently with deficits in adaptive behavior, and manifested during the developmental period."[58] While this definition appears similar to the 1961 definition, the reader will note that the word "significantly" has been added which according to the Grossman committee is to mean two standard deviations below the normal (IQ limit at approximately 70 depending on which intelligence test is used). In addition, the committee eliminated the classification category of borderline retardation. However, it should be borne in mind that while the former "borderline" classification has been excluded, it does not mean that such individuals are free from problems of learning and social adaptation or that they do not require appropriate supporting service. Only time will determine how significant this definition will be in meeting the needs of those so classified as mentally retarded.

Other individuals that many times have been considered mentally retarded, although they are not, include those with a variety of conditions that are categorized as *learning disabilities*. Some have difficulty connecting the printed word with something that makes sense to them. They may have difficulty distinguishing "b" from "d", "saw" from "was". The child may hear a spoken word or sound adequately, but be unable to remember the word or interpret the sound accurately. They may not remember how to spell a word from one day to the next. They may gaze out the window rather than listen to their teacher or aimlessly wander about the classroom. They may be hyperactive, continually drumming their fingers or shuffling their feet, or may act impulsively with sudden rages. These children continually cause frustration—for their parents, for their teachers, and most importantly for themselves.

Children with learning disabilities show a discrepancy between expected and actual achievement in written language or mathematics. This learning disability does not appear to be primarily the result of sensory, motor, intellectual, or emotional handicap or lack of opportunity to learn. "Learning disabilities" refers to those children of average or above average intelligence who have a disorder of one or more of the basic psychological processes involved in understanding or using language—spoken, or written.

Professionals are skeptical about estimating the number of children who might have a learning disability, though they do know that the majority of children with this problem are boys. Estimates range from 1 to 15 percent of the school population, although some state that as many as 35 percent of all children may have a learning disability which will cause them some kind of school problem. In addition, they come from all economic and social levels. Environment does not appear to be a direct cause. For example, Thomas Edison, Woodrow Wilson, and Sir Winston Churchill were just a few of the famous people who made significant contributions to society despite their learning disabilities.

It appears that no one really knows the causes of learning disabilities. Theories range from chemical imbalance to genetic heredity. These children may be labeled as perceptually handicapped, hyperkinetic, learning disabled or with minimal brain damage, minimal cerebral dysfunction, faulty neurological development, or dyslexia. These labels used by various professionals all overlap. None of them totally explains the cause.

Difficulty in evaluation of the percentage of learning-disabled youngsters may be caused, in some respects, by the fact that there are children who become unknown victims of the educational process but are never classified as "learning disabled." Early in life these children might be marked by teachers as troublemakers or attention-getters or as lacking motivation. There appears to be a correlation between deliquency and learning disabilities. Surveys of juvenile delinquents have shown that as many as 80 percent may have learning disabilities.

According to pediatricians and psychologists, children with learning disabilities don't socialize well with their peers because their peers realize they are different. They don't play the same way—often they are clumsy and have tempers. Often learning-disabled children play with children who are a year or so younger because they get along better with that age group.

nonsensory impairments

Effective human efficiency is dependent upon the smooth function and integration of bodily parts and the various systems, including the musculo-skeletal, cardiovascular, respiratory, digestive, genitourinary, endocrine, nervous, and reproductive systems. When an accident or a disease interferes with bodily parts or systems, a disabling condition may result. Furthermore, it is impossible to alter one organ or body system without producing changes in the other. The causes of disabling conditions may be hereditary (for example, hemophilia), congenital (spina bifida), traumatic (severance of the spinal cord), infectious (osteomyelitis), glandular (Addison's disease), metabolic (diabetes), neoplastic (cancer of the bone), circulatory (arteriosclerosis), respiratory (emphysema), myogenic (rheumatoid arthritis), or neurogenic (cerebral palsy).

Precise information concerning the numbers, locations, and types of physically disabled persons, as well as the extent of their needs for service, is not available. However, in 1970, the President's Task Force on the Physically Handicapped reported that over 25 million persons suffer from some type of nonsensory impairment.[59] As noted in Table 2.3, diseases and disabilities exist among all age groups—small children, students in school, working-age adults, and people in their advanced years.

A difficulty encountered when considering nonsensory impairments is determining what to include. This problem is further compounded because it is impossible here to identify and describe the variety of even the major diseases and conditions that result in disabilities. I have, therefore, selected for mention only those diseases associated with various organs and systems that are of greatest significance in terms of special population numbers, with a brief description of a few specific diseases.

Many of these conditions are usually apparent to the casual observer, as will be noted shortly. In other cases, the resulting disabilities are not so readily apparent. These individuals have a variety of chronic health problems that require long convalescent periods and/or restriction in their activity either periodically or chronically. However, much of the disability associated with chronic illness and impairment is a result of social definitions in contrast to physical incapacities.[60] The student who is considering offering recreation service to the nonsensory physically impaired should acquire further knowledge about these acute and chronic conditions.

While an exact number of physically disabling conditions cannot be given, there is baseline information on the use of special aids—artificial limbs, braces, crutches, canes, special shoes, wheelchairs, walkers, and other special aids for getting around. The Health Interview Survey by the National Center for Health Statistics estimated that over 6 million persons in the civilian, noninstitutional population of the United States (or 3.2 percent of the total population) used one or more special aids to assist in their mobility. A total of over 7 million such aids were reported in use. Special shoes were the most frequently reported aid, while artificial arms or hands were the least frequently reported. Persons 15 to 44 years of age reported the least use of aids and persons 65 years and over reported the highest use of aids (13.3) percent).[61] A later study prepared for the National Park Service indicated that over 400,000 individuals use wheelchairs, 1.1 million use

TABLE 2.3 PHYSICALLY HANDICAPPED PEOPLE IN THE UNITED STATES

Age Group	Estimated Total Number
0–4 years	270,000
5–19 years	3,660,000
20–64 years	15,000,000
65+ years	6,690,000

Source: President's Task Force on the Physically Handicapped, *A National Effort for the Physically Handicapped* (Washington, D.C.: U.S. Government Printing Office, 1970), p. 2.

leg braces, 172,000 use artificial limbs, and over three million use canes, walkers, and crutches to assist in mobility.[62]

Musculoskeletal Impairments

Bones, joints, and muscles make up the musculoskeletal system. *Bones* form the framework of the body. The places of contact of bones are called *articulations,* or *joints. Muscular tissue* is specialized for contractability while its functions are exceedingly numerous and varied. Disease or injury to any part of this system may cause a disabling condition that in turn may affect the capacity to work or to move. However, human movement, for example, is not dependent upon bones, joints, and muscles alone; it is also dependent upon the function of motor nerves, the cells in the spinal cord from which these nerve fibers arise, and the impulses from the motor areas in the cerebral cortex of the brain. In addition, other systems such as the cardiovascular and respiratory systems are also involved. Thus, when damage affects the stability of the musculoskeletal systems and interferes with the normal function of bones, joints, and muscles (specifically, abnormalities in locomotion), we consider the individual to have an orthopedic problem.

The term *orthopedic* is derived from two Greek words: *orthos,* meaning right, correct, true, straight; and *pardeia,* the rearing of children. Orthopedic is defined by many as the "straight child." In modern usage, the term refers to persons with muscular or skeletal impairments—i.e., those impairments associated with the proper function of bones, joints, muscles, tendons, and peripheral blood vessels and nerves. In many instances individuals with orthopedic impairments may require an appliance for body and limb support. The causes of orthopedic impairments may be congenital, infectious, osteochondritic, and traumatic. Furthermore, the term is also applied to a medical specialty concerned with the preservation and restoration of motor and locomotor functions.

Major disabling conditions of the musculoskeletal system associated with the site of the disturbance include the following:

Bone. A bone may become infected, and the resulting inflammation of the bone and its marrow is called *osteomyelitis.* Bone may be the seat of infections such as *tuberculosis of the bone.* Malignant tumors are by no means rare and usually require surgical procedures. If a tumor affects the limb, as it did the son of Senator Edward Kennedy, amputation is required. *Osteoporosia* is a metabolic disorder of the bone common in older persons that leads to excessive risk of fractures. Sometimes bones that should unite before birth fail to do so. One such failure leads to *spina bifida,* in which there is a defect of closure of the bony spinal canal. As a result, there is usually a protrusion of the spinal cord through this gap, causing varying degrees of paralysis in the lower extremities. Another such congenital malformation is *clubfoot,* either single or bilateral, in which the front part of the foot is inverted and rotated, accompanied by a shortening of the Achilles tendon and contracture of the fascia in the sole of the foot.

Joints. Among all chronic diseases in the United States rheumatism may be the most prevalent. More than 17 million persons are suffering from arthritis and related rheumatic diseases.[63] The three most common types are *infectious arthritis, osteoarthritis* (degenerative), and *rheumatoid arthritis;* the latter two are most prevalent. It is estimated that over 6.5 million persons suffer from rheumatoid arthritis and about one-half of these are partially or totally disabled.[64] Another form of this type found in children is *juvenile rheumatoid arthritis;* however, the prognosis for this condition is more favorable than for rheumatoid arthritis. *Scoliosis* (lateral curvature of the spine) is a joint deformity that may involve the entire length or only one portion of the vertebral column. A progressive disease, it can lead over the years to pain, disability, and cardiopulmonary and other complications. Lastly, joints may be dislocated, in which case there is a displacement of one of the bones or a derangement of the parts that compose the joint.

Muscles, Tendons, and Bursae. Skeletal muscles may undergo atrophy from unknown causes. A particularly distressing disease because it strikes children and teen-agers, weakening and gradually shriveling the voluntary muscles, is *progressive muscular dystrophy.* As the disease progresses, it may incapacitate the person so completely that he cannot stand or sit. However, there are several forms of the disease, and not all lead to total incapacitation. Other muscular diseases that may produce a disabling condition are *progressive muscular atrophy* and *myasthenia gravis.* While diseases of the tendons and bursae do not produce disabling conditions, they do cause limitations for a period of time in the more severe cases.

Two conditions associated with musculoskeletal dysfunction are *adhesions* and *contractures.* The etiology of both are either acquired or congenital. An adhesion is a pathologic band restricting the normal movement between two adjacent tissues. It is caused by serous or hemorrhagic exudate from the blood vessels which is either inflammatory or traumatic in origin. When a joint is stiff it is generally due to the presence of adhesions that may be found in or around it. Contractures are caused by structural changes in the soft tissue. A contracture is a fixed state of muscle, tendon, fascia, or ligament which does not disappear under anesthesia except in hysterical cases. Contractures are frequently seen following the removal of a cast and in individuals who have suffered a stroke or damage to the spinal cord.

Earlier it was indicated that when musculoskeletal stability is disturbed, function is lost. It is well to consider the effect of disease and traumatic injury upon the musculoskeletal system. Traumatic injuries include fractures, dislocations, strains, sprains, lacerations of every type, and thermal injuries. There are many traumatic injuries and, to a lesser degree, diseases that are accompanied or followed by temporary or permanent disability. In some instances the injury or disease is so severe that a brace or an amputation is required. Causes for amputation include the following: (1) accidents, (2) uncontrollable chronic infections, (3) malignant tumors, (4) circulatory insufficiency from peripheral vascular diseases, (5) uselessness of a deformed limb that is objectionable to the person, (6) thermal injuries, (7) congenital absence, and (8) other conditions that may endanger the life of the individual.

As a result of an amputation or other orthopedic impairment, an individual may be fitted with a prosthesis, brace, or orthopedic appliance. The amputee does not always have a prosthesis prescribed—i.e., some are not motivated to learn how to use the prosthesis, others may be too young or too old, and still others may lack the potential skill for the proper control and function of the prosthesis. Braces and splints are used mainly to render mechanical support to weak or paralyzed limbs and to prevent deformity.

Nervous System

The human brain and central nervous system are awesome instruments, far more advanced than the most sophisticated man-made computer. At the same time however, disturbances of the brain and central nervous system have historically been among the most tragic, disabling, and intractable scourges of mankind. Not only do these disorders claim lives, but they sentence many to a lifetime of total or partial disability, and sap medical and financial resources far out of proportion to the number afflicted.

The nervous system is divided into a central part consisting of the brain and spinal cord, and a peripheral part consisting of the nerves carrying motor messages from the brain and spinal cord to the muscles and those carrying sensory messages from the skin and other parts of the body to the spinal cord and brain. Any infection or injury at any time during the life of the individual or any lack of development of any part of this system is likely to result in disabilities of various kinds.

Exact figures on the prevalence of neurological impairments are not available. However, the National Institute of Neurological Diseases and Stroke (NINDS) estimates that as much as 10 percent of the total population of the United States may be suffering from one of the approximately 200 disabling neurological or sensory disorders. According to the NINDS, multiple conditions are common, and the vast majority of the neurological and sensory problems are still incurable.[65] The estimated number of cases and cost of care for selected chronic neurological disorders are given in Table 2.4.

One of the most tragic disabling illnesses because it strikes at infants,

TABLE 2.4 ESTIMATED NUMBER OF CASES AND COST OF CHRONIC NEUROLOGICAL DISORDERS		
Disability	Estimated Total Cases	Estimated Annual Cost of Care[1]
Cerebral palsy	750,000	$ 1.6 billion
Epilepsy	2,000,000	$ 2.0 billion
Multiple sclerosis	500,000	$ 1.0 billion
Spina bifida	27,500	$ 55.0 million
Spinal cord injury	125,000	$ 2.4 billion
Strokes	2,000,000	$ 4.0 billion
Tumors of the brain and other parts of the nervous system	140,000	$430.0 million

SOURCE: National Institutes of Health, *Neurological and Sensory Disabilities: Estimated Numbers and Cost* (Washington, D.C.: U.S. Government Printing Office, 1973).

[1] Estimates are calculated on per year maintenance (physician's fees, drugs, and special management) for partially and totally disabled at home and in public and private institutions.

many of whom are treated for the rest of their lives as though they were completely helpless, is *cerebral palsy.* Cerebral palsy may develop during the prenatal, perinatal, or postnatal period. It is estimated that each year about 25,000 babies are born with cerebral palsy — one every 21 minutes. Although the cerebral palsied child may present any combination of signs and symptoms that reflect cerebral malfunctions — such as neuromotor disability, convulsions, or vision, hearing, speech, tactile, or perceptual disturbances — the symptom that differentiates cerebral palsied children from others in the syndrome is the neuromotor disability. This disability may be spasticity (about one-half of the victims are spastic) and weakness, either alone or in mixed varieties. Dysfunction may be limited to a single limb or may involve the entire body. Frequently cerebral palsied children are diagnosed with multiple disabilities such as blindness, deafness, cleft palate, and congenital heart diseases.

While the public has adopted a more open attitude toward many illnesses, *epilepsy* (sometimes called *parorysmal cerebral dysrhythmia*) still appears to carry a social stigma. This stigma, to some degree, is nothing more than rank discrimination. And though there is less of it now than ever before, five states still have laws providing for involuntary sterilization of epileptics and five states permit parents who adopt children to annul the adoption if the child turns out to have epilepsy. In some parts of the world, epileptics are not allowed to marry.[66] The cause of *ordinary epilepsy,* the most common type, also called *genuine* or *idiopathic epilepsy,* is not known; it is not directly inherited, although a predisposition or tendency toward it runs in families. *Acquired epilepsy,* also called *symptomatic epilepsy,* may be the result of brain tumors, diabetes, infectious diseases, toxic cerebral irritations, and psychological disturbances. The word *epilepsy* is derived from the Greek word *epilepsia* meaning "a seizure" or "to seize" which includes the idea of being seized by a demon or god, and is applied to a type of seizure characterized by loss of consciousness and involuntary convulsive movements. There are different forms of seizures— namely, *grand mal, petit mal, psychomotor,* and *Jacksonian epilepsy.* Today, however, many physicians prefer to use an internationally agreed upon and simplified classification that divides the epilepsies into *generalized* (seizures involving the whole body) and *focal* (seizures affecting just one part of the body and limited to a single identifiable section of the brain). The seizure is due to a temporary disturbance of the brain impulses and abnormal electrical discharges. The student should remember that all seizures are not epilepsy. Seizures can result from a number of things: fever, for instance, hormonal or chemical imbalances, an alcoholic's withdrawal from alcohol and so on. Generally, only those occurring repeatedly are called epilepsy.

The term *cerebral-vascular accident* refers to a stroke. The condition was recognized and described by Hippocrates. In the United States alone, it occurs 1.5 million times a year. It often cripples and is the third ranking killer, responsible for 9.9 percent of all deaths.[67] A stroke is caused by acute vascular lesions in the brain that result in a sudden loss of consciousness, often accompanied by loss of sensation and motor power. The local ischemia responsible for the stroke may be due to (1) thrombosis (most common), (2) embolism, or (3) hemorrhage. In nearly all major cerebral-vascular accidents, paralysis results with the hemiplegic type (paralysis of one side of the body) being the most frequent. Other cerebral dysfunctions that were mentioned under cerebral palsy may be associated with the stroke.

Paralysis of a muscle or group of muscles is due to pathologic changes resulting from disease or injury in either the upper motor neuron within the brain and brain stem or the lower motor neuron within the spine and its periphery. Specifically, damage to the upper motor neuron causes *spastic paralysis,* and lower motor neuron damage causes *flaccid paralysis.* Furthermore, the degree and extent of the damage to the nervous system will determine the seriousness of movement impairment. There are four classifications, according to the limbs involved: the term *monoplegia* is used if one limb is involved; if half the body (both limbs on one side), *hemiplegia* is used; if both lower extremities, *paraplegia* is used; if all four extremities, *quadriplegia* is used.

Prior to World War II, a broken neck or back with severance of the spinal cord meant death, if not immediately from respiratory failure, then certainly within a short time from secondary infections. Today, there are thousands of paraplegics and quadriplegics. An estimated 125,000 persons have survived spinal cord injuries, and more than 10,000 are added to this population each year. The majority of such injured are young men and women. Approximately 62 percent of spinal cord injuries happen to adults between 16 and 30 years of age with the greatest number of injuries (53 percent) occurring during the summer months. The apparent cause is high velocity or high risk activities such as fast driving, skiing, diving, contact athletic events, and similar activities.[68]

Multiple sclerosis (MS) is another neurological disease surrounded by myths striking people (three out of five are women) mainly between the ages of 20 and 40. MS generally progresses in a series of exacerbations and remissions although it sometimes progresses rapidly, producing severe disability within a few years of onset. Exacerbations, attacks during which symptoms get worse or new symptoms appear, often last less than six weeks and are followed by periods of remission, sometimes lasting many years, during which symptoms remain the same or improve spontaneously. Motor symptoms are less likely to improve than sensory (touch, sight) symptoms.

Other disabling neurological diseases include *poliomyelitis; meningitis,* of which there are many forms; *Parkinson's disease;* and tumors of the brain and spinal cord.

Circulatory System

There are three parts to the circulatory mechanism—namely, the heart, blood vessels, and blood. Since food is delivered and waste removed by the blood stream, the nutrition of the body depends upon the efficiency of the circulatory system. Interference with any part of this system therefore impairs the function of the body.

There are three main conditions that may result in heart disease; (1) endocarditis, an inflammation of the valves; (2) narrowing of the coronary arteries; and (3) high blood pressure. Examples of heart diseases due to these conditions include *rheumatic fever, bacterial endocarditis, coronary artery occlusion* (heart attack, *hypertension,* and *congenital heart disease.* Of these, the commonest is hypertension. Approximately 35 million Americans are known to have high blood pressure. High blood pressure may actually be a mild condition and in many cases never causes symptoms. However, in others damage results. Hypertension means that there is too much pressure in the bloodstream. It's like a garden hose with a too-tight nozzle. Eventually either the nozzle or the hose bursts, which is exactly what happens to blood vessels when the pressure is too great. If the vessel bursts in the heart, you have a heart attack. If it's in the brain, you have a stroke

The etiology of hypertension is unknown, although emotional tension, tumors, and kidney ailments are suspected causes. Hypertension is followed in descending order of prevalence by coronary artery occlusion, rheumatic heart disease, bacterial endocarditis, and congenital heart disease. Each year more than 40,000 children are born with defects in the structure of the heart or of the large blood vessels connected to the heart.[69]

The heart is aided in its work mainly by the arteries and to a lesser extent by the veins. The arteries are active, contractible organs that not only drive the blood on by a peristaltic contraction, but also control the pressure by narrowing or widening the vessel walls. The most common disease of the arteries, and one that causes much disability in middle age and later life, is *arteriosclerosis,* or hardening of the arteries. This is a physiological process of wear and tear that produces degeneration, calcification, and decrease in elasticity of the tissue. The changes in function that follow such changes in structure are disturbing.

Varicosity is the most common disease of the veins. In individuals who stand a great deal of the time the valves of the leg veins wear out and eventually are unable to resist the pressure of the long column of blood that they are called upon to support. In these instances, the veins become tortuous and dilated, and we speak of them as *varicose veins.*

The function of the blood is to constantly circulate through the vessels bringing to all tissues their needed supply of chemicals and bearing away the waste products of their metabolism. The blood cells originate in the hematopoietic system—namely, the bone marrow and lymphoid tissue. There are a number of blood and lymphatic diseases that cause disability. Blood disorders of importance here are *pernicious anemia, sickle cell anemia,* and *hemophilia.* Hemophilia, "the bleeding disease," is characterized by excessive repeated hemorrhages, both spontaneous and following light trauma. The condition is inherited, being transmitted only to males, but the gene is transmitted by females of the family. Hemophilia affects the knee joint more frequently than any other region.

Difficult and distressing lymphatic diseases are the leukemias. In spite of its name, leukemia is not a disease of the blood, but essentially a generalized proliferative neoplastic disorder of the blood-forming *tissues* that usually results in a great increase in the white cells of the blood. Of the four types, two are common: *myelocytic leukemia* and *lymphocytic leukemia.* Either type may be acute or chronic. Children are more apt to be afflicted with *acute lymphocytic leukemia,* while adults more often contract the chronic form. Prognosis in both types is grave; however, chronic cases may live for 10 or 15 years.

Respiratory System

The respiratory system is responsible for taking oxygen into the body and giving off carbon dioxide. The organs concerned with this action are the nose, the pharynx, the larynx, the trachea, the bronchi, and the lungs. Of importance to us are those diseases that affect the bronchi and lungs.

Chronic bronchitis and *emphysema,* frequently grouped as chronic obstructive pulmonary diseases, result in an increasing number of disabilities each year. Individuals with chronic bronchitis and emphysema are partially or completely disabled for many years. Chronic bronchitis is a persistent or recurrent inflammation of the bronchial tubes. Emphysema is a disease in which the lungs lose their elasticity and cannot expand and contract normally to draw in and force out air. *Asthma* is another chronic obstructive respiratory disease, characterized by recurrent attacks of difficulty in breathing and a feeling of suffocation. Most attacks of asthma result from allergies, the person being hypersensitive or allergic to substances in the air he breathes or, less frequently, in the food he eats.

Although *tuberculosis* is not as prevalent as it once was, the number of new cases is declining only slowly. It is estimated that 25 million persons in this country have tuberculosis bacilli in their bodies and that over 150,000 have the active disease.[70] The most striking change in incidence is the shift from the young to the old. Some years ago a tuberculosis sanitarium resembled a college dormitory; today it is more like an old folks' home. A few generations ago it could be found in all socioeconomic classes. Today it is associated primarily with low-income groups, and the blacks carry a heavy load. It should be kept in mind that tuberculosis is not restricted to the lung, but may involve every organ of the body. However, it is found more frequently in the lung since its chief method of spreading is coughing.

Cancer is the second leading cause of death in the United States affecting every age group and almost any part of the body. It has been included here because cancer of the lung is the leading cause of death. Although lung cancer is much more common in men than in women, the rate of increase has been greater in recent years among women than men. The causes of cancer are quite varied, although there appears to be a link between cigarette smoking and cancer of the lung. While the death rate from cancer has increased steadily over the years, still many do not die immediately as a direct result of the disease. The future seems to be more encouraging, according to the American Cancer Society, which states that of every six persons who get cancer today, two will be treated successfully and four will die[71] There are over 950,000 Americans annually receiving medical care for cancer through office visits and in-patient treatments and in convalescent settings.

The most common chronic lung disease in children is that accompanying *cystic fibrosis* of the pancreas. The crippling effect is due to the almost regular appearance of a chronic infection and an obstructive process in the lungs. The condition usually becomes manifest at birth or shortly thereafter. The majority of the children with this disease appear thin and chronically ill. The thick secretions in the lung cause paroxysms of severe coughing. Exertion quickly leads to shortness of breath, and thus participation in more than mild exercise is difficult. Eventually the heart will be embarrassed by lack of oxygen, and heart failure with general dropsy will slowly develop. By this time the child is bedridden.

Endocrine and Metabolic Disorders

A *gland* is an organ that secretes one or more substances serving the chemical or physiologic needs of the organism. Glands of internal secretion have no ducts, but discharge their secretion by way of the veins and lymphatics with which they are abundantly supplied. They are called *glands of internal secretion, ductless glands,* or *endocrine glands.* They govern metabolism. One cannot have a serious disturbance of one gland of internal secretion for any length of time without other glands becoming affected. Disturbances of endocrine glands may play a major or minor part in producing a disabling condition such as arthritis, certain epiphyseal disturbances, and various disorders of bone growth and development. For example, *hypothyroidism,* an underactivity of the thyroid gland, causes the individual to be sluggish and overweight. *Hyperparathyroidism,* an overactivity of the parathyroid glands, causes pain in bones and joints, weakness, and loss of muscle power and tone. *Addison's disease,* another glandular disabling condition, in which there is weakness, low blood pressure, darkening of the skin, and weakness of other systems, is the result of a deficiency of hormones from the adrenal glands.

Metabolism refers to all the changes in foodstuffs from the time they are absorbed from the small intestine until they are excreted as waste products from the body. The processes of metabolism are carried out by means of enzymes within the cells. Many of the cellular enzymatic reactions depend on the presence of vitamins and are regulated by hormones.

Two of the more common metabolic problems are *phenylketonuria (PKU)* and *diabetes mellitus.* In the former, an enzyme deficiency apparently prevents the proper metabolism of phenylaline, one of the essential amino acids. Its subsequent buildup causes irreversible brain damage if the condition goes untreated and results in mental retardation. Treatment consists mainly of special dietary measures throughout the early years of childhood.

Diabetes mellitus, a chronic disease, is caused by a lack of insulin. There are two forms of this specific type of diabetes: *juvenile* or *youth-onset diabetes* and *maturity-onset diabetes.* It is estimated that approximately five percent of the population—10 million Americans—have diabetes, and 3 million of these are juvenile diabetics. Diabetes is a major health problem in that it is increasing by six percent a year, is the direct cause of more than 38,000 deaths per year and a factor in perhaps 260,000 more. It is the third leading cause of death by disease in the United States and the leading cause of blindness.[72] Men reach their greatest susceptibility to diabetes at about 51 years of age; women reach it at about 55. Juvenile diabetes, which is the most common long-term childhood illness, is the more severe, comes on more suddenly, and is usually more difficult to regulate. Juvenile diabetes almost always requires regular injections of insulin for its control, while mild cases of maturity-onset diabetes can sometimes be controlled by weight loss and diet. Older people in particular are susceptible to infectious and degenerative changes in arteries, nerves, and other tissues. Life expectancy is 25 to 30 years after the onset of the disease. The specialist should always be on the lookout for symptoms suggesting the onset of a diabetic coma, the severest complication of diabetes mellitus. Another diabetic condition which is just the opposite of diabetes mellitus is *hypoglycemia* (low blood sugar). However, with proper diet and rest, this disease presents no major problems.

Allergic Conditions

The term *allergy* denotes an altered reactivity or a hypersensitiveness, natural or artificial, of an individual to a variety of substances introduced into the body. Allergens may be classified generally as follows: inhalants, foods, drugs and biologicals, infectors, contactants, and physical allergens.

It is estimated that allergy is the third most prevalent illness in this country, responsible for a major disease in one out of every 10 individuals, and affecting in some degree perhaps as many as one out of every two people.[73] Individuals can develop an allergy at any time in their life. Fortunately, allergies are not contagious, but they can present problems and reduce activity.

sensory impairments

Sensory impairments are those disorders of perception and communication—specifically, special populations so affected include the visually impaired (blind and partially sighted) and the hearing impaired (deaf and hard-of-hearing).

Visual Impairment

Sight is the most important special sense that an individual has. According to the American Foundation for the Blind, it is estimated that about 6.4 million individuals in the United States have some type of visual impairment even with corrective lenses. They are categorized as having: partial sight, residual vision, partial blindness, low vision, or reduced central vision. Of the 6.4 million, about 1.7 million of these are considered "legally blind"—i.e., having central visual acuity that does not go beyond 20/200 in the better eye with correcting lenses. Of these, nearly 450,000 are totally blind or have no usable vision at all. As a result of an increased life expectancy, nearly 65 percent (one million) of the severely visually impaired are 65 years of age or older.[74]

Generally speaking, most of the severely visually impaired can perceive light and motion, and many can count fingers at arm's length. Some see only a portion of an object because their visual field is limited. Some can spot a pin on the floor, but fail to see a moving van on the road.

The precise causes of blindness and severe visual impairment are unknown although diseases, accidents, and heredity play their parts. Individuals who are born blind are considered to be *congenitally blind,* while those who become blind as the result of disease or accident are referred to as being *adventitiously blind.*

Some of the major causes of blindness in this country are as follows:

Glaucoma, which is caused by an abnormal accumulation of fluid in the eyes, produces elevated intraocular pressures that seriously impair vision. One out of every eight blind persons is a victim of this disease. It is responsible for much of the blindness after 40 years of age.

Diabetes of long duration results in *diabetic retinopathy.* Despite insulin therapy, it is present in about 6 percent of people with diabetes. Diabetic retinopathy is the leading cause of blindness in the United States.[75]

Cataracts are opaque areas that develop on the lens. They develop chiefly in older individuals and represent part of the aging process.

Detached retina can interfere seriously with vision and may eventually cause blindness. The retina, which is essentially an extension of the optic nerve lining the interior of the eyeball, receives the light rays and transmits the impulses to the brain where they register as sight. Injury or inflammation can cause a detached retina.

Retrolental fibroplasia, a form of blindness that formerly occurred among premature babies, has been virtually eliminated since physicians stopped administering oxygen in high concentrations to these babies. However, 8,000 or more children and young people in this country can attribute their blindness to this problem.

Hereditary defects are the result of an inherited predisposition.

The causes of partial sight include not only the above but also refractive errors (*myopia* and *hyperopia*), developmental abnormalities of structures, defects in muscle function, and defects and injuries of the eye.

Hearing Impairment

In popular parlance, the term *deaf* is used to designate any type of auditory impairment, ranging from slight to profound. Actually, there are various categories of hearing impairment. The designation *deaf* represents only one type; it is, however, the most unique. Its singular quality stems from the fact that individuals so affected are the only ones of all the hearing impaired population for whom the major portion, if not the whole, of life development takes place without benefit of effective auditory contact with the environment.

The hard-of-hearing are those whose hearing ability is significantly less acute than the normal individual, but still great enough to be used for the understanding of verbal communication and contact with the environment.

About one out of every 10, or 20 million people, in the United States have some hearing impairment, and over 200,000 cannot hear human speech.[76] Impaired hearing may come on suddenly or gradually, and may manifest itself in many ways.

There are two basic types of hearing loss: the *conducive type (conduction deafness)*, in which there is some disturbance in the passage of sound to the inner ear; and the *sensorineural type (nerve deafness)*, resulting from disease of the auditory nerve. Infection is the major cause of both types. However, inherited defects of the nervous pathways or organs of hearing appear in about 20 per 100,000 births. *Otosclerosis* is a fairly common cause of conduction hearing loss in the white race. This condition prevents movement of the bones of the middle ear that transmit vibrations. Nerve deafness is often noticed in people 60 years of age and older, resulting from degenerative changes in the auditory nerve. In addition to the obvious derangements of the ear that might ensue from a variety of physical traumas, acoustic trauma from loud and sustained noises can cause hearing loss.

Speech Defects

While not a sensory impairment, it seems important to mention here *speech defects*. Maldevelopment or complete lack of development of spoken language is estimated to present a problem or handicap for about 3.5 percent of our school-age children.[77] Of the so-called "functional disorders," the most prominent are stuttering and lisping, which account for about half of the 7 percent affected. Next most common are anatomic defects, followed by defects in the central nervous system.

In older persons, deterioration of speech may be associated with a number of systemic diseases and toxic states such as *Parkinsonism, multiple sclerosis, Huntington's chorea,* and *nutritional encephalopathy.*

emotional disturbance

The National Association for Mental Health (NAMH) reports that there are some 753,000 patients under psychiatric care in hospitals, 173,000 on trial visits or in supervised community care, and 1,350,000 in out-patient care in public and private clinics; it is estimated that 20 million persons in this country will at some time suffer from mental or emotional illness of sufficient degree to require professional help. Also included within these estimates are the 5 or 6 million alcoholics, the 500,000 to 700,000 narcotic addicts, and the 300,000 to 500,000 juvenile delinquents. Mental illness also accounts for a substantial percentage of divorces, crimes, work absenteeism, unemployment, and other personal troubles.[78]

The problems connected with mental illness or disturbances were dramatized in 1972 by the controversy surrounding the nomination of Senator Thomas Eagleton as the Democratic vice-presidential candidate. When it was revealed that Eagleton had been treated for emotional problems, the issue grew so heated that he was forced to withdraw his candidacy.

It is often stated that half the beds in all hospitals are for the emotionally disturbed. In 1972, according to the National Center for Health Statistics, there were 372,603 beds in psychiatric hospitals, which is included in a total of nearly 1.5 million beds in general medical and surgical hospitals and specialty hospitals. Further, of the 990 specialty hospitals in the United States, a majority were psychiatric hospitals.[79] However, a positive note can be found; rehabilitation of the mentally ill has moved forward faster than any other single category of the disabled.[80] When everything is considered, the reported estimate by the National Association for Mental Health that 10 percent of the population comprises untreated cases of mental illness seems conservative. This seems to be supported by First Lady Rosalynn Carter, honorary chairman of the President's Commission on Mental Health, who has long maintained that "mental illness touches every single family."[81]

Mental illness is probably the oldest and most baffling of human afflictions. The problem was first met, as one might expect, with sorcery and witchcraft, then with cruelty and incarceration, and until recently, merely with custodial care.

Like many physical illnesses, mental illness does not consist of a single disorder, but a host of them, and their classifications are far from clearcut. While the causes of mental illness are open to question in a technical sense, there is general agreement that mental illness involves both the body and the mind. In other words, some causes may be physical in nature, some predominantly mental, and some a combination of the two. These disorders may range from mild and temporary to chronic and severe. Regardless of the causes, the result is a personality that behaves in an abnormal way. In fact, mental illness can encompass virtually any departure from what is considered normal or socially acceptable behavior. All of us behave abnormally, irrationally, and unrealistically at times; it is only when unusual behavior persists that mental illness may be indicated. In a stricter sense, mental illness generally describes mental or emotional disturbances that cause so marked an alteration in thought, mood, or behavior that the individual finds it difficult or impossible to meet the everyday requirements of living.

Individuals suffer emotional conflict whenever anything interferes with their adjustment to demands or pressures. These demands are usually of two kinds. One kind is primarily social or interpersonal, resulting from having to live interdependently with other persons. A second kind of demand is primarily internal, arising in part from biological needs and in part from having learned from personal experience to desire certain kinds of social conditions such as approval and achievement. The external demands are closely related to the internal ones, and usually excessive demands from one side produce a counteraction from the other.

To live successfully requires coming to terms with external pressures as well as satisfying internal ones. If individuals cannot adequately adjust to the problems of living, various symptoms of adjustive failure appear. Whether the maladjustment is mild or severe, four types of symptoms are usually recognized. First are those varieties of negatively toned moods or affective states. These are known by the terms *anxiety* or *uneasiness, depression, guilt,* and *fear,* to list the most common examples. If these states of mind appear often and with high intensity, they make a person's life miserable. *Psychosomatic diseases* resulting from life stress are another symptom of maladjustment. Ulcers, intestinal colitis, and high blood pressure are a few of the organic ailments that result from pressures. A third symptom consists of *deviations in behavior* from the societal standards. When individuals do not behave in accordance with the usual rules, they pose a problem for the society in which they live, and for themselves because their deviation tends to isolate them from successful contact with others. Such behavior deviation is one of the main reasons why penal institutions and mental hospitals exist. Last is the symptom of *impaired effectiveness,* which takes many forms. For example, while taking a test, excessive anxiety may interfere with the thinking necessary for successful performance. Under conditions of stress or disaster, effective behavior may be disorganized.

The varieties of adjustive failure must somehow be classified and described. The approach to classification in predominant use today was developed originally in 1907 by the German psychiatrist Emil Kraepelin. The main basis of the classification consists of patterns of symptoms. While there are some differences among psychiatrists as to classification of mental disorders, the latest American classification system divides these disorders into two main groups: organic and functional.

Organic disorders result from impairment of brain tissue function through such causes as congenital defects, prenatal injuries, skull fractures, chronic exposure to poisons, advanced syphilis, hardening of the arteries in the brain, brain infection or tumors, severe alcoholism, and drug addiction. These disorders are of two types: acute and chronic.

Acute brain syndrome arises from temporary impairment of brain tissue function which, in turn, is the result of the causes just cited. In an acute attack the individual may recover. The disease is potentially reversible in that the particular attack may not necessarily cause permanent damage sufficiently severe to result in permanent symptoms, although sometimes such permanent damage will occur later as a result of a series of acute attacks.

Chronic brain syndrome refers to relatively permanent or irreversible damage to the brain tissue and the resulting widespread impairment of brain function. Even if the initial cause is successfully treated, the symptoms arise from the permanent damage to the brain tissues that may have resulted. The disorder is thus chronic or permanent, whether mild or severe, lasting the remaining life of the individual.

Functional disorders, on the other hand, have no known basis in neurological damage, and, even more important, functional disorders are generally believed to stem from adjustive failures rather than from organic defects. Some researchers, however, are not satisfied with this view, and have embarked on a quest for evidence of other more tangible causes. Currently, faults in body chemistry, deficiencies in essential nutrients, and low blood sugar are under suspicion. Changes in hormone levels, such as those that occur during menopause and after childbirth, are also being considered.

Within the functional group of mental disorders, further distinctions are made between psychotic disorders, psychophysiological disorders, psychoneurotic disorders, personality disorders, and transient situational personality disorders. Generally speaking, lay persons will find the functional disorders more familiar than the others since the terms *psychosis* and *neurosis,* and, in fact, many of the subvarieties such as *schizophrenia* and *depression,* or *hysteria* and *obsessional neurosis,* are in common usage today.

Within the classification system the largest group of mental illnesses comprises the neuroses. In addition to being far more common, neuroses are usually less severe, less destructive, and less disabling than psychoses. As some authorities explain it, a neurotic can manage to go about his daily business despite his problems, but a psychotic can't. Others have said, facetiously perhaps but vividly, that neurotics build dream castles and psychotics inhabit them.

Actually, a *neurosis* begins with the kind of nervousness and tension that can build up occasionally in anyone who finds himself in a stressful situation. It is only when the condition becomes prolonged, produces discernible patterns of behavior, or intensifies to the point of being disabling that it is called an illness at all. In neurosis, contact with reality is maintained, but it is inaccurate and faulty. A *psychosis*, on the other hand, is considered a serious illness, even in its milder forms and even when its effects are temporary. The psychotic person does not maintain contact with reality; instead he replaces the real world around him with internal imaginary thoughts and ideas. The fantasy is the reality.

Symptoms also differ. A neurosis is most often seen as a state of anxiety accompanied by such physical signs as trembling, insomnia, frequent headaches, and stomach upsets. Some neurotics develop what is called *conversion hysteria* and suffer physical impairments, such as paralysis of a limb or loss of one of the senses, without physical cause. In milder forms, a neurosis may show up as a compulsive habit such as excessive hand-washing or always stepping over the cracks in sidewalks, hypochondria, or fear of crowds, high places, and other phobias. Psychosomatic illnesses, as described earlier, are also an outgrowth of deepseated anxiety.

In the psychotic, not only are the emotions seriously disturbed, but also the mind becomes confused and the whole personality is markedly changed. In some cases, the psychotic state continues for months, years, or even decades. But in most cases, the individual will have periods of clarity in which he appears normal before lapsing back into his irrational state. Not all victims of psychoses are found in psychiatric institutions. Some are able to carry on a fairly normal life in the community, giving the picture of being "odd" or "strange." Some even raise families and hold down responsible jobs.

Consideration of the other forms of mental illness will be left to the student by reading some of the Suggested References. However, some attention should be directed toward mental illnesses that affect children.

The most serious illness found in children is *schizophrenia*, and it was not until some 30 years ago that psychiatrists began to recognize and report its presence in children. Prior to that, schizophrenic children were being diagnosed as mentally retarded or brain damaged, mainly because the symptoms are so similar. Some of the signs, such as dullness, apathy, and the inability to form or express whole thoughts, could be indicative of mental retardation; others resemble the symptoms found in some cases of brain damage and included, along with irrational rage and violent temper tantrums, hallucinations and delusions.

Psychiatrists now suspect that childhood schizophrenia comprises a group of mental illnesses. Two have been identified: the child suffering from *primary infantile autism* appears to be encased in a shell, withdrawn, unresponsive to people, overly preoccupied with objects, and out of contact with reality. *Symbiotic infantile psychosis* is characterized by abnormal attachment to the mother. The child literally clings to her; some authorities, in fact, believe that a symbiotic child actually feels that he is a part of his mother and never does think of himself as a separate individual.

Unusual fearfulness, a strong tendency toward destructive acts, extreme aggressiveness, and inability to learn, though intellectually capable of it, may be other indicators of children's mental or emotional disturbance.

Treatment of Emotional Disturbance

Just as there is no single accepted cause of mental illness, there is no accepted means of treating it. Usually, some form of *psychotherapy* (individual or group) that attempts to effect changes in ideas and emotions is combined with *chemotherapy* that involves administering antidepressants, sedatives, or tranquilizers to combat the symptoms. The discovery of tranquilizers in the early 1950s, incidentally, is credited with revolutionizing the treatment of mental illness and reversing the upward trend of long-term hospitalization of mentally ill patients for the first time in history. For more on drug therapy, see Appendix B.

Another method used in treatment, though less widely than it once was, is *electroshock therapy*. Limited for the most part to cases of severe depression in which other methods have proved ineffective or would entail extended treatment, shock treatments are said to often afford prompt and long-lasting relief. Insulin-induced shock therapy is sometimes used to achieve similar results in schizophrenic patients. In cases where suffering is extreme, psychosurgery or brain surgery is occasionally used, but only as a last resort.

One may ask whether mental illness can be cured. This is a difficult question to answer. Some professional workers would say yes while others would hedge, responding that the individual's ability to deal with the requirements of everyday living can be improved. Yet it goes without saying, of course, that recovery from mental illness, as from any illness, is dependent on many variables. How soon treatment is administered is one of them. The severity of the condition is another. And the type of illness is a third factor.

But the time has passed when people entered mental hospitals with little hope of ever leaving, and almost anyone suffering from a mental illness can expect to benefit measurably from treatment today. Several large health insurance companies report that the average stay for their policyholders is only 16 days. Growing recognition of the problem, increased knowledge, better staffed hospitals, and advances in treatment have all helped to improve the outlook for the mentally ill.

alcoholism and drug abuse

Chemical agents that alter consciousness have been widely used in many different societies throughout human history. They have served sometimes to facilitate socializing or celebrating among members of the tribe or community and other times as an acceptable means of relaxation or "escape" for the individual from the problems and anxieties of his daily existence. Until 1930, a liquid extract of marijuana could be found on many pharmacy shelves in the United States. It was a popular remedy with doctors and was prescribed for many complaints including loss of appetite, "nerves" and depression. In addition, some religions have used beverages or drugs as a means of achieving a closer union with their deities in their rituals. It is not difficult to see all three of these aspects reflected in our society today.

Alcoholism

The suffix -*ism* means "excess." Alcoholism is a condition resulting from excessive indulgence in alcoholic beverages. It is a disease of addiction not really profoundly different from the craving for narcotic drugs. Alcoholics usually evolve gradually from social drinkers to excessive drinkers to alcoholics. In some cases alcoholics proceed to a stage where their brains or their bodies have been physically damaged by alcohol. This stage is called *chronic alcoholism.*

Alcoholism is one of this country's major medical-social-economic problems. It affects men and women, young and old, rich and poor, the urban person and the rural person. In short, alcoholism has no boundaries. Recently, physicians are becoming aware of a dysfunctioning termed *fetal alcohol syndrome* wherein the child shows flattened facial features, slow physical growth, impaired mental functioning, and internal physical problems. The syndrome is associated with mothers who would be considered "social drinkers."[82] Conservative estimates have put the number of those with a drinking and alcoholism problem at 9 million, but many people working closely with problems of alcohol and with heavy drinkers feel that the number is much greater. *Medial World News* reported in 1972 an estimate that slightly less than 10 million or 4.6 percent of the population were alcoholics.[83] Alcoholics Anonymous report that 11.3 percent of its members are under 30 years of age, and that since 1974 the number of members in that age group has increased nearly 50 percent.[84] Among alcoholics, men outnumber women by a ratio of 6 to 1 in this country. *Cirrhosis,* chiefly a disease of alcoholism, takes roughly 26,000 lives each year.

Who is and who is not an alcoholic is difficult to define since no studies exist that clearly differentiate an alcoholic from a nonalcoholic in the chronic drunkenness offender group. The most common definition in statute is illustrated by Indiana's commitment law:

> The term "alcoholic" means any person who chronically and habitually uses alcoholic beverages to the extent that he loses the power of self-control with respect to the use of alcoholic beverages, or any person who chronically and habitually uses alcoholic beverages to the extent that he becomes a menace to the public morals, health, safety and welfare of the members of society in general.[85]

In summary, the social-psychological implications of alcoholism are many. For example, alcohol causes —

1. Over 50 percent (30,000) of all traffic deaths.
2. A life expectancy shorter by 10 to 12 years.
3. Cause of death on more than 13,000 death certificates yearly.
4. Half of all homicides and one-third of all suicides.
5. An absenteeism of two and one-half times as frequent as general work force.
6. An economic cost to the Nation of $15 billion yearly.[86]

Drug Abuse

They have been smoked, chewed, injected, sniffed, and mainlined, and referred to as a *joint, roach, H, coke, grass, smack, boo, meth, hog, super weed, cyclone, cadillac,* and *Angel dust.* Sometimes after they are used, an individual may become strung out, on a trip, crash, or get busted by the narcs. Strange terms? Not to those people who have experimented with, dabbled in, or abused certain drugs.[87]

We are a "drug-oriented society." Year after year pharmaceutical manufacturers have sales amounting to billions of dollars to satisfy a national demand for billions of prescription tablets and capsules. Further, according to a 1975 cabinet-level report, drug abuse costs Americans between $10 billion and $17 billion annually and is linked to 15,000 deaths a year.[88] In addition, like alcoholism, there is a problem of definition.

Until 1906, when the Federal Pure Food and Drug Act was passed, there was no control over drugs. It was not until 1914 that the Congress of the United States passed the Harrison Act to control narcotic addiction. The act did not make addiction illegal, but it did put controls on the production, manufacturing, and distribution of narcotics by imposing taxes. The Marijuana Tax Act of 1937 provided similar controls over marijuana. In 1965, the Drug Abuse Control Amendments extended the Federal Pure Food and Drug Act to control stimulant, depressive, and hallucinogenic drugs that may be subject to abuse.

The number of active narcotic addicts may be from 50 to 100 percent higher than the 68,864 reported by the Bureau of Narcotics in 1970;[89] and it appears to be climbing, particularly among young people. With increased support, the anti-narcotic campaign has led to many advances. Nevertheless, more information about the factors involved in addiction and about effective treatment is badly needed, as are additional treatment facilities and training programs for the staff to man them.

aging

The elderly make up the fastest growing group in the population, and they comprise an increasing proportion of the total. When the first census was taken in 1900, half the people were 16 years of age or younger. In 1981, it is projected that the median age of Americans will be 30; by 2000 it will pass 35, and approach 40 by the year 2030. In 1977 there were about 23 million (11 percent) Americans over what is generally regarded as the retirement age—approximately 3 million more than there were in 1970. Everyday, more than 1000 people in this country reach the age of 65. By the turn of the century it is estimated that nearly 31 million people will be 65 or older.[90] The rapid increase in the number of older Americans will certainly affect their economic, social, and political roles and will bring about changes in their position in American society.

The dramatic increase in the size of the elderly population doesn't mean that people are living longer than they used to; they're not. Instead, the number of people who live to reach old age is much greater than in the past, when there were so many deaths in infancy or childhood. If major breakthroughs continue to occur in the treatment and prevention of cancer and cardiovascular-renal diseases, the Nation's elderly population will live significantly longer, and will, of course, be even larger than the 31 million currently projected for the year 2000.

The majority of older Americans are women. In the oldest age brackets, most women are widows, and many of them live alone. By contrast, most elderly men live with their wives. Men are less likely than women to face the disruption caused by a spouse's death and to live alone in a house that is more and more difficult to maintain.

The imbalance between the number of older men and older women becomes more pronounced as their ages increase. One result of this is seen in nursing homes, where three out of four patients are women. In addition, while only five percent of the elderly—about one million—are found in nursing homes and similar institutions, most elderly who enter nursing homes die there; the average stay is 1.1 years. According to the U.S. Census Bureau, cancer and diseases of the circulatory and nervous system were the leading causes of death in the elderly in 1974. If medical breakthroughs occur, we can anticipate a doubling of the 65-plus population in nursing homes according to the director of the National Institute of Aging.[91]

Health is a major concern of the elderly. Certain ailments—heart disease, rheumatism, and arthritis, for example—are more prevalent among the old. Elderly people spend more time in hospitals, fill a third of the nation's hospital beds, and visit physicians more frequently than the young and middle-aged adult. Their annual medical bills are three times greater than those of other adult ages. The complexity of reimbursement procedures through Medicare, Medicaid, and private insurance carriers discourages many elderly people from obtaining as much health care as they need.[92]

A social problem which affects the elderly is poverty. Poverty restricts the lives of many of the Nation's aged. Contrary to popular belief, the number of elderly living in poverty has declined. Today, it is estimated that approximately 15 percent of the elderly—slightly more than 3 million persons—fall below the official poverty line. However, government sources do say that another 10 percent live in "near poverty."[93] Those facing the most severe problems in income, housing, and health are elderly widows or those who have never married.

As a rule, elderly people have less money to live on than other adults. The money comes from a variety of sources—Social Security, private pension plans, income from assets in real estate and investments, and public assistance. While these resources are sufficient for many, a large number are also in need of Supplemental Security Income, food stamps, subsidized housing, and Medicaid.

Even though these brief comments may be discouraging to some, public awareness of the elderly is growing. Public attention to the elderly over the past decade or so has produced an outpouring of public and voluntary efforts, many highly imaginative and truly effective. Pressure to expand and improve these efforts is not likely to abate.

To summarize the conditions, the onset and subsequent severity of most diseases typically depend on the combined effects of several factors. Within the pattern of causes related to any given case, one may commonly find genetic, physical, emotional, and social factors. The typical coronary thrombosis provides the clearest example, as it often involves a genetically acquired deficiency of fat metabolism that is aggravated by socially derived eating habits, a lack of sufficient physical exercise, and undue emotional stress resulting from family or job tension. Neurotic problems provide another fine example. Neurotic conditions by definition involve inappropriate reactions to emotional stress; however, social conflicts provide a common source of this stress; the potential effects of such physical factors as fatigue and poor nutrition are well known, and the contributing role of genetic factors is a widely supported possibility.

Although the rule of multiple causation generally applies, it should also be recognized that a particular agent or event is often so dominant that it becomes, for all practical purposes, the single cause. Examples are such genetically caused conditions as hemophilia and PKU.

Regardless of the specific nature of any one causative factor, it tends to produce disequilibrium within the soma or psyche of the affected individual. These pathogenic activities involve either a direct attack upon tissue structure or an interference with the functioning of physiological or psychological processes.

SUGGESTED REFERENCES

Albrecht, Gary L., ed. *The Sociology of Physical Disability and Rehabilitation.* Pittsburgh: University of Pittsburgh Press, 1976.

Barry, John R., and C. Ray Wingrove. *Let's Learn About Aging.* New York: John Wiley and Sons, 1977.

Becker, Marshall H., ed. *The Health Belief Model and Personal Health Behavior.* Thorofare, N.J.: C. B. Stack, Inc., 1974.

Bleck, Eugene E., & Donald A. Nagel, eds. *Physically Handicapped Children: A Medical Atlas for Teachers.* New York: Grune & Stratton, Inc., 1975.

Bowe, Frank. *Handicapping America: Barriers to Disabled People.* New York: Harper and Row Publishers, Inc., 1978.

Cobb, A. Beatrix. *Medical and Psychological Aspects of Disability.* Springfield, Ill.: Charles C. Thomas Publisher, 1973.

"The Crime Wave," *Time* (June 30, 1975), pp. 10–24.

Dubos, René. *Man, Medicine and Environment.* New York: Praeger Publishers, 1968.

Feingold, B. A., ed. *Developmental Disabilities of Early Childhood.* Springfield, Ill.: Charles C. Thomas Publisher, 1978.

Freidson, Elliot, and Judith Lorber, eds. *Medical Men and Their Work: A Sociological Reader.* New York: Aldine-Atherton Publishing Co., 1972.

Furth, Hans G. *Deafness in Infancy and Early Childhood.* New York: Medcom Press, 1974.

Goldfarb, Ronald L., and Linda R. Singer. *After Conviction.* New York: Simon and Schuster, 1973.

Goldensen, Robert M., ed. *Disability and Rehabilitation Handbook.* New York: McGraw-Hill book Co., 1978.

Gordon, Gerald, and others, eds. *Disease: The Individual and Society.* New Haven, Conn.: College and University Press, 1968.

Johnson, Elmer H. *Crime, Correction, and Society* (4th ed.). Homewood, Ill.: The Dorsey Press, 1978.

Kaplan, John. *Marijuana: The New Prohibition.* New York: Pocket Books, Inc., 1971.

Koestler, Frances A. *The Unseen Minority: A Social History of Blindness in the United States.* New York: McKay Publishing Company, 1976.

MacDonald, A. P., Jr., "Attitudes Toward the Poor that Militate Against Effective Upgrading," *Rehabilitation Literature,* 32:1 (1971), pp. 2–5.

Patrick, D. L., J. W. Bush, and Milton M. Chen. "Toward an Operational Definition of Health," *Journal of Health and Social Behavior,* 14:3 (1973), pp. 6–23.

Rosow, Irving. *Socialization to Old Age.* Berkeley, Ca.: University of California Press, 1974.

Solomon, Philip, and Vernon D. Patch, eds. *Handbook of Psychiatry* (2nd ed.). Los Altos, Ca.: Lange Medical Publications, 1969.

Stubbins, Joseph, ed. *Social and Psychological Aspects of Disability: A. Handbook for Practitioners.* University Park, Penn.: University Park Press, 1977.

Suran, Bernard G., and Joseph V. Rizzo. *Special Children: An Integrative Approach.* Glenview, Ill.: Scott, Foresman and Company, 1979.

Wright, Beatrice A., "Changes in Attitudes Toward People with Handicaps," *Rehabilitation Literature,* 34:2 (1973), pp. 354–357, 368.

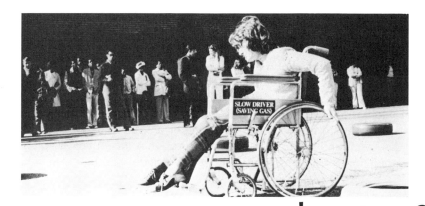

chapter 3
agencies and institutions providing service to special populations

One naturally tends to think of rehabilitation progress in the removal or mitigation of the end effects of disease or injury, in the number retrained to work and participate in activities of daily living, in the rapid numerical growth of education programs for handicapped children, in the individuals who "go straight" after serving prison sentences, or in the recognition of the needs of the disabled and disadvantaged. However, the key contributors to this progress are the organizations, services, personnel, and facilities that assist the individual in reaching the maximum of his physical, emotional, social, intellectual, and vocational potentials. Concerted action for rehabilitation can be attained only through the organization of the means to overcome the effects of the problem.

organizations

During the past three decades there have been more publicity, more legislation, more money appropriated, and more community campaigns related to meeting and serving the needs of special populations than at any other period in our country's history. Likewise, over the years, many organizations have been established in response to the obvious need for service and rehabilitative action. These organizations are of either a governmental or a nongovernmental nature. Furthermore, they are usually directly concerned not with the rendering of a specific service but rather with the social and political interest that produces incentives for planning and organizing to realize specific service to special populations.

governmental organizations

Activities of a health, correctional, and special service nature are organized along the same lines as many other areas of responsibility that are organized at federal, state, and local levels. The national government has only certain limited powers granted to it by the Constitution. The protection and welfare of individuals are among general responsibilities that are reserved for the states by the Constitution. The various state legislatures have sought to meet these responsibilities by establishing departments or boards at the state level through appropriate legislation and by encouraging and supporting the development of local departments, when necessary, for delivery of direct services to individuals.

Federal

Because of its constitutional authority, the federal government has gradually developed a formidable array of agencies and bureaus. The development of field health services began in the eighteenth century when the 13 colonies depended on the seas for both protection and trade. To encourage enlistments and expansion of the small merchant marine, the government established a Marine Hospital Service within the Department of the Treasury to provide medical care for seamen when they came ashore. As our frontiers moved westward, greater extension of public health services soon became necessary because of widespread epidemics of yellow fever, smallpox, and cholera. As a result of the evolution from a rural to an urban civilization, it became apparent that some public health organization would have to be responsible for studying and regulating the relationship of people to their total environment.

In 1912 the Marine Hospital Service was disbanded and the U.S. Public Health Service was established. It is interesting to note that this branch of government still fulfills its historic function, still controlling the marine hospitals for the benefit of members of the merchant marine. In 1939 the government's activities in the fields of health, education, and welfare were transferred to the Federal Security Agency. In 1953, under President Dwight D. Eisenhower's administration, most of the health activities were brought together as part of the newly created Department of Health, Education, and Welfare (HEW).

Apart from HEW, other government agencies carry on important activities related to health and health protection. The Army, the Navy, and the Air Force all have major medical departments to provide health care and treatment for their personnel and certain dependents. Their programs are the responsibility of the Department of Defense. The Veterans Administration has a major responsibility to provide medical care and rehabilitation for veterans. Agencies that protect the public's health include the Department of Justice (through the FBI) and the Treasury. They are concerned with the illegal distribution and use of narcotics. Other agencies involved are the Environmental Protection Agency, the Federal Trade Commission, and the Federal Communications Commission.

In the area of federal correctional activities, the Bureau of Prisons in the Department of Justice is responsible for providing programs of custody and treatment based on the individual needs of the offender. The Law Enforcement Assistance Administration, an agency in the same department, offers advice to state and local correctional agencies on how to improve their programs and operations. In the same department, the Federal Bureau of Investigation (which exercises full police jurisdiction over all crimes not the concern of the other federal police agencies) serves as a clearinghouse of records pertaining to criminals, collects crime statistics, and provides training for selected police officers from law enforcement agencies in this country at its National Police Academy. The Children's Bureau has also played an important role in corrections through collection of juvenile statistics and assistance in the promotion of uniformity and higher standards in the juvenile courts.

Health-Oriented Legislation. Health care legislation as it has developed in our democratic society over the past 179 years has been an interesting and many-faceted process. It has involved vested interest groups that have reflected the climate of the times and the various forces that act and react on a particular environment. Social legislation originates with a specific need and, given the legislative process and the influence of political forces, often requires decades in which to complete. Legislation does not just happen; it is a result of the relationship of six elements at work in the total process—conceptualization of an idea, political support, leadership, negotiation, public debate, and finally, decision making. The political process in a democratic system is founded on laws that represent the collective decisions of the community. While it is impossible to review here all of the health care legislation since the founding of this country, it is worthwhile to comment that through the democratic system a trend has developed whereby legislation has gradually become more representative of the entire community.

It was not until 1918 that Congress enacted the first nationwide rehabilitation act: the Smith-Sears Veterans Rehabilitation Act. This act provided vocational training and placement for disabled veterans of World

War I. The initiation of this act for disabled veterans was destined to play a major role in the establishment and development of services for the civilian disabled.

Congress passed the Vocational Rehabilitation Act in 1920, which provided vocational training, counseling, and job placement for disabled civilians through federal grants to each state. Since 1920 there have been many amendments to this act. Although this program was established with meager resources and under the narrow concept of vocational training and placement, the assistance rendered today to all kinds of disabled persons in all states covers a wide range of services.

The Rehabilitation Act of 1973 (P.L. 93–112), for example, authorized expenditures of over $1.5 billion over two years, placing major emphasis on services for the most severely handicapped. It provided for a study of services for individuals for whom vocational rehabilitation is not a feasible goal but who can, through rehabilitation, improve their ability to live independently; established an Architectural and Transportation Barriers Compliance Board to ensure compliance with existing standards under the Architectural Barriers Act; authorized programs to support state vocational rehabilitation agency programs, training, research, demonstration, and construction and improvement of rehabilitation facilities; required the rehabilitation counselor and the client (or his parent or guardian) to jointly develop a written program for rehabilitation.

Sections 503 and 504 of the 1973 Rehabilitation Act have specific implications for recreation and leisure programs and activities. Section 503 eliminates employment discrimination based on physical or mental handicaps in those agencies or industries that have a contract with any federal department or agency in excess of $2,500 to provide either personal property or nonpersonal services, including construction. This means that more emphasis and greater consideration will have to be given recruiting and hiring individuals with different limiting disabilities and conditions for recreation and leisure programs.

A major effort to provide greater opportunity for individuals with disabilities and impairments to enjoy and participate in recreation and leisure programs and services was afforded through Section 504 which required that federal fund recipients make their programs and activities accessible to the handicapped. Section 504 of the Act states:

> No otherwise qualified handicapped individual in the United States . . . shall, solely by reason of his handicap, be excluded from the participation in, be denied the benefits of, or be subjected to discrimination under any program or activity receiving federal financial assistance.[1]

The statute, Section 504, covers all grant programs from general revenue sharing to categorical grants. It also defines—handicapped individuals broadly, including physical and mental disabilities, diseases such as cancer, diabetes and heart ailments, and conditions such as alcoholism and drug abuse. It includes individuals who have a record of a handicap and those who are regarded as disabled even if they are normal.

Since the passage of the 1973 Rehabilitation Act, there have been amendments to Section 504 (P.L. 93–156 and P.L. 95–602) which have further guaranteed the rights in federally funded programs and activities to persons who qualify as handicapped. In addition, several court cases already tried under Section 504 have guaranteed the *right to education, right to treatment,* and *right to community services.* In short, recreation, leisure, and related activity areas have been affirmed and reaffirmed by both legislation and litigation. In is important therefore to emphasize that students and teachers become familiar with the interpretations of Section 504. It is anticipated that federal agencies will have their proposed Section 504 regulations finalized during early 1980.

Equally as important as the Rehabilitation Act from a recreation service standpoint was the enactment of the Education for All Handicapped Children Act of 1975 (P.L. 94–142). This Act requires that all handicapped children ages 3 to 21 starting in 1980, be provided a free appropriate public education and includes recreation as a related service area. Recreation services must be provided as a support service in schools, institutions, or the child's home to assist the handicapped child to benefit from special education. According to many educators this Act may be by far the most significant education law passed in the last two decades. Recreation professionals feel the law has great importance to the field of recreation. This is the first time recreation has been included in education legislation. Because of the implications of this legislation for recreation services, all potential recreators, regardless of eventual employment, should make every effort possible to have knowledge and understanding about this law.

Other important legislation that has marked social and economic significance in the twentieth century for the disabled as a group or for those with specific health-related impairments, as well as providing direct or indirect sanctions and support for programs for a recreation and leisure nature, includes the Social Security Act (workmen's compensation, public assistance laws, hospital and medical insurance programs—Medicare), the Randolph-Sheppard Act, the National Mental Health Act, the Hill-Burton Act, the Mental Retardation Facilities and Community Mental Health Centers Construction Act, the Developmental Disabilities Act, the Elementary and Secondary Education Act (Titles I, III, and VI), the Lead-Based Paint Poisoning Prevention Act, the Land and Water Conservation Act, the Captioned Films for the Deaf Act, the Demonstration Cities and Metropolitan Development Act, the Housing and Urban Development Act, the Narcotic Addict Rehabilitation Act, the National Employ the Handicapped Week Act, the National Health Planning and Resources Development Act, the Older Americans Act, and the Community Services Act.

Correctional Legislation. Correctional legislation is of recent concern. Correctional institutions and programs have received little attention because the idea of retributive punishment is deeply rooted in human emotions as well as in the administrative fragmentation of our justice system.

It was not until prison riots, parole scandals, and correctional maladministration following World War II that the public and political leaders began to give attention to correctional problems. The Ford Foundation in 1959 provided funds for the American Justice Institute to conduct a survey of modern correctional practices in the Western world.[2] In 1963, President Lyndon B. Johnson established the Commission on Law Enforcement and Administration of Justice, which subsequently issued the report *The Challenge of Crime in a Free Society*[3] in 1967. The report recommended "sweeping and costly changes in the administration" of corrective institutions throughout the country. The Congress in 1964, recognizing the deplorable conditions within correctional institutions, appropriated over $2 million to conduct a study of correctional manpower and training.

In 1965 Congress enacted the Federal Prisoners Rehabilitation Act. This act was directed toward those offenders in federal institutions and concerned itself with community-based treatment programs wherein inmates work at jobs and attend academic or vocational schools in the community. Furloughs, another provision of the act, allow inmates to make unescorted trips home for emergency visits, to seek jobs, and for other approved purposes. The idea behind the program is that the offender is more likely to make a successful transition from the institution to the community if given an opportunity to participate to a limited degree in the community.

As a result of the Hayes-Cooper Act (1934) and Ashurst-Summer Act (1935) excluding prison-made goods from interstate commerce, interest in vocational training within state correctional institutions waned. However, with new funds available through the Manpower Development and Training Act, the Economic Opportunity Act, and the vocational rehabilitation amendments of 1963, interest is once again on the rise. Likewise, academic training is available under the Elementary and Secondary Education Act.

In attempting to combat the crime problem of youth, Congress passed the Juvenile Delinquency Prevention and Control Act in 1968. The act was directed at rehabilitating delinquents and aiding potential troublemakers. Rehabilitation services include diagnosis, treatment, and training. Money was also provided for counseling to prevent delinquency, for training juvenile court social workers, and for constructing and revamping juvenile institutions. In 1974, the Juvenile Justice and Delinquency Prevention Act was passed. One purpose of the Act was the development of programs designed to divert and prevent youngsters from entering the Juvenile Justice System.

State

At the state level, the responsibilities of the various departments concerned with public health, mental health, rehabilitation, welfare, and correction vary considerably among different states, depending largely on their wealth and the progressiveness of their administration. In the main, their responsibilities are found in the general area of planning, coordinating, and offering supportive-type service. Most state departments establish standards of service and personnel quality, and provide educational opportunities. In addition, they have responsibility for the disbursement of federal funds and the development of new and improved methods for the provision of health, rehabilitation, and correctional service. Direct services are fairly limited but important: state mental, retardation, tuberculosis, and cancer hospitals, as well as correctional institutions, are the most common examples.

Local

At the local level, health responsibilities are primarily restricted to community public health departments. They vary from small rural county departments to large departments responsible for the health needs of populated metropolitan areas. In general, they provide a comprehensive variety of services. Some county and city health departments have responsibilities also for the operation of public hospitals, clinics, and outpatient services.

For the most part, the correctional process takes place at the local level. Apprehension and detention of the offender, whether adult or juvenile, begins at this level. Pretrial detention or actual detention of the offender, which can be for a period of a few days up to a year, falls into four classes: (1) the city lockup; (2) the municipal jail; (3) the county jail; and (4) the specialized facilities for women, juveniles, narcotic addicts, alcoholics, and the like. Probation and parole with supervision are also administered here. Likewise, community-centered programs, halfway houses, and prerelease guidance centers whose purpose is to aid the reentry of the offender into society are part of the local level's responsibilities.

nongovernmental organizations

Nongovernment organizations are perhaps even more diverse in their origins and functions than their government counterparts. In this country, however, a vast amount of health, rehabilitation, and social welfare work is being done by these organizations. Some of them are voluntary organizations supported by contributions or membership dues; others are endowed philanthropic foundations; others are professional organizations; others are large business enterprises, such as insurance companies and industrial corporations. Still others are local organizations for various types and purposes, such as educational institutions, labor unions, and community chests. They have the largest investment in health, social, and welfare problems.

Voluntary

National voluntary health, rehabilitation, and social welfare organizations are composed of individuals, both lay and professional, whose primary purpose is either combating a particular disease, disability, or social problem (or group of diseases, disabilities, or social problems) or improving the health or social welfare of a particular group of people. The movement for voluntary organizations began with the Anti-Tuberculosis Society of Philadelphia in 1892. Three-quarters of a century later over 30,000 voluntary agencies had been organized. They are supported largely by voluntary contributions from the public at large rather than by government sources or endowments. They primarily engage in programs of research, education, and service to individuals and agencies or institutions in their particular spheres of interest.

Prominent among these organizations that operate in this country are the National Association for Mental Health, the American Lung Association, the American Cancer Society, the American Heart Association, the American Red Cross, the National Association for Retarded Citizens, the United Cerebral Palsy Association, the Muscular Dystrophy Association, the American Foundation for the Blind, and the National Easter Seal Society for Crippled Children and Adults.[4]

Philanthropic

Most of the philanthropic foundations have been established and endowed by wealthy individuals. They have interests that are broader in scope than any particular health, rehabilitation, or social welfare problem. Some operate in local areas or special fields; some are national or even international in scope. Their main source of financial support is often the investment earnings resulting from securities provided by the philanthropic individual or family. The Ford Foundation, the Rockefeller Foundation, the Commonwealth Fund, and the Kellogg Foundation are prominent examples. They often support new lines of research, training of personnel, and pilot programs. In this manner they often open up new approaches that government agencies may have overlooked or cannot provide.

Professional

Various groups of professional workers have formed organizations to promote their professional interests. These national organizations usually have affiliates at the state level, and some may also have local chapters. Such organizations strive to improve the social and economic welfare of their members, to keep their members informed, of changes and developments in professional practice, to set standards of ethical conduct and of professional practice and to aid in the enforcement of these standards, to engage in research to improve practice and utilization of professional services, to speak for and on behalf of the profession in planning and action groups, to monitor government activities in relation to their profession, to represent the profession in the determination of public policy, to mediate for the profession with the various governments and their agencies, and to provide the public with information relative to their profession. Examples of such organizations are the American Correctional Association, the National Rehabilitation Association, the National Therapeutic Recreation Society, the American Physical Therapy Association, the American Medical Association, and the American Nurses Association.

Becoming a member of a professional association or society usually implies that the individual has met certain qualifications of education and/or experience. Associations usually maintain records on current and past members. In turn, the individual may receive the journal of the association, listings of employment opportunities, and other informational items.[5]

As health organizations developed in this country, the need to provide for an exchange of ideas and for the coordination of certain services became obvious. This led to the formation of the National Health Council. All major voluntary health agencies, professional associations concerned with health, and major units of government concerned with health are members of the National Health Council. Among its activities the council conducts an annual forum devoted to the consideration of major health issues, the improvement of community health services, and the promotion of careers in the health fields.

Some people ask whether these nongovernment organizations are needed since federal, state, and some local governments are appropriating money for similar types of work. The answers to such questions are many, but prominent among them are the following: (1) voluntarism is an essential element of a free, democratic society; (2) nongovernmental organizations are better able to deal with amny controversial problems and to experiment with new ideas and programs; and (3) research people should have more than one possible source of support. No one speaks more positively about this subject than those who administer federal research programs.

services

Rehabilitation services are numerous, varied, and broad in nature, and are offered for the direct benefit of the individual. Services may be rendered in any one of a variety of facilities. However, this does not mean that all kinds of rehabilitation services are offered in the same facility. One facility may provide only one kind of service while another facility may render any number of services. Also, one individual may provide one service while another may render more than one kind of service.

The services provided in the health rehabilitation process are as follows:

- Clergy-medic services
- Corrective therapy
- Dentistry and allied services
- Dietetic and nutritional services
- Health aide services (directed primarily toward various ethnic and socioeconomic minorities)
- Health care institutional services (in-patient, out-patient, and nonpatient services — hospitals, institutions, day care facilities, rehabilitation centers, extended care facilities, etc.)
- Health education services (community, public, school, etc.)
- Homebound services
- Library services
- Manual arts or training therapy
- Medical services (prevention, cure, and alleviation of diseases)
- Music therapy
- Nursing and related care services
- Occupational therapy
- Ombudsman services
- Optometry services
- Orthotic and prosthetic services
- Podiatric services
- Psychological services (diagnosis of mental health problems, testing, counseling — personal and group, etc.)
- Social work service (medical, psychiatric, welfare, etc.)
- Therapeutic recreation service

- Sheltered employment
- Speech pathology and audiology service
- Suicide prevention centers
- Vocational rehabilitation service (vocational guidance, training, and placement)

While many of the above services are also found in correctional rehabilitation, the practical application of these services is directed toward:

- *Adult probation:* a type of sentence which is imposed on one convicted of a crime and requires the individual offender to remain in the community under the supervision and jurisdiction of the court.

- *Furloughs:* temporary release for family visits, especially in family emergencies, interviews with prospective employers in preparation for permanent release; training or medical care; and participation in religious, educational, social, civic, and recreational affairs.

- *Halfway house:* a homelike residential facility located in the community for offenders who need more control than probation or other types of community supervision can provide.

- *Institutional training and treatment:* academic and vocational as well as individual and group counseling and therapy, testing, etc.

- *Juvenile aftercare:* release of a juvenile from an institution or training or school facility at the time when he can best benefit from release and from life in the community under the supervision of a counselor.

- *Parole:* release of an adult felon offender from an institution after he has served part of his sentence under the supervision of the State and under prescribed conditions.

- *Pretrial intervention:* a program designed to provide a rapid rehabilitation response for young first-offenders following arrest, but prior to trial. The court suspends prosecution for a 90-day period and places the youth into a program of counseling, training, and employment assistance.

- *Prerelease centers:* supervised program designed to ease the transition from total confinement to freedom by involving people from the community who come to the prison to provide information in areas of vital interest to the inmate who is about to be released.

- *Work-release:* the offender is confined in an institution only at night or on weekends, but is permitted to pursue normal routine the remainder of the time.[6]

personnel

One of the major concerns in offering provisions of health and social rehabilitation is to make it available to all persons. It has been said that the "health care industry" in this country now has a combined manpower force large than that of any other industry. About one out of every 20 of the nation's employed is involved in the health care industry. In 1974, approximately 200 career specialties made up the health care industry, which employs 4.7 million people.[7] By 1980 an additional million people will be required.[8] In 1970 a white paper reflected the Administration's concern and suggested that several factors have contributed to this expansion and increased demand for health workers. These factors include large population growth, increased public awareness of the value of health care, the expansion of health care services for low income groups, government subsidies for hospital construction, and enlargement of the scope of medical services through research and technological progress.[9]

According to various investigators, the shortages are massive and at all levels, from the highly skilled professionals to the newly educated worker to the paraprofessional. Even the federal government has recognized the need for health manpower and has attempted to alleviate the problem in the past decade by passing such legislation as the Health Professions Educational Assistance Act, the Allied Health Professions Personnel Training Act, and the Health Manpower Act, as well as the Manpower Development and Training Act. In spite of these efforts, the basic fact remains that such legislation, while helpful, has not increased the supply of health workers. Therefore, it appears unrealistic to expect the need for professional and paraprofessional personnel to be met in the near future.

In 1967 the National Recreation and Park Association (NRPA) conducted a study of the manpower needs of the total field of parks and recreation projected through 1980. The NRPA estimated a need for 11,552 therapeutic recreation specialists having two or more years of formal training in 1967, for 12,091 such specialists in 1970, and for 18,786 in 1980.[10] In addition, the study indicated that many positions requiring a baccalaureate degree could possibly be filled by persons with an associate degree. If the estimates are a true projection, or even a close projection, the field of therapeutic recreation service is presently in a manpower crisis since the National Center for Health Statistics reported that between 6,000 and 8,000 (full- and part-time) therapeutic recreation specialists and aides were employed in health fields in 1974.[11]

function of service personnel

The number of types of workers in the health and social rehabilitation field has increased almost as rapidly as has the total number of persons in the field. The shortage of professional workers and the need for people with highly specialized skills have been two major factors contributing to this trend. The term *allied health discipline* is now used to encompass the large and rapidly growing family of occupational groups that are involved in providing health services.

In addition to the traditional health and social rehabilitation professions of medicine, nursing, psychology, social service, and vocational rehabilitation, a cadre of highly specialized workers has developed. Many of these people provide direct services to individuals that are extensions of health and social care, as do, for example, the physical therapist, the occupational therapist, and the therapeutic recreation specialist. Some are technologists whose occupation has evolved because of the need for people with specific skills. Other groups have emerged as a result of the delegation of certain functions by many professionals. These latter groups include licensed practical or vocational nurses, therapeutic recreation assistants, and speech therapist aides.

A complete listing of personnel found in the health and social rehabilitation field has increased so greatly that it is hard to enumerate them all, let alone describe their responsibilities here. Also, it is not possible to include the hundreds of interested people who participate indirectly in rehabilitation programs — volunteer groups, fund-raising groups, parent groups, service and fraternal organizations, and others. However, it is important to identify some having a more significant role in the rehabilitation process as well as those who may work closely with the therapeutic recreation specialist.

health services[12]

1. *Administration of health services*
   a. *Health Officer, commissioner, or public health administrator of state health department:* with few exceptions, a physician with specialized professional education and training in public health, psychiatry, or other specialty.
   b. *Hospital administrator, executive director, superintendent, or director of hospital, nursing home, or related institution (rehabilitation center, training school, sheltered workshop, or similar facility):* may or may not be a physician with specialization; recently individuals with professional education and training in administration as a specialty have been employed.

c. *Administrator or executive director of voluntary health agency* (the National Easter Seal Society for Crippled Children and Adults, the National Association of Mental Health, and the like): administrative professional education and training vary; however, the administrator usually has some sort of professional or technical health skill—e.g., physician, psychologist, social worker, physical therapist, and nurse.

2. *Correctional therapist:* uses assistive, resistive, and active exercises designed to strengthen and coordinate functions and to prevent muscular deconditioning.

3. *Educational therapist (special educator):* administers medical treatment through the use of educational activities and materials designed to develop the mental and physical capacities of the patient.

4. *Library services*

   a. *Medical librarian:* provides library services to meet the needs of professional staff and of professional schools. May be assisted by a *medical librarian technician.*

   b. *Patients' librarian (hospital librarian):* develops library facilities to meet interests of bedridden and ambulatory patients, provides book cart service, and encourages reading as part of therapeutic program.

5. *Medical records administrator (librarian):* is responsible for planning, organizing, directing, and controlling medical record services; for developing, analyzing, and evaluating medical records and indexes; and for cooperating with the medical and administrative staff in research projects utilizing health care information. May be assisted by a *medical records technician* who performs the technical tasks associated with the maintenance and use of medical records.

6. *Medicine and osteopathy—M.D., Doctor of Medicine, and D.O., Doctor of Osteopathy:* both are concerned with the prevention, cure, and alleviation of disease and may use surgery, drugs, and other accepted methods of medical care. While not restricted to any specialty, of which there are over 30, all doctors contribute to rehabilitation.

7. *Manual arts therapist:* administers a program of actual or simulated work situations through the use of industrial arts activities to help prepare the patient to become a productive member of the community.

8. *Music therapist:* uses instrumental or vocal music to bring about changes in behavior that can serve as a basis for improved mental and physical health.

9. *Nursing services*

 a. *Registered Nurse (R.N.):* is responsible for rendering nursing care to patients, carrying out physicians' instructions, and supervising personnel who perform routine care and treatment of patients.

 b. *Licensed practical nurse (L.P.N.):* provides nursing care and treatment of patients under the supervision of a licensed physician or registered nurse.

 c. *Nursing aide:* assists R.N. or L.P.N. by performing less skilled nursing tasks in the care of patients.

 d. *Orderlies and attendants:* usually men, they assist in performing a variety of duties associated with male patients and certain heavy duties in the care of all patients.

10. *Occupational therapist:* uses a variety of activities in a therapeutic manner to evaluate learning and performance abilities in relation to physical or emotional conditions so as to improve social well-being and ability to function independently. May be assisted by an *occupational therapy assistant* and/or *aide* and *noncertified assistants* who have received on-the-job training.

11. *Orthotist and/or prosthetist:* orthotist makes and fits orthopedic braces while the prosthetist makes and fits artificial limbs.

12. *Physical therapist:* is responsible for the restoration of function and the prevention of disability following disease, injury, or loss of bodily part through the use of exercise, heat, cold, electricity, ultrasound, and massage. May be assisted by a *physical therapy assistant and/or aide.*

13. *Psychology*

 a. *Clinical psychologist:* engages primarily in the diagnosis and treatment of mental illness.

 b. *Counseling psychologist:* is responsible for helping the individual understand himself so that he can utilize his own strengths to deal effectively with his own problems.

14. *Social worker:* is responsible for helping patients and their families cope with problems related to severe or long-term illness, recovery, and rehabilitation. Assists physicians and other personnel in understanding the social and emotional factors related to a patient's health problems. Social workers may specialize in social welfare, medical, and psychiatric services.

15. *Speech pathologist and audiologist:* identify persons with disorders in the production, reception, and perception of speech and language, as well as determining the etiology, history, and severity of the disorders through interviews and special tests.

16. *Vocational rehabilitation counselor (rehabilitation counselor):* is concerned with evaluating the vocational potential of the patient or client, thereafter matching the abilities of the client with a suitable job. Counselors may specialize in services to the blind, mentally ill, and others.

All of the above major titles require educational preparation at the baccalaureate level or above; however, as noted earlier, occupations have evolved because of the need for people with specific skills or as a result of the delegation of certain functions to assistants. The amount of education and training varies for these assistant positions from a few weeks of on-the-job training to two or more years of education or an associate degree. Attempts have been made to standardize the titles in relation to the level of training. The distinction is as follows:

1. *Technician or assistant:* educational preparation at the associate degree level (two years of college education or other formal preparation beyond high school.)
2. *Aide:* specialized training of less than two years' duration beyond high school, or on-the-job training.

Correctional Services

In the correctional setting many of the above personnel are also found; however, there are other personnel who are unique to this professional field. They are as follows:

1. *Correctional commissioner or administrator of state correctional department:* is an individual with specialized professional education and training in criminology, penology, police administration, or other closely allied specialty.
2. *Warden or superintendent:* is administratively responsible for the function and operation of an institution within the framework of the laws and departmental policies and procedures.
3. *Associate warden, custody (or care) and treatment:* usually two administrators and separate divisions; one is responsible for custody or security, the other for treatment.
4. *Classification officer:* is responsible for diagnosing and planning the custodial care and constructive treatment program for the offender as well as preparing the preparole report.
5. *Parole officer:* administers a program of supervision and guidance of parolees; may be assisted by specialized parole officers responsible

for preparole investigation, employment placement, training, or research.

6. *Probation officer:* is responsible for presentence investigation and supervision of probationers under the administration of the judicial system; probation officers administer to either juveniles or adults.

7. *Parole board:* is responsible for all parole decisions; membership consists of persons usually appointed by the governor of the state, by a panel of government officials, or by a board of corrections where such exists.[13]

Taking into account the type of population found in our correction system, the rate of turnover, and the mission of the various institutions, over 132,000 individuals were employed in federal, state, county, and local correctional institutions, according to the Bureau of the Census, in 1970.[14] In the field of correctional recreation no accurate figures are available. At best, a survey conducted in 1966 by the Children's Bureau of public institutions serving delinquent children found less than 200 recreation workers.[15]

human service teams

Perhaps one of the most important influences in recent years, resulting from the tremendous advances in scientific knowledge and technology and the trend toward specialization throughout our entire society, has been the creation of so-called *teams.* No one person can be expected to be knowledgeable about the "whole person," but by bringing together experts from various professions, the agency or institution can give the individual who is receiving service the advantage of their combined knowledge and skills.

Generally speaking, the team is usually composed of a variety of personnel representing professional disciplines concerned with the health and welfare of people. The membership varies with the needs of the individual. Each member of the team possesses knowledge and skills specific to his discipline. In many situations the members of the team confer regularly about the care and treatment of the individual. In this way, each member augments the services of the others in orienting their functions toward goals that will assist the individual.

As an example of a team meeting, the physician, the nurse, and the dietitian may pool information relative to the diet of the patient in a general hospital. Or the psychologist, the social worker, the vocational rehabilitation therapist, and the therapeutic recreation specialist may be members of a team planning the discharge needs of an educable mentally retarded adult in a residential institution for the retarded. Or the parole officer, the therapeutic recreation specialist, and the municipal recreation supervisor may act as a team in developing a leisure program for the social offender during a preparole investigation. In prison, a classification committee in many instances is a team. The team and the function of the therapeutic recreation specialist on the team will be discussed further in Chapters 7 and 8.

facilities

The spectrum of health and social rehabilitation services in a community ranges from preventive and health maintenance services, through primary care facilities, to in-patient services for the sick, and homecare and restorative and rehabilitative services for those who require them. A wide variety of agencies provide these services, and many agencies combine a number of them. Mental health centers, for example, often have outpatient services for diagnosis and treatment as well as in-patient facilities for the acutely ill. In many instances, two or more agencies combine to provide a more complete range of services for individuals. For example, a special school for the mentally retarded may work with a vocational training center to provide vocational training and with the municipal recreation department to provide recreation service.

The scope of correctional services as compared to that of health and social rehabilitation services is much more restricted. The rehabilitation services offered in the specialized institutions are designed to meet the needs of those offenders presenting specific problems. Correctional services include probation, institution care and treatment (in-city lockups, municipal or county jails, prisons and penitentiaries, reformatories, farms, camps, etc.), and parole.

health and health-related facilities

Types

There are many kinds of health and health-related facilities; they can be described according to their size, ownership, control, or services, or the length of stay of the patient. In most instances, hospitals and institutions are described in terms of number of beds. The facility may be owned or controlled by the government, by private groups, or by one person. Government ownership may be at the federal, state, county, or local level. Often general medical and surgical hospitals situated in a city or county are governed jointly by representatives of the government and representatives of the community. Religious organizations and physicians are examples of private groups that own and operate hospitals.

In relation to services offered, a hospital may be a general hospital—that is, one that offers a diversity of services, such as surgery, medicine, obstetrics, and pediatrics. Or it may be a special hospital, institution, center, or agency, admitting only patients of one sex, people with a particular illness or disability, or people of a specific age group. Hospitals that treat only female diseases and children's hospitals are examples of the former and latter, respectively. Hospitals or institutions for the mentally ill, hospitals for cancer or heart patients, and residential schools or training centers for the mentally retarded are examples of specialty hospitals or institutions.

The length of stay recently has become a basis upon which to classify an institution. There are two types: patients are permitted to stay 30 days in *acute care institutions,* after which they are transferred to the other type, *chronic care institutions.* As the latter term implies, chronic care means "long-term." Rehabilitation centers, nursing homes, and extended care facilities are examples of long-term care facilities. Emphasis in rehabilitation centers is put upon retraining and rehabilitating so that the patient may return to community living, while in nursing homes the patient usually requires an extended period of nursing care or services.

In 1973 there were an estimated 34,108 in-patient health facilities representing nearly 3.2 million beds. Nursing care and related homes accounted for 64 percent of the total number of in-patient facilities (and over 1 million beds); hospitals, including specialty hospitals (psychiatric, chronic, orthopedic, alcoholic and narcotic, and others) represented 22 percent; and the remaining 14 percent included facilities that primarily offer services such as training and sheltered care, as opposed to medical or nursing care in homes or residential facilities for the deaf, blind, physically disabled, mentally retarded, and the like.[16] A more detailed description is given in Table 3.1.

An interesting aspect for discussion relative to care and treatment is presented in Table 3.2. It will be noted that in-patient facilities (the general medical and surgical and the specialty hospitals) are usually operated by government or are nonprofit in nature, while nursing care and related homes are proprietary, which means they are privately owned and operated for profit. The question is, therefore: Who receives the best care and treatment? Recent reports also indicate that there will be a large increase in the number of proprietary general medical and surgical hospitals during the next decade.

Out-patient and nonpatient health services such as hospital outpatient departments, psychiatric out-patient clinics or centers, and day care facilities for the mentally retarded are increasingly being utilized to meet community needs. These facilities usually provide a full range of health and medical services, including prevention of disease, early diagnosis, and treatment.

TABLE 3.1   IN-PATIENT HEALTH FACILITIES BY TYPE—1973

Type of Facility	Number of Facilities	Number of Beds	Number of Patients[1]
Hospitals	7,438	1,449,062	1,120,159
General medical and surgical	6,458	1,030,432	775,359
Specialty hospital	980	418,630	344,800
Psychiatric	508	338,574	282,634
Chronic	70	22,350	18,675
Tuberculosis	65	10,215	6,517
Other	337	47,491	36,974
Nursing care and related homes	21,834	1,327,704	1,197,517
Nursing care	14,873	1,107,358	1,011,092
Personal care home with nursing			
Personal care home without nursing	6,961	220,346	186,425
Domiciliary			
Other	4,836	400,899	340,697
TOTAL	34,108	3,177,665	2,658,373

SOURCES: National Center for Health Statistics, *Health Resources Statistics: Health Manpower and Health Facilities,* 1975 (Washington, D.C.: U.S. Government Printing Office, 1976), pp. 383, 351, 361, 374.

[1] Number of average daily patients for general hospitals, and number of residents for specialty hospitals, nursing care and related homes, and other in-patient health facilities.

TABLE 3.2   OWNERSHIP OF HOSPITALS, NURSING HOMES, AND OTHER IN-PATIENT FACILITIES—1973

Ownership	General Medical and Surgical Hospitals[1]	Specialty Hospitals[1]	Nursing Care and Homes[2]	Other[3]
Government	2,239	505	1,319	720
Proprietary	818	182	16,712	1,307
Nonprofit	3,401	293	3,803	2,809
TOTAL	6,458	980	21,834	4,836

[1] SOURCE: National Center for Health Statistics. *Health Resources Statistics: Health Manpower and Health Facilities,* 1975 (Washington, D.C.: U.S. Government Printing Office, 1976) p. 354.

[2] SOURCE: Ibid., p. 373.

[3] SOURCE: National Center for Health Statistics. *Health Resources Statistics: Health Manpower and Health Facilities,* 1975 (Washington, D.C.: U.S. Government Printing Office, 1976), p. 385. (Includes facilities for the mentally retarded, dependent children and orphans, unwed mothers, alcoholics and drug abusers, deaf or blind, and physically handicapped.)

Listed below are other types of services more commonly found in a majority of communities:

1. *Neighborhood health center:* concentrates on providing and coordinating comprehensive care, including preventive care and early diagnosis, and physical, social, and vocational rehabilitation of those with residual disabilities.

2. *Day facilities for the mentally retarded:* concentrate on the treatment, education, training, personal care, or sheltered workshop services. One or more of these services may be offered in a single facility.

3. *Home health services:* concentrate on providing services in the home to those individuals who may have chronic diseases. Services may range from programs offering one type of health care such as nursing care or Meals on Wheels to physician-directed medical, social, and related services.

4. *Hospital out-patient services:* concentrate on services of a medical nature for those individuals who are generally ambulatory and who do not require or presently receive services as an in-patient.

5. *Psychiatric out-patient clinic or center:* concentrates on offering nonresidential mental health services and programs to individuals with mental or emotional disorders. Services usually cover diagnosis and treatment. The clinic may be a distinct facility or associated with a general medical and surgical hospital as an out-patient service.

6. *Rehabilitation center:* concentrates primarily on the restoration of the physically disabled to their fullest physical, mental, social, vocational, and economic usefulness. A wide variety of organizational patterns and service activities is found. A single facility may serve all disability groups or only those in a specific disability category. Likewise, program services may include only one service, such as a vocational workshop, or a variety of services.[17]

Health Organizational Structure

Most health and health-related facilities grow out of the needs of people. Each facility sets its own functions designed to carry out the purposes set forth in its articles of incorporation. The purposes may be broad, as they are for a general hospital, or they may be limited, as for a public or private institution for the mentally ill. Some facilities may be concerned only with research, such as the Clinical Center, National Institutes of Health. Others may have education as their primary purpose. Still others may be set up for "day care" or "night care" only.

According to MacEachern, no modern enterprise is more complex than the hospital, and only through organization can efficiency result.[18] In a general hospital, hospital policies are usually set by the hospital board of directors or trustees. The board usually consists chiefly of people who are representative of the community served by the hospital. There is usually one or more representatives of the medical department or service on the board; likewise, the hospital administrator is a member. In government institutions, such as state institutions for the mentally ill or mentally retarded, the members of the board are appointed by the governor and function in an advisory role. Some may say that the institution is weakened by this procedure; however, the institution is also represented through the democratic process that ultimately affects the operation of the institution through the government's legislative, judicial, and executive branches.

During the past decade there has been a trend toward decentralization of authority in institutions for the mentally ill and retarded. The most common method of decentralization has been the *unit system*. The institution is divided into autonomous units, each responsible to a unit director. In some institutions, the respective units may be further divided into sections. More will be said about this type of organizational structure in a later chapter.

correctional facilities

Types

It was not until the late sixteenth century that prisons as places for the reception of ordinary criminals developed.[19] Earlier, prisons were used to confine military captives and those who committed crimes against landowners and the government.[20] Houses of correction were established in colonial America soon after the colonists arrived. The first penitentiary (Walnut Street jail) was established in Pennsylvania (Philadelphia) in 1794. By 1835, America was credited with the establishment of the first genuine penal system in the world, although practices varied widely in the different states.[21] The first separate institution for women was the Indiana Women's Prison, which opened in 1873. In 1972, it was estimated that there were over 4,700 prisons and jails in this country. Many of the state prisons and local jails were built during the 1800s and early 1900s.[22]

There are many types of correctional institutions for men, women, and juveniles; the more common ones are prisons and penitentiaries, reformatories, farms, ranches, camps, jails, houses of correction, workhouses, and training and industrial schools. Some are designed to provide maximum, medium, or minimum security for older and youthful felons while others are used for misdemeanants.

Correctional institutions, like health and health-related facilities, may be classified according to control and length of stay as well as type of security. All correctional institutions are government controlled at the federal, state, county, or local level. At the federal level, 35 institutions of various types are under the direction of the U.S. Bureau of Prisons, which was established by an act of Congress in 1930. Over 200 prisons, reformatories, farms, camps, and ranches are operated by state governments. State prisons or penitentiaries have been established in every state. They are administered in three ways, though some overlapping exists: (1) by boards, (2) through an independent department, or (3) within a larger existing department.[23]

Jails, houses of correction, workhouses, farms, and road camps make up over 4000 institutions (jails) at the county and local government levels.[24] Federal and state institutions handle those convicted of felonies, which involves a long-term sentence, while county and local jails handle those offenders serving sentences for misdemeanors, a short-term sentence.

The type of security is another way of classifying correctional institutions. There are three types used: (1) Maximum-security institutions are walled, and the majority of prisoners are housed in cells, work within the walls, and are guarded. (2) Medium-security institutions are usually not walled, but are surrounded by a wire fence. Prisoners are usually housed in dormitories and work outside the compound, and there is less security. (3) Minimum-security institutions are open institutions, usually with no fence, where prisoners live in unlocked buildings or dormitories and work outside the institution; guards are at a minimum, with supervision during work by overseers. There is a tendency today to provide all levels of security in each institution. It would appear that the correctional institutions to which the guilty defendants are sent range from maximum-security prisons to open forestry camps without guards or fences, from short-term detention homes or training schools for juveniles to penitentiaries where men or women may spend the rest of their lives.

The various types of correctional facilities are as follows:

1. *Juvenile detention center:* a facility for holding children of juvenile court age in secure custody for court disposition.

2. *Juvenile institution:* a facility whose role is to provide a specialized program for those who must be treated; may be and usually is referred to as a *training* or *school facility.*

3. *State correctional institution for adults (prisons, penitentiaries, reformatories, road and forestry camps, or farms):* a facility that receives felons sentenced by the criminal courts for more than one year.

4. *Local jail:* a facility that in most situations houses both those offenders awaiting court action and those serving short sentences, usually up to one year but may be up to several years.

FIGURE 3.1 INSTITUTION FOR ADULT MALES, UP TO 2,000

CENTRAL
STATE AUTHORITY

WARDEN OR
SUPERINTENDENT

STAFF

Industries Manager	Business Manager	Associate Warden (Custody)	Associate Warden (Classification and Treatment)	Medical Services Manager
Functions	*Functions*	*Functions*	*Functions*	*Functions*
Industries	Budget	Security guarding	Classification	General health
Farms	Accounting	General work crew	Release procedures	Clinics
Accounts, stores, records, etc., for production enterprises	Procurement	Supervision	Inmate education and training	Hospital administration
	Stores	Control of routine	Religion	Dental services
	Canteen	Movement of inmates	Recreation	Psychiatric services
	Feeding	Discipline	Inmate records	Institution sanitation
	Clothing		Mail	
	Plant maintenance		Visits	
	Personnel payrolls and records		Casework and counseling	
	Fire protection		Library services	

Source: American Correctional Association, *Manual of Correctional Standards* (1966), p. 319.

5. *Lockup:* a facility that is secured, usually operated by the police department for temporary detention of persons held for investigation or awaiting a preliminary hearing.[25]

Correctional Organizational Structure

The organizational structure of correctional institutions varies with the type, size, and objectives and goals of the specific institution. At present the organizational patterns of various institutions are undergoing widespread change. The more or less traditional organizational framework in institutions for adult males with a population up to 2,000 is shown in Figure 3.1.

accreditation, licensure, certification, and registration

Licensing requirements and other forms of credentialism were initiated during medieval times to protect the public by ensuring that high standards of performance were met. Today, there are essentially two types of credentialing. One recognizes the competence of educational programs to prepare personnel; this is generally referred to as accreditation. The second recognizes the competence of individuals to deliver services. This includes the practices of licensure, certification, and registration. The various types of credentialing are defined as follows:

- *Accreditation:* the process by which an agency or organization evaluates and recognizes a program of study or an institution as meeting certain predetermined qualifications or standards.
- *Licensure:* the process by which an agency of government grants permission to persons meeting predetermined qualifications to engage in a given occupation and/or use a particular title or grants permission to institutions to perform specified functions.
- *Certification:* the process by which a nongovernmental agency or association grants recognition to an individual who has met certain predetermined qualifications specified by that agency or association. Such qualifications may include: (a) graduation from an accredited or approved educational program; (b) acceptable performance on a qualifying examination or series of examinations; and/or (c) completion of a given amount of work experience.
- *Registration:* the process by which qualified individuals are listed on an official roster maintained by a governmental or nongovernmental agency.[26]

In practice, the distinction between certification and registration is not always as clear as the standard definition of "certification" and "registration" would seem to indicate.

There are two types of accreditation: institutional and specialized. *Institutional accreditation,* or general or regional accreditation, is concerned with the quality of the total institution. Institutional accreditation is conferred on a regional basis by the secondary and postsecondary commissions of six regional accrediting associations that cover the United States. Institutional accreditation indicates that the total institution is achieving its own specified objectives in a satisfactory manner. It is not the equivalent of specialized accreditation since it does not validate a specialized program of study.

Specialized, or *program* or *professional accreditation,* is conferred on a national basis by a number of national organizations, each representing a professional, technical, occupational, or specialized educational area. Specialized accreditation applies to an individual curriculum, department, or program within the educational institution and is aimed at protecting the public against professional or occupational incompetence.

Since January 1976 the Council on Accreditation of the National Recreation and Park Association (NRPA), in cooperation with the American Association for Leisure and Recreation (AALR) has been accepting applications for accreditation of recreation, leisure services and resources curriculum. At the present time, only baccalaureate and master's degree programs are being considered. In addition, therapeutic recreation is one of a number of professional options within the total curriculum which the department may request to be accredited.

As of 1974, 31 health professions and occupations were licensed by one or more states.[27] Legislation usually establishes education, experience, and personal qualifications, requires successful completion of an examination, and provides for issuance of a license as a prior condition for entrance into the occupation. As most readers know, physicians and nurses, for example, are required to have a license before they can practice their speciality. Therapeutic recreation specialists are licensed by only one state—Utah; it passed a recreation therapy act in 1975. It should be noted that exclusions and exceptions from licensure requirements are always made for federal employees and in some instances for state and municipal workers.[28]

Certification and registration recognizes the professional competence of individuals in their health field. The certifying or registering function may be retained within the association or may be transferred by the parent association to independent agencies under its sponsorship. The groups, whether committees, boards, or registries, have the sole purpose of distinguishing the quality of personnel.

Certifying boards or registries usually encourage the use of professional designations to honor the professionals who have met their requirements of education, experience, and competency. Their names may be published on registries, and they may have been authorized to use the designations "certified" or "registered" or, more frequently, to use initial abbreviations indicative of such professional status. For example, O.T.R. means that an occupational therapist (by education, experience, and competency) has been registered by the Board of Registry of the American Occupational Therapy Association. A therapeutic recreation specialist might use M.T.R.S., which means the person is registered as a Master Therapeutic Recreation Specialist (by education, experience, and competency) by the Board of Registration of the National Therapeutic Recreation Society.[29]

It should also be noted that licensure and accreditation exist in relation to health facilities. The licensure of health facilities is a form of business licensure to conduct or engage in the provision of health services within a specific type of institution or setting. The objective is to regulate the opening of new health facilities and to support and enforce standards of performance.

An effective force in promoting and upgrading health care is the voluntary accreditation program carried out by the Joint Commission on Accreditation of Hospitals (JCAH) formed in 1951 through the cooperative efforts of various medical organizations. The commission can accredit a hospital, provisionally accredit it, or not accredit it at all. In 1971 the JCAH formed the Accreditation Council for Long-Term Care Facilities which consist of organizations representing the American Association of Homes for the Aged, the American Medical Association, and the American Nursing Home Association. Another accrediting body concerned with rehabilitation centers, sheltered workshops, homebound programs, and other like facilities and programs is the Commission on Accreditation of Rehabilitation Facilities.

While correctional facilities are presently not accredited, the American Correctional Association is in the process of developing an accreditation program.

SUGGESTED REFERENCES

Aday, Lu Ann. *The Utilization of Health Services: Indices and Correlates.* Washington, D.C.: U.S. Government Printing Office, 1972.

Alford, Robert. *Health Care Politics: Ideological and Interest Group Barriers to Reform.* Chicago: University of Chicago Press, 1975.

Butler, Robert. *Why Survive? Being Old in America.* New York: Harper and Row Publishers, Inc., 1975.

Greenfield, Harry I. *Allied Health Manpower: Trends and Prospects.* New York: Columbia University Press, 1969.

Hasenfield, Yeheskel and Richard A. English, ed. *Human Service Organizations.* Ann Arbor: University of Michigan Press, 1978.

Heydebrand, Wolf V. *Hospital Bureaucracy: A Comparative Study of Organizations.* New York: Dunellen Publishing Company, Inc., 1973.

Mechanic, David, ed. *Politics, Medicine, and Social Sciences.* New York: Wiley-Interscience Publishers, 1974.

National Advisory Commission on Criminal Justice Standards and Goals. *Criminal Justice System.* Washington, D.C.: U.S. Government Printing Office, 1973.

National Recreation and Park Association, "Position Statement for the White House Conference on Handicapped Individuals," *Therapeutic Recreation Journal,* 11:1 (1977), pp. 3–5.

The President's Committee on Mental Health. *Report to the President.,* Vol. I. Washington, D.C.: U.S. Government Printing Office, 1978.

Rothman, David. *The Discovery of the Asylum.* Boston: Little, Brown and Co., 1971.

Shapiro, Ira G. "The Path to Accreditation," *Parks and Recreation,* (January 1977), 29, 112.

United States Senate Special Committee on Aging. *Long Term Care Facility Improvement Study.* Washington, D.C.: U.S. Government Printing Office, 1975.

United States Senate Special Committee on Aging. *Nursing Home Care in the United States: Failure in Public Policy.* Washington, D.C.: U.S. Government Printing Office, 1974.

Yale, David R. "Certification: A Mistake," *Parks and Recreation.* (February 1975), 24, 36–37.

chapter 4
the historical development of rehabilitation and therapeutic recreation

In the consideration of therapeutic recreation as a helping profession, it is important to devote attention to the development of recreation services in hospitals and in settings of a rehabilitation nature including correctional settings. Similarly, it is desirable to consider the development of recreation services for the ill, disabled, and disadvantaged in community settings. But first, however, we must consider the historical background and development of health and correctional rehabilitation since therapeutic recreation service, as we know it today, was born within the settings concerned with rehabilitation.

The concepts of rehabilitation and therapeutic recreation are not new, although a definitive history of both has yet to be written. The origin of rehabilitation in the history of the human race is dim, and is even dimmer as it relates to therapeutic recreation. While little work has been done to uncover the therapeutic values of recreation in its infancy, we are indebted to Virginia Frye and Elliott M. Avedon for their historical sketches of recreation as a therapeutic agent in an earlier time.

In this chapter we will look to other times and places in an attempt to capture the beginnings of recreation service to those with limiting conditions and disabilities in various settings and rehabilitation. The chapter will also attempt to show how people in the past have used the many possibilities of recreative experiences to change behavior. It is hoped that from this historical overview the student will gain a greater understanding of the heritage of therapeutic recreation and an appreciation of the influences that have made it what it is today. To know and understand is to offer a better service.

historical development

prehistoric civilizations

Disease and disability are as old as life itself. Anthropologists and archaeologists tell us that paleolithic man suffered from the pains of disease. For millions of years before human history animals likewise suffered from many conditions we still recognize today. Disease is in reality a part of all life since it is the reaction of the living organism to abnormal stress or stimulus. We know little about early humans' reaction to disease and disability except what can be pieced together from the study of artifacts and through comparative studies of those remnants of primitive cultures that still exist.

The view that humans were savage first and then became civilized and that good treatment of the sick, disabled, and aged is a criterion of higher civilization is contradicted by the facts, so far as primitive societies are concerned. Indeed, we find quite generally that food-gathering, fishing, and hunting communities were inclined to treat their ill and disabled members well. However, where life was hard, the sick and infirm were sacrificed in special circumstances: when the food or water gave out, when the tribe was starting out on a long migration, or when epidemics caused such fear of the sick that they were abandoned.[1] In general, it appears that the chief cause for the elimination of the sick and infirm was economic conditions. When they were economically useless, there was no point in preserving them.

In the early period of human history, it seems safe to assume that only the "fittest" survived. Each person had to play his role in self-protection and self-preservation. If he was not able to do so, he died. Leading a life of hardship, surrounded by the hostile forces of nature that they could not understand, humans developed supernatural explanations for the unknowns of life. A great body of religious and magical beliefs and practices developed. It is apparent that many, if not all, primitive people used recreation activities in the forms of dancing and music to drive away the evil spirits of disease. There is also some evidence that the disabled and sick were thought to be agents of a hostile world and were treated accordingly, and that malformed babies were destroyed.

primitive civilizations

With developing civilization, social life became more complex. Families joined to form larger social groups, living and working together and following definite sets of rules. Woman played an increasingly important part in the life of the group, doing farm work and attending to the home, while the men took care of the animals and were hunters, fishermen, traders, and also warriors.

At this stage of human history, there seem to be some inconsistencies in the beliefs and actions toward the sick, disabled, and aged. There are some indications that while many cultures did not destroy their disabled as a general practice, they subjected them to other types of personal and social abuses and torment. On the other hand, there were groups that practiced the other extreme and considered the disability a mark of distinction that brought special privilege or consideration to the individual. Perhaps we might speculate that here was the dawn of the new approach to human differences and infirmities—the beginning of a shift from automatically eliminating life to the idea that there might be some worth or value in preserving the disabled.

Practices that hundreds of generations later were to be called *rehabilitation* seem to have started their development here. Archaeological findings reveal that certain mineral and hot water springs were used for special purposes other than drinking. We might speculate again that the water was used for the treatment of ailments, as it is today. It seems reasonable to assume that instinct may have been a source from which other methods of treatment sprang. An individual hurt his leg and spontaneously, without thinking, rubbed it. This rubbing developed into a system and became what we call *massage*. Another individual, suffering from arthritis, crawled to the fire and discovered that the heat relieved his pain. These simple instinctive reactions may then have developed into more controlled methods and forms for the application of heat and cold, using water, steam, sand, or other available materials. Such media are used today by physical therapists.

Before these instinctive acts became a system of treatment of the injured or disabled person, however, another important attitudinal change had to take place—that of mutual aid, of caring for the person involved. The idea that one human being could help to eliminate the suffering of another and perhaps thus prolong or save life appears to have been an early development. For whatever magical or religious reasons this was done, the important consideration here is the fact that care was taken of human life by others.

ancient civilizations

As people invented writing and recorded their traditions and practices, we find explanations of the phenomena of nature, including disease, disablement, and old age. The explanations possess a similarity in all ancient civilizations, based as they are on religious-magical concepts that undoubtedly precede the oldest written records. Two persons were primarily concerned with these concepts and practices: the medicine man and the minister of religion, whose function it was to appease the deities. Eventually these two persons became united in one—the priest-physician.

   This medicine man or priest-physician was the first "professional." He was not just the forerunner of what we now call the *physician,* but also probably the model for many professions. He was the wise man and the person who possessed the learning and specialized knowledge of the group. Practices became a confusion of superstition and fact, of natural remedies and religious rituals. Yet, these practices were logical for these cultures; they were in accord with the philosophy and religion they possessed. Medical practice in ancient Egypt was divided into two schools: the empiric, which was costly and reserved for the royal family and the wealthy, and the magico-ritual, which was inexpensive and popular. One cannot help but be struck by the idea that even though much early care was purely magical in nature, it nevertheless included elements that are also found in rational therapy. Early Egyptian writings indicate that to receive forgiveness from the gods, one must "walk in the gardens which surround the temple, row on the majestic Nile, and embark upon . . . planned excursions . . . dancing, listening to concerts, and acting in representations. These are the ways required for those possessed by illness."[2] According to Frye, "Priests are said to have been aware that the dispelling of morbid moods was aided by the temple atmosphere, the beauty of lotus gardens, and the ritual songs and dances of the temple maidens."[3] From the very beginning, therapy seems to have been an interwoven combination of empirical, rational, magical, and religious elements.

   Paralleling the Egyptian civilization, although not quite as ancient, was the civilization that flourished in the Indus river valley of India, comprising people of unknown origin and the great Aryan migration that peopled India and parts of western Asia and Europe. Some of the most ancient Indian medical texts contain magic formulas against demons. At this time, medicine was almost entirely in the hands of the ruling caste of Brahmins. In the Brahmanic period, physicians belonged to a caste lower than the priests. The physician Charaka is considered to be one of the founders of

Indian medicine.[4] As noted by Avedon, Charaka not only advocated the use of toys and games but felt that hospitals had the responsibility to provide them for patient use.[5]

In its turn, Chinese medicine influenced by the Buddhist philosophies imported from India and by Confucianist principles became an extremely intricate art. The use of recreative activities as a form of therapy and as an adjunct to treatment was not unknown. Various forms of gymnastics and massage were suggested as a prevention to disease.[6] Other recreational activities were used in association with surgery.[7]

The idea that an individual should be compensated for injury, or loss of a part of the body, was accepted by most ancient civilizations. The rights of the person injured or afflicted were first expressed in Babylonia in retaliatory terms: "Eye for eye, tooth for tooth, hand for hand, foot for foot."[8] This was the usual compensation between persons of like social status; however, monetary compensation was usual for the injured person who was considered to be of lower status and thus inferior to the injurer. The great code as given by Hammurabi provided regulations in regard to fees and compensations for injured persons as well as employment practices[9] The provisions were mixed with superstition and magic and were harsh, but perhaps for the first time groups or communities were responsible for the individual, both the injured and the injurer.

The Mosaic code given to the Hebrews also provided for individual rights by the group. These were perhaps the first public health regulations, providing rules for sanitation, cleanliness, and reporting and isolating contagious disease, as well as specifying hours for work and rest[10] The Twelve Tablets of Rome and the Anglo-Saxon codes provided for monetary compensation for injury.[11] Our current concepts and laws of workmen's compensation undoubtedly developed from the same basic ideas embodied in these early regulations.

The Jews, as a result of the strength of their faith in one God, began to stem the tide of superstition and magic. Their God was recognized as the source of health, and the Jews held the extreme view that disease and illness were punishment for sins of the individual and his family. This belief is still held by many people as part of our attitudinal pattern toward disease and disability.

greek-roman civilization

These beginnings covered a great deal of time in human history, providing the background for the growth of knowledge attained by the Greeks. In contrast to other ancient peoples, the Greeks desired to live according to reason, and they searched for perfection and first causes. Their desire for "a good mind in a good body" seems to have been responsible for a great shift in the philosophy of care for the sick and disabled. For the first time the part that a person's mind and feelings play in his treatment was recognized. The idea of the whole man, so important in present rehabilitation activities, apparently started at this time.

The healing arts were practiced in temples. These temples were apparently situated in scenic places. It is reported that the temples of Aesculapius were built in healthful pastoral settings, usually with mineral springs at hand; they were equipped with bathing pools, gymnasia, and gardens. At Epedauros, the temples included excercise grounds, a race track, a library, a stadium, and a theater seating 20,000 persons.[12] The effect of the environment and recreational activities on the patient was apparently recognized.

The genius of ancient medicine was a Greek—Hippocrates, the philosopher-physician, the "Father of Medicine." His oath, defining the ideals, duties, and responsibilities of a physician, is still used today in the medical profession. One of his great contributions was the *case study method* as the approach to medical education.[13] The clinician taught and learned by observation and study at the bedside of his patient. Up to this time knowledge about illness and disease was handed down from father to son. Hippocrates' fundamental belief was that illness and defects of the body were due to natural causes. In this way he helped to free the field from superstition and convert it into something of an empirical art to be studied and mastered by the slow process of trial-and-error learning. For the first time the patient became the center of attention. He was studied as an individual; records were kept so that the same signs might be recognized in another person.

Following Greece, Rome became the undisputed master of the world. Her own native system of care for the sick and disabled was very primitive and unscientific when compared with that of the Greeks. Rome made few if any contributions to the healing arts. Romans were suspicous of and reluctant to use the medical knowledge they took over from the Greeks. However, in the story of modern rehabilitation they contributed greatly through their organizational genius in public health measures. They introduced sanitary measures through the issuing of government decrees. One prohibited burials within the city; another ordered officials to look after the cleanliness of streets and to the water supply; still another established a public medical service of physicians to look after the needs of the poor. This probably was the first attempt of government to meet the needs of its citizens regardless of class—perhaps the first such community program.

The greatest of all Roman innovations, however, was the hospital system, although according to some historians, the beginning of a hospital system can be traced back to 1550 B.C.[14] The Roman hospital system was established chiefly by the army. Infirmaries were built for the poor, and it is reported that physicians' homes were used as "nursing homes" for better-class patients.[15] Patients were moved outdoors to enjoy the sunshine. A physician named Soranus prescribed music to relieve pain. In a later period of Roman history, another physician, Galen, prescribed recreational activities to assist in relaxation of the body and mind.[16] This latter type of care is one of the modern approaches to rehabilitation.

Jesus, the great teacher of Christianity, in his compassion for those who suffered from physical, mental, and social problems at the hands of their fellow men, emphasized the human, individualized approach to care and treatment. His teachings were based on the Jewish faith in one God and emphasized the dignity of each human life, regardless of race, class, or infirmity—a concept present since the beginning of the recreation movement.

The philosophy that all care and treatment should be based on love and the brotherhood of mankind is directly responsible for much that is included in modern rehabilitation practice. The Christian church as a social organization often failed to live up to these teachings, but it has served to preserve the emphasis on the importance of the individual, which is at the heart of Western democratic culture.

the middle ages

The downfall of the Roman Empire left Europe without a single unifying governing structure, and health efforts reverted to a primitive level. What was needed at this time seemed to be a ruling authority under the protection of which some new form of social organization might grow. It was the Christian church with its excellent organization, its strong central authority, and its discipline that helped make the growth of new Europe possible.

For about eight centuries the classical learning and science passed into the church's keeping. This was fortunate or it might have been lost forever. However, the intellectual independence of the individual had to be sacrificed to the authority of the church. The church also took over the role of physician of the body as well as of the mind and soul, and it was again a strange mixture of physical remedies, magic, and ritual that was dispensed. Hippocrates had freed treatment and care from religion and superstition, and had taught men that illness and disability were not sent by the gods as punishment, but rather natural phenomena to be studied. Under the church rule the view of the supernatural origin of disease was revived, partly the result of the fact that to be a physician one first had to be ordained a priest. Very little progress was made in theory and research during the Middle Ages—the doctrine of the four humors prevailed, and few had the knowledge or courage to question its authority.

The idea of the hospital was carried forward by the Arabians and the Christian church. Islamic hospitals became models of human kindness, especially in the treatment of the mentally ill. Cairo's Mansur Hospital cooled its fever wards by fountains; contained lecture halls, a library, chapels, and a dispensary; and was staffed with nurses of both sexes. It employed reciters of the Koran, musicians to lull patients to sleep, and storytellers for their distraction; discharged patients were given money to tide them over during convalescence.[17,18]

Arabian hospitals so impressed Christian pilgrims to the Holy Land that in the eleventh century a hospital was founded in Jerusalem. This was later expanded by the Crusaders and formed the kernel of the religious Order of the Knights of St. John of Jerusalem, the famous Knights Hospitalers who played a major role in the Crusades. Hospitals were also opened for the care of orphans and the aged, crippled, and blind.[19]

The separation between medicine and surgery lasted throughout the medieval period. In the ancient world the physician traced his art to scholars; he was a man of dignity who served the upper class. The surgeon who worked with his hands was of low social status; his professional ancestry was in barbering. It was not until the seventeenth century that surgery was considered a profession fit for men of upper classes. Ambroise Paré brought together in a working relationship the long-robed university physicians and the barber-surgeons whom the people relied upon. He believed in treating the complete man and was known for his ability to inspire his patients. It is reported that he attended to all details of a patient's treatment and recovery, even to methods of relieving boredom through games, music, and reading during convalescence. His practical genius was shown in his construction and development of artificial limbs and the glass eye. He is also credited with the statement: "I treat them, God cures them."[20]

The seeds of knowledge planted in preceding centuries came to fruition in the fourteenth, fifteenth, and sixteenth centuries, initiating the cultural transition from medieval to modern civilization. Some of these forces that changed the existing medieval social order were the Renaissance, the Reformation, nationalism, the discovery of a new world, and the diffusion of knowledge through the printed word. All of these factors influenced the healing arts in one way or another.

It was during this period that the crippled and the mentally retarded came into prominence as "fools" or "jesters." The greater the deformity, the greater the mirth and laughter it provoked. Courts sought them. It is reported that the demand for jesters created a scarcity of them, increasing their value to such an extent that parents are said to have crippled their own children in order to enhance their value. For the first time the disabled were able to earn their living, however distasteful the method must have been to some.[21]

The church, in providing custodial care in its monasteries, may have been a forerunner in the development of educational oportunities for those in its care. Up to this time no attention had been paid to the educational or training needs of physically disabled and intellectually handicapped people. With the church serving as the center for both physical care and education, it can be speculated that the idea arose that custodial care alone was insufficient for the individual's needs. Education and training of the handicapped, however, was to occupy a minor role until the eighteenth and nineteenth centuries.

As we move into the eighteenth and nineteenth centuries, one cannot help but speculate about the possible influence of Locke and Rousseau on scientific medicine. According to some health historians, these philosophers were able to both generate considerable concern for the welfare of the common person and provide general guidelines for their improvement.[22]

the eighteenth and nineteenth centuries

With the growth of scientific medicine during the late eighteenth century and throughout the nineteenth century, the concept of the dignity of man was emphasized more and more. Many persons began to regard the mentally and physically disabled with pity and to treat them with special care. Also, as financial fortunes began to accumulate, the philanthropic concept evolved and was directed toward the medical and custodial care of the poor.

Phillippe Pinel, in the latter part of the eighteenth century in France, attempted to prove that kind and humane treatment of the insane would do much toward their recovery. Likewise, Jean Itard, also in France, initiated the first scientific attempt at training a retarded child. As a result of the concerns of others in France, England, and the United States about the care of those considered insane and feebleminded, care, treatment, and education in hospitals and residential schools were improved, and a new attitude of optimism was engendered. For example, in 1751, prior to the American Revolution, the Quakers, with the aid of Benjamin Franklin, established the Pennsylvania Hospital in Philadelphia, which was the first general medical hospital in the United States. This was a voluntary hospital designed to provide care for the sick, poor, and "lunatics." Some fifteen years later in this same city, John Morgan is credited with establishing the first medical school in America.[23]

The first American asylum exclusively for the mentally ill was opened at Williamsburg, Virginia in 1773.[24] It was not until 1817, in Hartford, Connecticut, that the first private school for the deaf was organized, and the first and only college for the deaf, called Deaf-Mute College, opened its doors in Washington, D.C. in 1864. This college was renamed Gallaudet

College in honor of the early work of Thomas Hopkins Gallaudet, a teacher of the deaf and mute. Schools for the blind were founded in New York, Pennsylvania, and Massachusetts between 1829 and 1832. In 1899, the first tax-supported school program for physically disabled children was established in Chicago. The first public institution for the mentally retarded was not established until 1848 through legislative action in Massachusetts.[25] The first club for older persons, a forerunner of the senior citizen clubs, was established in 1870 in Boston.[26]

During this period there was evidence of renewed interest in the use of recreational activities as aids in helping those considered to be mentally ill. Physicians were beginning to prescribe physical exercise, handicrafts, reading, and music for their patients. Dr. Benjamin Rush, the first American psychiatrist, wrote a letter to the managers of the Pennsylvania Hospital in 1810 advocating the use of many homely tasks, such as weaving, spinning, and other domestic occupations, for their therapeutic effect. Likewise, he recommended playing chess and checkers, listening to the flute or violin, reading, and making trips to the community.[27]

Patients selected by the physicians on the Committee of the Asylum of New York Hospital in 1821 participated in approved exercises and amusements. A doctor at McLean Hospital, Massachusetts, in 1822 described the use of "draughts, chess, backgammon, nine-pins, swinging, sawing wood, gardening, reading, writing and music" as therapeutic in the diversion they provided the "lunatics."[28]

Bockoven[29] and Zilboorg[30] inform us that the moral therapists of the nineteenth century believed that psychiatric hospitals should exist to retrain patients so that they could live more fruitfully in society. So firm was their conviction in the value of planned recreation that they involved all staff members and their children, as well as the patients, in the work of the hospital and in its games, social functions, and intellectual pursuits. For example, at the dinner hour, all waited until the superintendent had taken the first bite of food; at the annual ball, the grand march was headed by the superintendent and his wife; and in daily living on the wards, the patients, attendants, and children of the staff had their recreation together.

Norman Dain[31] in his investigation of the history of psychiatric thought in the United States, reports that the patients of Friends' Asylum in Frankford, Pennsylvania, beginning in 1830, participated in social gatherings, played ball, flew kites, threw quoits, went fishing, and made trips to places of interest near the asylum. He continues that in the late 1830s and early 1840s many asylums had annual fairs that were open to the public. Patients also published weekly newspapers and presented theatrical performances.

It was not unusual for hospital superintendents of the day to assume that activities were the best remedy for functional brain disorders. The

"Code of Rules and Regulations for the Government of Those Employed in the Care of Patients of the Pennsylvania Hospital for the Insane at Philadelphia" contains this statement: "It is highly important that patients should, as far as possible, be kept constantly at some pleasant kind of employment—either work of some kind, or riding, walking, or amusements. . . ."[32]

While the opinions of leaders in psychiatry in the past century have been presented with sufficient examples to influence the reader, there is one other that is especially appealing. In the first edition of *System of Practical Therapeutics* (1892), the section on the treatment of insanity written by Dr. Edward N. Brush included the following:

> Amusements should not be lost sight of in the enumeration of the remedial measures to be brought into play in caring for the insane. The sane mind enjoys laying aside the cares and perplexities of the hour and being simply amused. In the theatre or opera the outside world is forgotten; the mimic scene becomes real and supplants all else. Many institutions have distinct buildings devoted to the purposes of amusement. Theatrical performances, concerts, negro minstrels, lectures, views shown by the stereopticon, constitute some of the means which may be brought to use. These are of undoubted value and may, with benefit, be enjoyed by all classes of patients.[33]

Although therapeutic recreation activities have been of greatest use in the field of psychiatry until recent years, they have also been used sporadically by some as a muscle builder for those with disabilities of muscles and joints. Dr. Clement-Joseph Tissot of France in his book *Gymnastique Medicinale et Cherurgicale*, published in 1780, recommended "shuttlecock, tennis, football, dancing . . . and the game of barriers."[34]

Florence Nightingale not only led the way toward modern nursing techniques and care, but also introduced and provided recreational opportunities for hospitalized soldiers. In her book *Notes on Nursing*, she recommended pets for chronically ill patients and commented on the good effects of music upon patients.[35]

Industrial growth and urbanization during this same period brought about changes in working conditions and a demand for protection through labor legislation. This period was also marked by increased social consciousness and feelings of social responsibility on the part of the upper class and the educated for the welfare of lower income groups. This concern resulted not only in social legislation, but also in the establishment of settlement houses. The first such house was established by Oxford and Cambridge students in Toynebee Hall, East London, in 1875. The University Settlement, on the East Side of New York, opened in 1886 and Hull House in Chicago, under Jane Addams, in 1889.[36]

The humanitarian outlook was also carried over into a concern for those in special classes—the mentally retarded, the deaf, the blind, dependent children and others—through federal and state legislation and private interest.[37,38] The agitation against owning slaves, and their eventual emancipation, was also an aspect of this humanitarian concern. However, it was not until the twentieth century that social and economic conditions for blacks and other minority groups changed for the better.

The humanitarian movement was also felt in prison reform in the way of changes in social conditions within the prisons, in sentences, and in architecture. In the beginning, prisons were places of detention or confinement for military captives, those awaiting trial or execution, and those who aroused the ire of the sovereign.[39,40] However, it should be pointed out that the concept of financial compensation for injury to an individual or agency as a result of a criminal act is not of recent origin. As early as the fourth century, kinship groups offered payment to other kinship groups if a member was killed to avoid a blood feud.

It was during the sixteenth century that houses of "correction" were established in England and Europe. Although reformation was intended, the unsanitary conditions of these prisons resulted in widespread agitation against them. The cry was the same then as now—the prisons don't so much reform criminals as foster crime.

Prison advancement began late in the eighteenth century, concurrent with a growth of new philosophies of human conduct based largely on a decline of vengeance. However, until well into the nineteenth century, penalties against the convicted criminal consisted almost entirely of execution, public degradation, corporal punishment, and banishment plus fines and confiscation of property. Thick stone cells and high stone walls patrolled by armed guards provided security for those confined. Offenders often wore leg irons or were chained to walls.

The reformers' goal of changing the mentality of offenders was prominent in the Pennsylvania prison system, initiated by the Quakers in 1790, where each inmate was given a solitary cell with a Bible, and solitary work was performed in the cells. New York's Auburn Prison, constructed in 1816, featured small cells and congregated silent work. The lockstep and striped suit were Auburn innovations.

Although the Auburn system was an adaptation of the Pennsylvania system, the two came to be thought of independently, and vigorous competition developed between them. However, the Auburn system was eventually adopted in all states except Pennsylvania.

Between 1830 and 1870 practical reforms took place within institutions. Males were segregated from females, the old from the young, the hardened criminal from the first-time offenders. In addition, there was differential treatment for the offenders because some crimes were considered more serious than others. Likewise, institutions were constructed to handle those not considered a serious risk or a danger to society.

A prison that opened at Elmira, New York, in 1877 was the first establishment for young offenders to be called a *reformatory*. However, the concept behind the reformatory movement was short lived, and by 1910 it was generally admitted that the idea was a failure.

Probably the most important correctional developments were probation and parole. The first use of probation generally is ascribed to the efforts of John Augustus, in Massachusetts, starting in 1841. In 1878, the Massachusetts Legislature provided that the mayor of Boston should annually appoint a probation officer as part of the police force.

A series of statutes enacted by New York State in the latter part of the nineteenth century marked the earliest significant established parole system. The system provided indefinite sentences and a return to custody for parole violation.

Almost immediately after New York's lead, other states began enacting parole laws, and by 1900 such statutes were in effect in nearly half of the states. By 1922 the federal government and all but four states had enacted parole laws, and by the second half of the twentieth century, parole was a part of the penal system of every state.

Correctional institutions received little public attention between World Wars I and II. According to McGee, the conditions most characteristic of our prisons

> were enforced idleness, inadequate and untrained personnel, gross overcrowding, and indeed, an almost complete negation of the high sounding principles enunciated at the first convention of prison executives at Cincinnati in 1870.[41]

It was not until some 10 years later that the effects of neglect were recognized. These problems led to new correctional reform, both in theory and in practice.

Most of the essential ideas basic to the philosophy of modern comprehensive rehabilitation had been developed by 1900. The beginnings are deep and interwoven in human cultural history. It was left to our time, however, to fuse the ideas of recreation services to special populations, rehabilitation, and humanitarianism into a working whole.

twentieth century

The expansion of therapeutic recreation during the twentieth century can best be appreciated if it is presented in terms of recreation service and professional development.

service development

The first half of the twentieth century saw a gradual trend toward the development of organized recreation service for special populations in various institutional settings. This was especially so in the employment of full-time recreation workers to develop and direct recreation programs in federal and state hospitals/institutions serving the mentally ill and mentally retarded and, to a lesser degree, in general medical and surgical hospitals, special schools, and correctional institutions. Likewise, community-based programs were developed to meet the varied needs and interests of the physically disabled, mentally retarded, racial minorities, economically deprived, aged, and other special populations.

During this period and thereafter came the organization of recreation specialists working with special populations, which culminated in the formation of the National Therapeutic Recreation Society, the establishment of standards and a national voluntary registration program, and the appearance and development of therapeutic recreation curricula in colleges and universities. However, the student should realize that from the beginning of this century until the present, the road of organized recreation service to special populations and of professional development has not been without its problems, failures, and successes.

Hospitals/Institutions

To consider the development of formal organized recreation programs in hospitals/institutions, it is necessary to retrace our steps to 1863. In September of that year delegates from 16 nations gathered in Switzerland at the request of a Swiss banker for a conference that led to the formation of the Red Cross. As a result of the charter commitments of this organization, the American Red Cross services to the armed forces, including recreation services, were developed. However, it was not until the entry of the United States into World War I that the Division of Recreation in Hospitals was organized. The function of this division was "to provide, in cooperation with the Educational Service of the Surgeon General's Office of the United States Army, supplemental recreation for soldiers, sailors, and marines in military and naval hospitals."[42] The Red Cross continued to provide recreation leadership and services to military hospitals and Public Health Service hospitals until 1931. At that time, the treatment of exservicemen was transferred to the United States Veterans Bureau, and Red Cross recreation personnel were assigned to these hospitals.[43]

Between 1920 and 1930, recreation programs were appearing more and more in state hospitals for the mentally ill and retarded. Also, shortly after 1931, a recreation service was established in St. Elizabeth's Hospital in Washington, D.C.

While these programs, in most instances, were still diversional in nature, psychiatrists and others increasingly recognized the therapeutic value of recreation. As early as 1921, Dr. R. F. L. Ridgway, a psychiatrist at Harrisburg (Pennsylvania) State Hospital, wrote an article on recreation for the mentally ill to arouse more interest in providing therapeutic recreation in such hospitals.[44] William Menninger and Isabelle McCall published an article in 1937 describing the value and use of recreation at the Menninger Clinic, a world-famous center for the care and treatment of the mentally ill in Topeka, Kansas.[45] An early experimental study in recreation for the mentally retarded was reported by Bertha E. Schlotter and Margaret Svendsen at the Lincoln State School and Colony in Illinois in 1932. They reported on the two-year success they had obtained in the use of recreation activities in developing social skills in retarded children.[46]

While the provision of recreation service to other special population groups—physically disabled, blind, deaf, and the like—during these early years can be traced, such services were scattered throughout hospitals/institutions in the United States. Recreation service to the physically disabled and medically hospitalized individual was primarily the responsiblility of the occupational therapist; teachers and physical educators assumed the responsibility in special schools.

Although World War I had given great impetus to the use of recreation in hospitals, its development thereafter was slow until World War II. World War II brought about tremendous expansion and acceleration in the recreation movement in hospitals and institutions. Red cross hospital recreation workers were again called upon by the military to provide recreation services in military hospitals here and overseas. While medical approval was required for patient participation in recreation activities, the services were not narrow or limited, as indicated by the description below:

> Individualized as well as group activities were conducted indoors on wards, in recreation halls, auditoriums, craft shops, game rooms, and the like; outdoors on lawns surrounding the hospital as well as in other areas such as picnic grounds or small parks often provided on military installations. Offpost trips to nearby communities and to various special events were popular with convalescent patients.[47]

Following the war, recreation services in armed forces hospitals became an established service provided by Red Cross recreation workers.

World War II also bought an expansion in recreation services in veterans' hospitals, although not of the quality found in military hospitals. However, with the increased number of servicemen patients and the expansion of treatment programs in veterans' hospitals at the close of hostilities and thereafter, the Veterans Administration in 1945 established the Recreation Service as a part of its Hospital Special Services Division.[48] This resulted in the Recreation Services' offering a program of recreation services at each veterans' hospital domiciliary in the United States. In 1960 the Recreation Service was placed in the Physical Medicine and Rehabilitation Service. This organizational change was made, according to Bream, "to add even greater strength to Recreation and improve patient care by placing it under the immediate direction of a physician."[49]

As a result of the importance placed on recreation service in military and veterans' hospitals during World War II, recreation programs and services in state institutions for the mentally ill in the years thereafter were greatly affected. Not only were there acceleration and increase in providing recreation programs in such institutions, but also there was a shift in the concept of recreation and its value. In the past, the objectives of the program were primarily diversion and entertainment; now, however, recreation service took on a more therapeutic responsibility of assisting the medical staff in treatment, assisting patient adjustment to hospitalization, and assisting the patient in developing skills that could be used for recreative experiences following discharge.[50] In more recent years, we have seen another shift to include the concept of rehabilitation and reintegration of the patient into the community through the use of recreation programs and services. The recreation specialist is no longer saying "good-bye" to the patient at the institutional door, but instead is offering a leisure counseling service prior to discharge as well as following the patient personally or through referral into the community to assist the patient in leisure adjustment. Thus, recreation programs and services for the mentally ill have shifted from custodial services to treatment and to rehabilitation, and today we are talking about recreation services as a preventer to mental illness.

A similar expansion of recreation programs and services since World War II has been witnessed in institutions for the mentally retarded. There is probably no public or private hospital/institution in the United States today providing care and treatment to the mentally retarded that does not provide recreation service.

Generally speaking, recreation services in all types of hospital/institutional settings have grown rapidly under the impetus of an increased concern for the ill and disabled. Recreation programs are now available to patients in general medical and surgical hospitals; specialty, chronic disease, and convalescent hospitals; rehabilitation centers; and, more recently, comprehensive centers and clinics for the mentally ill and mentally retarded, sheltered workshops, halfway houses, and nursing homes and homes for the aged.

Prisons

Only since the turn of the century has it been common to find time allotted for informal, unsupervised recreational pursuits in many prisons. As early as 1912, the first theoretical rationale for the encouragement of recreational activities had been formulated.[51] This was primarily the result of a decline in prison industries and an attempt to reduce prolonged idleness. The following two decades witnessed a continuing interest in the rehabilitative functions of recreation activity, but not to the extent found in hospitals/institutions. By 1930, the American Correctional Association, in a revision of its Declaration of Principles, noted that "It has come to be recognized that recreation is an indispensable factor of normal life. This principle is now heartily endorsed by prison administrators."[52]

In subsequent years there was increased interest in the organizational and administrative aspects of organized recreation programs in correctional institutions. In the 1950s, in particular, a number of recreation publications gave attention to the value of recreation in prisons as well as the adoption of penal recreation standards by the United Nations.[53,54,55] The 1950s also saw the first scientific surveys of recreational practices in correctional institutions. Principal findings indicated that approximately half of all prisons for adult males employed a full-time director of recreation, that recreational programs in federal institutions were far more advanced than those in state institutions, and that the failure to implement recreational programs could be attributed to lack of funding and not to the resistance of prison administrators.[56,57]

The following decade witnessed a continuing trend. The American Correctional Association (ACA) developed a substantial elaboration of its recreation standards in 1960.[58] The Task force on Corrections of the President's Commission on Law Enforcement and Administration of Justice gave the weight of its support to these standards when in 1967 it included the ACA recreation standards in its own listing of standards.[59] More recently, the ACA has officially incorporated the standards.

In 1971 the National Therapeutic Recreation Society established a task force on recreation and corrections. In 1972 the state directors of correction from throughout the nation formed a task force on exercise and recreation to make recommendations for the improvement of recreation and exercise programs within penal institutions as well as to provide recognition of the problems that exist.[60]

The interest within the correctional community in the rehabilitative value of recreational programs is matched by the support of such programs by many offenders. The *Proceedings of the Annual Congress of the American Correctional Association* are marked by frequent testimony to this effect. Inmate autobiographies and scientific observation provide additional confirmation, although there are dissenting voices.

This history of correctional recreation in institutions, training schools, and camps for deviant children and youth is a part of the development of recreation in adult institutions, although physical education and team sports have been a part of the educational curriculum since the establishment of the first training school for juveniles in 1825. The development of recreation programs in halfway houses, detention centers, and the like is of recent origin.

The value of recreative experiences as a positive force in correctional rehabilitation is well summarized by the Hormacheas, specialists in correctional recreation, as follows:

> There is no doubt of the value of recreation as a rehabilitative tool. When the inmate leads a more balanced life combining work and recreation, treatment personnel as well as custodial personnel are able to work more effectively with the individual and his problems and thus prepare him for eventual release.[61]

Communities

Meanwhile, in community services to special populations, the recorded history of recreation services has not enjoyed the attention that it has in various hospital/institutional settings. It is interesting to note, however, that according to some historians, the formation of the Playground Association of America (1906) is a direct result of the concern early recreators had for the slum environment and its effects on children. Upon review of the charter of the Playground Association of America, one would find reference, as is found in the present National Recreation and Park Association charter, to the provision of "broad recreation opportunities to all people regardless of age, sex, and religious faith."[62]

Despite this auspicious beginning, there was a definite decline in the provision of recreation service to meet the recreation needs of special populations, or at least those needs of minority group members, through public recreation agencies until the 1960s. The rational for this inactivity is summarized by Hutchison:

> . . . it could be said that at its highest point of success, the recreation profession unwittingly allowed the prime focus of its mission to shift from the delivery of specialized human services to professional development and facility management. Unfortunately, it appears that the provision of services to people became a means to broader goals, purposes, and professional status, rather than remaining a vital and satisfying end unto itself.[63]

Despite the shortcomings of municipal recreation agencies in offering recreation services to special populations during the first half of this cen-

tury, a number of national organizations concerned with various impairments and disabilities, service organizations, and special agencies did
provide such services. In 1900, for example, the Association for the Aid of
Crippled Children was providing recreation service in homes, schools, and
hospitals, as well as operating summer programs for the physically disabled. Camping for physically disabled children was first recorded in 1888.
But not until the 1930s, however, did residential camping develop on a national scale. Easter Seal Societies throughout the United States have led in
this field; many of the state affiliates own and operate resident and day
camps serving children and adults, individuals and families. The
Lighthouse, a service center operated by the New York Association for the
Blind in New York City, has for many years offered recreation and camping
programs. Similar programs for the blind are found in other cities. In 1959,
the New York Service for Orthopedically Handicapped established an integrated program of recreation activities for physically disabled and able-
bodied children. Other national organizations and their affiliates that offer
recreation services include the United Cerebral Palsy Association, the
Muscular Dystrophy Association, the National Multiple Sclerosis Association, Goodwill Industries, the Kennedy Foundation, the American Foundation of the Blind, and the National Association for Retarded Citizens.

Service organizations such as the Kiwanis, Elks, Lions, Moose, and
Eagles have provided financial support and assumed in many instances
total responsibility for offering recreation services. Voluntary youth
associations such as the YMCA and YWCA, Boy and Girl Scouts, Boys and
Girls Clubs, the Police Athletic League, and others have either directly
assisted or sponsored programs for the disabled or made their facilities
available for others to offer programs for the disabled.

During the 1920s and early 1930s public school systems began to offer recreation programs after school for disabled children. Today, one of
the nation's most extensive year-round community recreation programs for
the physically disabled and mentally retarded is conducted by the Division
of Municipal Recreation and Adult Education, Milwaukee Public Schools.
A similar program is conducted by the Flint (Michigan) Community Schools.
Today, more and more public school systems in cooperation with
municipal recreation agencies are offering programs to the disabled.

In the early 1950s a small number of cities established special centers
to offer recreation services to the physically and mentally disabled. The
Recreation Center for the Handicapped in San Francisco, established in
1952 under the direction of Janet Pomery, is an excellent example of such a
center. In 1955, Kansas City established the Greater Kansas City Council on
Recreation for the Handicapped, a citywide council organized to better
coordinate recreation service to special population members as well as to
establish and develop new services. Since the late 1950s, and especially in

recent years, municipal recreation departments in major cities have employed specialists in therapeutic recreation or supervisors of special recreation to initiate and develop comprehensive programs of recreation service for those with physical, emotional, and social limitations. Of special note is the Washington, D.C. Recreation Department which has developed during the past two decades an excellent community recreation service program for the districtwide needs of the disabled.

While the first Senior Center opened in New York City in 1943, it was not until the 1950s that municipal agencies began to develop senior citizen centers and golden age clubs for the elderly.[64] Since then, and with the assistance of the government, special residential centers also have been built. The value of centers and clubs is reflected in the 1975 report of the National Council on the Aging on senior centers: "Opportunities that give recognition and status to participants are considered a major potential function of Senior Centers and Clubs."[65]

Although there has been an increase in the provision of recreation service to those with limiting conditions and disabilities, there is still a need for greater community recreation services. While the following statement by David Park is now nearly ten years old and the 1973 Rehabilitation Act and Education for All Handicapped Children Act is ever present, it is still very applicable today.

> If the public recreation program is to provide adequate recreation programs and resources for the total population, we must realize that there are significant numbers in our communities who require special programs and it is the communities' responsibility to provide special programs for these special groups.[66]

As early as 1911, the National Recreation Association recognized the needs of the disadvantaged.[67] Early efforts at meeting the needs of the disadvantaged are found in the program of the Cincinnati Park and Recreation Department, which, in 1933, established special centers to conduct programs for the unemployed and their families. In 1941 the San Fancisco Park and Recreation Department developed recreation services for those living in public housing developments.

However, it was not until the 1960s that a new perspective on recreation service for the socioeconomically disadvantaged and for minority group members developed.[68] This new perspective appears to be the result of three factors:

1. The social upheaval and civil disturbances that occurred during the 1960s: The Kerner Commission report as well as other reports indicate that the lack of recreation programs and facilities was one of the major causes of civil unrest and riots. As early as 1964, municipal recrea-

tion departments with assistance from the federal government initiated "crash" programs to relieve the pressure that was beginning to
develop in depressed sections of cities. In many instances, these programs were restricted to the summer months or were too late in developing to alleviate some of the inadequacies that existed.[69]

2. The financial assistance provided by the federal government to communities and agencies resulting from the social unrest: The 1960s
   witnessed the involvement of recreation service in the "war on poverty" through the variety of federally funded programs under the
   Economic Opportunity Act of 1964, such as Head Start, Upward
   Bound, Community Action Program, and Job Corps. Likewise, recreation service was provided through the Land and Water Conservation
   Fund Act of 1965, the Housing and Urban Development Act of 1965,
   the Demonstration Cities and Metropolitan Development Act of 1966,
   and the Public Health Service Act of 1966.[70]

3. The return to the earlier view on the part of the recreation profession
   that the recreation needs of all people should be met regardless of
   their station in life.

While recreation service to the disadvantaged and minority groups
since the 1960s has expanded, there is much yet to be done. Some
municipal administrators and educators feel, and rightly so, that recreation
service to these groups has only just begun. What can happen if more is
provided is answered by Nesbitt:

The recreation and leisure service professions can perform a major role in
overcoming disadvantagement. They can make a major contribution to the nation by making the lives of the disadvantaged as rich as possible in terms of
recreation and leisure. First, this is a meaningful end unto itself. It will enhance
the quality of America's recreational, cultural and leisure environment. Second, this will also contribute significantly to the health, education and welfare
of the disadvantaged. Bringing the disadvantaged into the mainstream of
American experience increases their ability to function in many settings—education, work and the local community.[71]

professional development

Origins

In the early years of this century, provision of recreation service in
hospitals/institutions was the responsibility of nursing personnel and craft
teachers (later called *occupational therapists*). As noted earlier, American
Red Cross personnel provided recreation services in military and naval
hospitals during World War I. During the 1920s and 1930s, individuals with
varied backgrounds and representing various disciplines directed programs

in hospitals, institutions, and special centers and schools. World War II found Red Cross personnel and volunteers providing recreation services. Also, military personnel with an education or interest in physical education or recreation were assigned to hospitals and reconditioning units. It was not until the years shortly after World War II that individuals employed as *recreation therapists* or *hospital recreation workers* in military and Veterans Administration hospitals and in state institutions for the mentally ill and mentally retarded began to organize themselves into professional organizations.

As a result of this concern, three organizations formed within a period of six years. The first of these organizations was the *Hospital Recreation Section of the American Recreation Society* (HRS–ARS). In October 1948, during the Thirtieth National Recreation Congress in Omaha, a group of approximately 37 recreation workers employed in various hospital settings met to discuss the advisability and importance of uniting recreation workers into an organized group. As a result of the enthusiasm generated for a special group, an interim committee was formed to work out affiliation with the American Recreation Society. Malcolm Randall of the Veterans Administration presided at this initial organizational meeting, and C.C. Bream, Jr., also of the Veterans Administration, was appointed Affiliation Committee chairman.

The following year, during the National Recreation Congress at New Orleans, the Hospital Recreation Section was officially recognized as a section of the American Recreation Society—the first group to organize as a section within the society. At this first official meeting, Malcolm Randall was elected chairman; Thomas Rickman, Jr., chairman-elect; and Carolyn Nice Lyle, secretary. From its beginning in 1949 to 1966 the section has been chaired by Malcolm Randall, Thomas H. Rickman, Jr., Carolyn N. Lyle, C. C. Bream, Jr., Dorothy Taaffee, Fred M. Chapman, Edith L. Ball, James F. Pratt, Lillian Summers, Albert L. Meuli, Sidney H. Acuff, John J. Gehan, Frances Cleary, Gerald S. O'Morrow, Francis W. Heinlen, and Fred Humphrey.[72]

The section issued its first quarterly newsletter in 1950. It was later incorporated into the American Recreation Society's *The Bulletin,* and still later, *American Recreation Journal.* The section also published in 1954 a well-received document, *Basic Concepts of Hospital Recreation,* which reported on the concept and applicability of recreation in various medical and rehabilitation settings. The publication underwent several revisions until 1962.

The second organization, the *Recreation Therapy Section of the American Association for Health, Physical Education, and Recreation* (*AAHPER*) (now called the *American Alliance of Health, Physical Education, and Recreation*) was formed in 1952 during the annual meeting in Los

Angeles of the AAHPER. This section developed as a result of a division in the Institutional and Industrial Recreation Section, one of three sections of the Recreation Division of the AAHPER. Membership consisted primarily of those employed in special schools with an educational background in recreation, physical education, and adapted physical education. The section's first chairman was Dr. Martin W. Meyer.[73] For a number of years the section had a monthly column titled "Recreational Therapy" in the AAHPER's *Journal of Health, Physical Education, and Recreation.*

The *National Association of Recreation Therapists (NART),* established in 1953 at Bolivar, Tennessee, was the last of the three organizations. This organization consisted primarily of recreation workers employed in public and private institutions and schools for the mentally ill and mentally retarded in the southern and midwestern states. Its first chairman was Floyd E. McDowell, followed by Frank Longo, William T. Lawler, Philip Walsh, Steven Chiovaro, Edward Karpowicz, Hayden Walker, Charlotte L. Cox, Samuel Seabolt, William L. Smith, and Anne K. Bushart.[74] The organization published a quarterly publication, *Recreation for the Ill and Handicapped.*

As might be expected, philosophies, interests, programs, and opinions differed among the three organizations; thus, a desire arose for some form of organization through which ideas could be exchanged and concerted action be taken. In 1953 representatives from each organization met, which resulted in the formation of the *Council for the Advancement of Hospital Recreation (CAHR).* The council not only provided a framework wherein communication was established to further the concepts and interests of hospital recreation, but also eventually established standards of qualifications for hospital recreation workers in 1956. These standards were incorporated into a program called the National Voluntary Registration of Hospital Recreation Personnel, which provided for the registration of personnel at the following levels: hospital recreation director, hospital recreation leader, and hospital recreation aide. This plan established the first national registration program within the total recreation movement.

With the establishment of HRS–ARS and NART, hospital recreation personnel in several states thereafter initiated action to establish like sections within their respective state recreation associations (as in Indiana, Illinois, California) or initiated state chapters that affiliated with the NART. Likewise, some state associations developed voluntary registration programs for hospital recreation personnel modeled after the national program or included them within their own statewide registration programs.

Within a few short years it became apparent that while the CAHR did provide a channel for communication among the three organizations, a strong single organization was also needed that would speak for all recreation specialists working in various settings that provided care and treatment to the ill and disabled. Between 1958 and 1962, representatives from the three organizations met for the purpose of resolving differences of philosophies so as to unite in one organization that could speak for the needs of this profession in its own right. Differences could not be resolved, however, and the Committee on Merger was disbanded.

During the early 1960s, an interesting phenomenon was occurring. There was a concern for unity within the total park and recreation movement. As a result of this concern, five national organizations representing various park and recreation interest areas (one being the American Recreation Society) merged in 1965, forming the *National Recreation and Park Association (NRPA).* To represent the various interests of those organizations that had merged, branches were established. Sensing the urgent need to maintain unity, representatives from NART and the former HRS–ARS again met in 1965 to attempt to resolve previous differences. By mid-1966, both organizations had received favorable response from their membership toward the movement to develop a branch within the NRPA. During the National Park and Recreation Congress in October 1966, the *National Therapeutic Recreation Society* (NTRS) was born.[75]

The duly elected Board of Directors of the newly organized NTRS met in Kansas City in early 1967 and elected Ira J. Hutchison as its first president. Since 1967, the organization has been led by presidents John Logue, Fred Humphrey, William L. Smith, Gerald S. O'Morrow, John A. Nesbitt, Sidney H. Acuff, Jerry D. Kelley, William A. Hillman, Jean R. Tague, Richard L. Stracke, Lee E. Meyer, Gary M. Robb, and David C. Park. During the years since its inception, the NTRS has been served by three executive secretaries—Ira J. Hutchison (1967–1968), David C. Park (1968–1975) and Yvonne Washington (1975–present).

Elements of Growth

In highlighting the activities of the NTRS since 1967, it is difficult to do justice to its many accomplishments. Certainly, a variety of factors have contributed to the growth of the NTRS and the profession of therapeutic recreation in general. We will focus here on only a few elements which seem particularly important for the potential therapeutic recreation specialist. These elements include publications, standards, education and training, and internal assessment. The "body of knowledge" unique to the profession and its practitioners should also be included. However, this element will be discussed in a subsequent chapter.

The advancement and acceptance of NTRS as a professional organization, to a great extent, can certainly be attributed to its various publications. The official quarterly publication, the *Therapeutic Recreation Journal,* has been widely accepted by recreation professionals as well as by other professionals in other disciplines. An earlier publication was the

Therapeutic Recreation Annual which evolved from *Recreation in Treatment Centers,* a publication initially produced by the HRS — ARS. Other publications have included *Impact, Communique* (a joint branch publication of NRPA), *NTRS Yearbook,* and various Society newsletters. In association with NRPA, a number of specific publications and special magazine issues concerned with a variety of topics as they relate to special populations have come forth; examples include: *Recreation in Nursing Homes,*[76] *Community Recreation Programming for Handicapped Children,*[77] "Trends for the Handicapped,"[78] and "Leisure and Handicapped People,"[79] Of special note is the publication entitled *Therapeutic Recreation — State of the Art,* prepared for the 13th World Congress of Rehabilitation International in Israel.[80]

Equally as important as publications are standards — registration and program standards respectively. The voluntary registration program established through CAHR has continued throughout the years with various revisions. In 1969, there were 283 persons registered.[81] Today, the approximate number of registrants in the NTRS voluntary program is 2200.[82] Moreover, various agencies and departments in state and local government now require registration as a requirement for employment while other such governmental units have used the registration standards to develop job description. Still other organizations such as national voluntary accrediting bodies have made reference to the standards when discussing personnel qualification. Regarding the registration program in its totality, Park comments:

> Through the efforts of NTRS–NRPA in promoting quality therapeutic recreation services, this program has gained national recognition. Some states and employment agencies are now requiring this registration before they will hire an individual. Others, while not requiring registration, are strongly encouraging it. The standards included in the Joint Commission on Accreditation of Hospitals manuals refer to the registration program when discussing qualified personnel.[83]

During the years following the merger, NTRS was quite active in developing, establishing, and promoting therapeutic recreation service program standards for use in various settings — psychiatric and mental retardation facilities, nursing homes, and alcohol and drug abuse centers. Recently, the Society upgraded standards relative to clinical and residential facilities as well as developing standards for use in community settings providing services to special populations.[84,85]

The NTRS has always been concerned about the education and training of therapeutic recreation specialists. Educational sessions and mini-institutes concerned with aspects of therapeutic recreation have been a part of the annual NRPA Congress since the formation of NTRS. In addition, NTRS has sponsored or co-sponsored in association with NRPA regional conferences, symposiums, institutes, and workshops, some annually, to further the knowledge and professional growth of therapeutic recreation specialists in the field and those about to enter. In 1975, the NTRS Board of Directors approved a 750-Hour Training Program directed toward personnel who should potentially qualify for national registration with the NTRS at the assistant and technician level. More recently, the Therapeutic Recreation Management School was established at Oglebay Park, Wheeling, West Virginia. This school is co-sponsored by the Wheeling Park Commission and the Department of Recreation, University of Maryland in cooperation with NTRS/NRPA. The school is under the direction of a Board of Regents consisting of national authorities in therapeutic recreation and offers a program of study of two annual one-week sessions of classroom study and lectures. It is the first attempt at continuing education in the field.

The growth of university curricula in therapeutic recreation has been extensive and varied. Since the 1950s, until recent years, curricula incorporated courses which reflected the functions, duties, and/or responsibility that a therapeutic recreation specialist might encounter in the performance of a specific job.[86] Likewise, courses were directed toward specific conditions or impairment. Since the early 1970s, a shift has occurred wherein attention is focused on specific competencies the student should have attained at the time of graduation from either an undergraduate or graduate program of study. This approach is primarily the result of the various NTRS education and accreditation committees coupled with the NRPA accreditation program.

As any professional organization develops there is always a need to examine future goals and directions. In an attempt to meet these ends various task forces over the years were established, some in association with NRPA and others only within NTRS. Of particular importance was the Presidential Commission on Assessment of Critical Issues (PCACI) established by Gary Robb as he took office in October 1977. This high priority commission was created (as the result of a NTRS Self-Evaluation study in 1976–77) in an effort to consider and resolve some of the major issues facing the field of therapeutic recreation. The issues that were considered included: credentialing, accreditation, personnel and program standards, branch governance, PL 94–142, and a definition and philosophical statement regarding therapeutic recreation. As an added impetus to the importance of the PCACI, arrangements were made with the coordinators, directors, and institutes to allocate a period of time for presentations and discussions of the issues during the 1977–1978 year. In the end, thousands of therapeutic recreation professionals had input into issues of primary concern to them. At present, some issues are still in the process of being finalized. However, this approach is indicative of the concern that the officers and directors of NTRS have in coming to grips with most important concerns of the field.

There have been other elements, indvidually and collectively through committee work, which have propelled the growth of the Society. In passing, the Society has worked jointly with NRPA in their sponsoring of various conferences and workshops concerned with aspects of recreation for special populations. The National Forum on Meeting the Recreation and Park Needs of Handicapped People in association with the President's Committee on Employment of the Handicapped in 1974 and the research needs assessment conference in the area of leisure time activity for handicapped people are good examples.[87,88] The Society has provided consultation to federal, state and local governmental units, as well as to various private agencies. The Society has represented not only itself but NRPA at Congressional hearings. In addition, it has been accepted as a therapeutic recreation lobby and has assisted in promoting legislative matters in the area of public welfare. The Society has worked with many State Societies in the development of a therapeutic recreation section. Lastly, the Society through its committee structure has not only promoted the concept of rehabilitation and community services to the handicapped but established a liaison with various other national medical, paramedical and allied health organizations. Certainly, the society has done much to contribute to its own growth; however, forces external to the Society have also assisted.

Contributors

No profession or professional organization can grow and sustain itself without the assistance of external forces. There are any number of forces which influenced, contributed, and shaped the development of therapeutic recreation and its professionalization. Such forces include professional and service organizations, federal and state agencies and bureaus, legislation, universities, publications, research, and the like. Only a few will be highlighted here and to fully appreciate these forces it will be necessary for us to consider some of those forces which were active prior to the merger as well as after the merger.

Two national service organizations that contributed greatly in their time to the growth and development of recreation services to those with limiting conditions and impairments were the *National Recreation Association* (NRA) and Comeback, Inc. The NRA(an outgrowth of the Playground Association of America, established in 1906 and one of the organizations that merged with others to form the NRPA) offered consultation service to communities and agencies and provided funds from governmental grants for special projects and studies from the early 1950s until the time of merger. In 1958, for example, the NRA supported a study involving more than 6000 hospitals/institutions in the United States. This study, the first comprehensive study ever attempted and completed in recreation service to the ill and disabled, considered the number of organized recreation programs in these hospitals/institutions, the personnel responsible for conducting the programs, and the number of patients participating in these programs. The study also considered whether programs were medically prescribed or voluntary, and evaluated salaries and titles of recreational personnel.[89] In still another study conducted in 1964, the NRA in association with the National Association for Retarded Children and Adults assisted Ruth Marson in surveying over 2000 public recreation agencies to determine the extent of community recreation services provided to the mentally retarded.[90]

Relative to professional education, the NRA in 1961 sponsored a Therapeutic Recreation Curriculum Development Conference to identify the competencies needed by recreation specialists working with the ill and disabled.[91] As a result, a large number of educational institutions implemented suggestions from the conference. Likewise, the term *therapeutic recreation* began to appear more frequently in the literature and to be used by agency departments in lieu of just *recreation service* or *recreation therapy*. Through its consulting service on recreation for the ill and handicapped, the Association published two early publications which received considerable distribution: *Starting a Recreation Program in a Civilian Hospital* (1952)[92] and *Recreation for the Handicapped in the Community Setting* (1965).[93] In addition, its monthly publication, *Recreation,* contained a column called "Hospital Capsules."

Comeback, Inc., headed by Beatrice H. Hill, was established in 1960 specifically to promote service for special populations through its consulting staff. Much like the NRA, it provided literature, secured grants for studies, and sponsored workshops and institutes.

The American Association for Health, Physical Education, and Recreation (now known as the American Alliance for Health, Physical Education and Recreation) (AAHPER) is a professional organization which has been concerned for some years in promoting recreation services for the disabled. Of special note here is an early national conference it sponsored on recreation for the mentally ill.[94] Participants included not only individuals actively engaged in directing recreation activities in hospitals/institutions, but also representatives from 18 professional health associations and organizations. Attention was given to professional attitudes and practices, preservice and in-service training, facilities and equipment, and evaluation and research. Since then, the AAHPER has given its support to many conferences and has published proceedings from these conferences. In 1973, for example, AAHPER reported on the results of materials developed during seven workshops it sponsored through funds provided by the United States Bureau of Education for the Handicapped (BEH) between 1971 and 1972 concerned with developing guidelines to assist in graduate preparation in adapted physical education and therapeutic recreation.[95] Also, during the mid-1970s, an information and retrieval center was established by AAHPER called Information and Research Utilization Center in Physical Education and Recreation for the Handicapped (IRUC). The center was funded through a grant from BEH and existed until just recently. During its operation, it collected, analyzed, categorized, described, packaged, and distributed information and materials about various aspects of adapted physical education, therapeutic recreation, and related programs. A summary of the activity of IRUC and the state of the art in physical education/adapted physical education, recreation/therapeutic recreation, and related impairment areas was published in an excellent publication entitled *Physical Education and Recreation for Impaired, Disabled and Handicapped Individuals — Past, Present, and Future.*[96] During the years, the Association has been quite active in publishing manuals and booklets on physical education and recreation for the disabled, in encouraging research and demonstration projects directed toward and for the disabled, and in showing a genuine concern for the recreation needs of special populations.

Service and professional organizations outside the therapeutic recreation arena that have contributed to the movement are the American Psychiatric Association (APA) and the American Medical Association (AMA). In 1952, the APA published a compilation of philosophies, trends, and comments about recreation service in its member hospitals of the Mental Hospital Service under the title *Recreation Trends in North American Mental Institutions.*[97] Still later, an APA committee on leisure time published an interesting publication on leisure and mental health from a psychiatric viewpoint entitled *Leisure and Mental Health: A Psychiatric Viewpoint.*[98] The AMA in 1961 designated professional recreation service as an allied health field.[99] This acknowledgement was the result of recreation's contribution to the promotion of health, the prevention of illness or further disability, the treatment of illness, and the rehabilitation of persons with physical, psychological, mental, or social disabilities. The implications of such an acknowledgement had far-reaching effects upon the delivery of recreation services in various settings.

Another organization, the American Foundation for the Blind (AFB), has in recent years worked closely with the NTRS in sponsoring workshops and conferences for the purpose of expanding recreation and leisure services to visually impaired persons. The AFB is not alone; many special-interest voluntary organizations such as the American Association on Mental Deficiency, National Association for Retarded Citizens, National Association for Mental Health, National Easter Seal Society for Crippled

Children and Adults, as well as philanthropic organizations, for example, the Joseph P. Kennedy, Jr. Foundation, have contributed directly and indirectly through funds, demonstration projects, and educational training to the advancement of therapeutic recreation.

The part that legislation has played in contributing directly to the promotion of recreation services to special populations and indirectly to professionalization has been extensive as noted elsewhere. One cannot help but wonder at what stage of growth therapeutic recreation would be if federal funds were not available for recreation research and demonstration projects, professional training, and curriculum development, to name a few areas of interests and concern. In 1963, the Rehabilitation Services Administration of the U.S. Department of Health, Education, and Welfare provided funds to selected colleges and universites for graduate study in therapeutic recreation. Since 1969, BEH has provided funds to various colleges and universities to institute new approaches in graduate studies in therapeutic recreation. A large number of higher educational institutions have received funds to pursue various topics of extreme importance to improving recreation services to special populations and to the profession. Still other educational institutions have received grants to study and develop competency-based curriculums at various academic levels.[100,101,102] The federal government has been quite consistent in its financial support for therapeutic recreation service.

With the initiation of more recreation programs in hospitals/institutions and the demand for trained leaders and administrators, educational institutions began to offer concentrations and options in hospital recreation, recreation therapy, and therapeutic recreation service. The first institutions to offer a concentration in this specialization at the graduate level were the University of Minnesota and the University of West Virginia in 1951.[103] Kraus, in his review of professional education, indicates that in 1953 six colleges and universities were offering undergraduate and graduate degrees in "hospital" recreation.[104] Still later, Stein reported in 1969 that 35 of 114 institutions indicated they offered a major in therapeutic recreation.[105] Most recently, Stein reported that 95 institutions in the United States and Canada were offering degree concentrations or options in this specialization.[106] This rapid growth certainly reflects the demand for recreation services in various settings and the concern for trained personnel.

As more and more demand developed for a greater and better recreation service to special population as well as for better trained leaders, many universities initiated institutes, workshops, and seminars. In the early 1950s, the University of North Carolina conducted biennial institutes on a broad range of topics. For a number of years during the 1960s, the University of Minnesota alternated with the University of North Carolina. In

1971 the University of Illinois initiated the first Midwest Symposium on Therapeutic Recreation. In recent years, the Universities of Maryland, Temple, George Washington, Pennsylvania State, Indiana, New York, Oregon, Iowa, Missouri, San Jose State, and California State at Northridge have sponsored a variety of conferences, all concerned with therapeutic recreation services to special populations.

As noted earlier consideration of the development of philosophical concepts of therapeutic recreation will be discussed in subsequent chapters. But it is well to mention that as the professionalization of therapeutic recreation developed, it became clear for those involved in offering services and those in academic settings to consider and develop an ideology. To meet this need, a position statement on therapeutic recreation was drafted and initiated during the Ninth Southern Regional Institute on Therapeutic Recreation at the University of North Carolina in 1969. During the annual conference of the NTRS in the same year, the statement was further discussed. Later Frye[107] and Ball[108] published papers on the philosophy of therapeutic recreation. And in 1970, at Indiana State University, the statement was the topic of a work-study conference. Since the early 1970s the statement has been further discussed and refined. Most recently, as indicated earlier, it is one of the critical issues under consideration.

In summary of the steady growth and development of therapeutic recreation, it is well to refer to the present president of NTRS, David C. Park, who writes:

> During the first 25 years of our development, we have grown a great deal and have experienced significant changes. We began as a profession that was almost exclusively hospital oriented, but we have since developed and declared a broader interpretation of therapeutic recreation. We have recognized the needs of all disabled individuals regardless of where they may reside, including such new areas as nursing homes, day care centers, and penal institutions. We were a profession that was split by semantics and even, to a degree, by philosophy. We now agree that therapeutic recreation is a process which is applicable in many different types of settings. Finally, we began as a profession that included several professional groups, but now there is one strong central organization that is becoming instrumental in bringing about acceptance and the realization that therapeutic recreation is a significant part of the rehabilitation process.[109]

SUGGESTED REFERENCES

"A Report on the NTRS President's Commission for the Assessment of Critical Issues," *Therapeutic Recreation Journal,* 12:2 (1978), pp. 38–41.

Carter, Marcia, "Articulation of Therapeutic Recreation Curricula,"*Expanding Horizons in Therapeutic Recreation III,* Gary M. Robb and Gerald

Hitzhusen eds., Columbia, Mo: Department of Recreation and Park Administration, University of Missouri, 1975, pp. 45–48.

Dolan, Josephine A. *The History of Nursing.* Philadelphia: W. B. Saunders Co., 1969.

Goldstein, Judith E. "Looking for Something? Selected Resources: Recreation and Leisure Services for Disabled Persons," in *Expanding Horizons in Therapeutic Recreation V,* Gerald Hitzhusen, ed., Columbia, Mo: Department of Recreation and Park Administration, University of Missouri, 1977, pp. 149–152.

Gunn, Scout Lee, and Carol Ann Peterson. *Therapeutic Recreation Program Design.* Englewood Cliffs, N.J.: Prentice-Hall, Inc., 1978, pp. 7–9.

Guthrie, Douglas. *A History of Medicine.* Philadelphia: J.B. Lippincott Co., 1946.

Hospital Recreation Section. *Basic Concepts of Hospital Recreation.* Washington, D.C.: American Recreation Society, September 1953.

Kraus, Richard. *Urban Parks and Recreation: Challenge of the 1970s.* New York: Community Council of Greater New York, 1972.

Lindley, Donald. "Relative Importance of College Courses in Therapeutic Recreation," *Therapeutic Recreation Journal,* 4:2 (1970), pp. 8–12.

Martin, Fred W. "Survey of College and University Coursework in Therapeutic Recreation Service," *Therapeutic Recreation Journal,* 5:3 (1971), pp. 123–129, 140.

National Therapeutic Recreation Society. *NTRS 1972 Yearbook.* Arlington, Va.: National Recreation and Park Association, 1972.

Nesbitt, John A., and Larry L. Neal. "Therapeutic Recreation Service: State of the Art, 1971," *Therapeutic Recreation Annual,* 9 (1971), pp. 1–7.

———, Paul D. Brown, and James F. Murphy. *Recreation and Leisure Service for the Disadvantaged,* pp. 87–131. Philadelphia: Lea and Febiger, 1970.

Norris, Albert S., Anthony E. Raynes, and Robert L. Kelley. "Mental Hospitals," in *Handbook of Psychiatry* (2nd ed.), eds. Philip Solomon and Vernon D. Patch. Los Altos, Ca.: Lange Medical Publications, 1969.

Park, David C. "The Effects of Future Shock on Our Profession," *Expanding Horizons in Therapeutic Recreation III,* Gary M. Robb and Gerald Hitzhusen eds., Columbia, Mo: Department of Recreation and Park Administration, University of Missouri, 1975, pp. 7–16.

Park, David C. "NTRS Task Force Reports," *Parks and Recreation,* (September 1974).

Park, David C. "NTRS-Year in Review," *Therapeutic Recreation Annual,* 8 (1971), pp. 55–57.

Park, David C. "The Effects of Future Shock on Our Profession," in *Expanding Horizons in Therapeutic Recreation III,* Gary Robb and Gerald Hitzhusen, eds. Columbia, Mo: Department of Recreation and Park Administration, University of Missouri 1975, pp. 7–16.

Parks and Recreation. Special Issue — Recreation in Corrections, IX, No. 9 (1974).

Shivers, Jay S. "New Understanding of Therapeutic Recreational Services and a Look at the Future," *Recreation in Treatment Centers,* 6 (1969), pp. 21–23.

Stewart, Morris W. and Yvonne A. Washington. "Credentialing," in *Therapeutic Recreation Management School: Second Year Curriculum,* Gerald S. O'Morrow and Morris W. Stewart, eds. College Park, Md: Department of Recreation, University of Maryland, 1979, pp. 28–35.

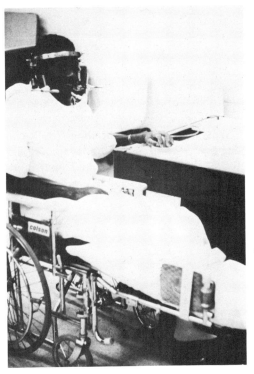

chapter 5
therapeutic
recreation

Therapeutic recreation, therapeutic recreation process, and *therapeutic recreation service* are terms that elicit a kaleidoscope of perspectives and attitudes. Since the way a task is executed depends to a considerable degree on one's interpretation of that task, what we may wish to apply any of these terms to will be determined by our definition of these terms.

therapeutic recreation

The term *therapeutic recreation* was not prevalent in the literature until the late 1950s. Prior to that time such terms as *hospital recreation, medical recreation, recreational therapy,* and *recreation for the ill and handicapped* were used. Today, few of these terms are in use except where they are used to identify the department or service in a particular setting.

Briefly, *hospital recreation* referred to the offering of recreation service within a hospital/institution setting; *medical recreation* suggested that recreation service was under medical supervision or guidance; *recreational therapy* had the connotation that recreation was therapy and had to be medically prescribed; *recreation for the handicapped* implied recreation service to those who were ill or disabled (however, the term *handicapped* in this description is misused since not all conditions that may be described medically as disabilities are perceived as handicaps).

The word *handicapped* has social implications. In other words, the individual himself and/or society determine who is handicapped. It is closely associated with the concept of attitude that was discussed in Chapter 2. A physical disability, may or may not be a physical handicap. My daughter's best girl friend has one leg slightly shorter than the other one. While medically she has a disability, she is certainly not handicapped in her thinking about what she can do and what her friends think she can do. Thus, the term *handicapped* has fallen into disuse.

In recent years another term has developed, *recreation for special populations*. This term appears to be associated with the provision of recreation service to individuals with limiting conditions and impairments who live in the community. In a study completed by Meyer concerning the extent of agreement and disagreement among professional leaders from the NRPA branches of the American Park and Recreation Society (APRS), the Society of Park and Recreation Educators (SPRE), and the National Therapeutic Recreation Society (NTRS), it was found that practitioners (APRS and NTRS) considered recreation for special populations "... as an umbrella term designating a continuum of recreation and leisure services for the ill and disabled." Educators (SPRE and NTRS), on the other hand, "... considered it to be referring only to the provision of recreational opportunities to ill and disabled and other special groups." In the opinion of educators, no "therapy" is intended.[1] More than likely this term will be replaced in a few short years since it appears there is lack of agreement.

As we begin this discussion of therapeutic recreation, it is important to preface our comments about the philosophy of recreation since it cannot be separated from the concepts of therapeutic recreation, therapeutic recreation process, and therapeutic recreation service. At the same time, the student is strongly urged to review those publications that define and discuss recreation as a philosophy, an experience, an institution, and a service.

Recreation is not a tangible, static thing, but a vital force that influences the lives of everyone. Recreation meets certain personal needs that cannot be satisfied in everyday living because of the restrictions and demands made upon our lives. It is essential to happiness, to a sense of belonging, to creativity, to accomplishment, and to satisfaction in living. Through recreative experiences the individual grows and develops physically, emotionally, socially, and intellectually. According to Gray's conceptualization:

Recreation is an emotional condition within an individual human being that flows from a feeling of well being and satisfaction. It is characterized by feelings of mastery, achievement, exhilaration, acceptance, success, personal worth and pleasure. It reinforces a positive self image. Recreation is a response to esthetic experience, achievement of personal goals or positive feedback from others. It is independent of activity, leisure or social acceptance.[2]

What then is therapeutic recreation? It is extremely difficult to say because each person has a different mental image of the term *therapeutic recreation.* Today, a number of variables determine the complexion of this image, ranging from the actions of a mother surrogate to a top-level administrator. The discussion of *what therapeutic recreation is* can be approached from any one of a number of avenues. Therapeutic recreation can be defined or discussed according to: the actions used in performing the service; the roles of the specialists who offer the services; the functions of the specialists; the consumer's image of therapeutic recreation; the image of therapeutic recreation that therapeutic recreation peers have; the philosophy of therapeutic recreation as perceived by practitioners; the settings where therapeutic recreation is offered; the value placed on the individual who needs therapeutic recreation. These are just a few examples of points from which one can begin to discuss or to define therapeutic recreation.

Definitions, concepts, and theories of therapeutic recreation are appearing with increasing frequency. More than two decades ago, however, recreators working in various health and correctional settings seemed to rely upon persons in other disciplines to show the way and define theories upon which recreation action and roles could be based. Persons in the behavioral science disciplines were generous, often too generous, in their assistance to the fledgling group that had just begun to assume aspects of a profession.

Today, a number of therapeutic recreation educators and specialists have defined a concept of therapeutic recreation, others have stated beliefs about therapeutic recreation, and still others have defined a philosophy of therapeutic recreation. These efforts suggest a qualitative, deliberate approach to a thorough analysis and study of the whole of therapeutic recreation. Such constructive efforts will provide those working in this specialized area with the structural framework within which the process and knowledge of therapeutic recreation can be examined, analyzed critically, revised, and improved continually in a sound scientific manner.

Some recreation personnel and members of other professions have contributed to the efforts made to define therapeutic recreation, each developing and making a statement as to what therapeutic recreation is according to his own philosophy of recreation, education, and experience.

Although many have developed statements of therapeutic recreation independently, the various statements convey similar ideas but use different words and various frames of reference.

Several selected definitions and statements about recreation in relation to special population members in various settings are presented here.

One of the earliest statements of the value of recreation to special population members having emotional problems was presented in 1948 by Dr. William C. Menninger, who wrote:

> It has been the privilege of many of us practicing medicine in psychiatry to have some very rewarding experiences in the use of recreation as an adjunctive method of treatment. Along with direct psychological help, hydrotherapy, shock and insulin therapy, many of us have, for years, used various forms of education, recreation, and occupation in the treatment of our patients. . . . Recreation has not only played an important part in the treatment program of many mental illnesses, but it has been a considerable factor in enabling former patients to remain well.[3]

In 1953 a committee within the Hospital Recreation Section of the American Recreation Society was appointed to conduct a study on recreation concepts in hospitals. Their findings were reported in a publication titled *Basic Concepts of Hospital Recreation*. A part of the Statement of Tenet of this publication reads as follows:

> WE BELIEVE,
>   That wholesome recreation is an essential ingredient of mental, emotional, and physical well-being.
>   That in keeping with the modern medical concept of treating the whole man, recreation, under medical guidance, has a vital and an important role in the treatment, care, and rehabilitation of ill and disabled people.
>   That recreation assists the physician in his work of helping the patient get well by:
>
> 1. Facilitating favorable adjustment of the patient to treatment and hospital environment.
> 2. Contributing to the development, restoration, or maintenance of sound mental, emotional, and physical health.
> 3. Providing the physician with opportunities to observe patient response to medically approved recreation activities.[4]

In this same report, Dr. Howard A. Rusk, an international authority in physical rehabilitation and director of the Institute of Physical Medicine and Rehabilitation in New York City, commented:

> I firmly believe that both individual and group recreation for patients have a direct relationship upon their recovery—these, in my opinion, are definitely adjunctive therapy.[5]

The late Dr. Paul Haun's writings and presentations are frequently referred to by therapeutic recreation specialists. Central to his thesis is that recreation cannot be considered therapy or clinical but is certainly therapeutic. As Haun states:

> I like to think of recreation . . . as an important means of increasing the effectiveness of therapy. While not curative in itself, it helps create the milieu for successful treatment. . . . In essence, recreation services help to create in the patient a desirable psychological state by contributing to his self-confidence, his optimism, and his ability to accept the inevitable discomfort of his illness.[6]

Dr. J. B. Wolffe, a cardiologist and former president of the American College of Sports Medicine, has stated:

> . . .recreation activities are an effective form of therapeutics and prophylaxis. Many patients do not yet understand the medical value of properly supervised recreation activities.[7]

Dr. Martin W. Meyer, a pioneer worker and spokesman for recreation workers in health settings, often commented about the importance of recreation as supportive psychotherapy. He said:

> Supportive psychotherapy is directed toward the strengthening of existing defense mechanisms, and when necessary, developing new mechanisms to maintain adequate controls and to establish an adequate equilibrium. Some of the common defense mechanisms often strengthened or developed through recreation activity . . . are repression, displacement of affect, substitution, sublimation and compensation.[8]

Dorothy Mullen, a recreation consultant to nursing homes in Connecticut for over 12 years, has this to say:

> There is the realization that . . . recreation . . . can create the climate for better medical and nursing care, and for more satisfied patients. . . The new nursing home is concerned with more than the physical needs of the patient. Nurses realize that patients sleep better and need fewer tranquilizing drugs when engaged in worthwhile, enjoyable activity. Confused patients become decreasingly so, thereby requiring less supervision and fewer restraints. The atomosphere changes to a preoccupation with living, rather than with death.[9]

Although Frye identified her ideas and concepts much earlier than 1972, in this year Frye and Peters' book *Therapeutic Recreation: Its Theory, Philosophy and Practice,* the first published by professionals in this specialized field, brought together the various concepts, theories, and science of therapeutic recreation. They contend that the concept of therapeutic recreation can be stated only in terms embodied by the concept or philosophy of recreation. The addition of the term *therapeutic* does not alter the concept of recreation per se, but denotes accompanying effects since the term used in a "broad sense describes anything of a positive or beneficial nature. [Further] the difference between recreation and therapeutic recreation is mainly a matter of degree, particularly with respect to the increased responsibility of the therapeutic recreator to direct conscious effort toward emphasizing potential beneficial effects of recreation."[10]

An article in *Parks and Recreation* in 1974 by Edith E. Flynn discussed the therapeutic importance of recreation in corrections. Flynn writes:

> Recreation activities in correctional facilities should, at the very least, provide constructive outlets to pent-up energies of inmates. But they really should do more than that. In jails, they could increase the ability of the accused and the convicted offender to cope with the fears and anxieties that are so understandably pronounced during incarceration. Additional benefits could accrue by instilling in inmates the foundations of teamwork, a sense of fair play, and the willingness to accept reasoned authority. But most importantly, recreation programs should teach inmates to use leisure time more constructively. . . Further, the point has been made that the majority of inmates returning to society from incarcerative settings do not go back to environments that provide for wholesome leisure activities.[11]

And most recently, Gunn and Peterson in their publication *Therapeutic Recreation Program Design: Principles and Procedures* view therapeutic recreation as being ". . .concerned with enabling individuals with physical, mental, emotional, or social disabilities to acquire appropriate socio-leisure life-styles."[12] As they point out, the process to accomplish this life style can be complex and depends upon the settings for success to be reached.

Additional statements to indicate the beneficial effects of recreative experiences for special populations can be found in the literature; however, it would appear that despite the variables that exist in relation to the various definitions and statements, *therapeutic recreation may be defined as those experiences of a recreational nature having the potential of being therapeutic for all.* Because of the contribution recreative experiences make in our daily living experience, the use of such experiences to prevent bio-psycho-socio dysfunctioning, and its influence on treatment, it cannot be considered other than having therapeutic implications.

Before leaving this subject it is well to note from the Meyer study that there was disagreement as well as nonagreement relative to a definition of therapeutic recreation among therapeutic recreation practitioners and therapeutic recreation educators.[13] This division of opinion may be the result of what Witt refers to as "The Outmodel Label."[14] However, I am more inclined to believe as indicated earlier, that the definition and concept of therapeutic recreation as developed by each therapeutic recreation specialist may vary according to the language used, the setting one has in mind, and the personal orientation of the specialist according to his/her education and experience. Because therapeutic recreation is multifaceted and multidimensional and is concerned with humans—the consumer is human, the specialist is human—there probably will be many definitions, concepts, and theories yet to come before one emerges that can be labeled the concept of therapeutic recreation.

therapeutic recreation process

The concept of therapeutic recreation as a "process" is of recent origin. However, I would suspect that recreative experiences have been utilized for some years as a process to bring about a positive change in the behavior of an individual. This is probably more the case in those institutions providing care and treatment to the mentally ill and retarded.

The appearance of a position paper in the late 1960s provided the impetus for general acceptance of the concept of therapeutic recreation as a process. While debates still exist about the concept, each person learns from the other and benefits from open-minded exchanges to the ultimate benefit of the recipient of therapeutic recreation—the special population member.

Despite variables in stating a concept of the therapeutic recreation process, individuals and groups of students, educators and practitioners should continue to strive to assemble words that represent their ideas and reflect the therapeutic recreation process as they see it. This would seem to be more important at this stage of therapeutic recreation development than continuing to look for one concept of therapeutic recreation as a process that will be universally accepted.

In 1969 a selected group of participants attending the Ninth Southern Regional Institute on Therapeutic Recreation at the University of North Carolina defined therapeutic recreation as

> . . . a process which utilized recreation services for purposive intervention in some physical, emotional, and/or social behavior to bring about a desired change in the behavior and to promote the growth and development of the individual.[15]

Frye and Peters state:

> . . . therapeutic recreation is a process through which purposeful efforts are directed toward achieving or maximizing desired concomitant effects of recreative experience.[16]

Fred Humphrey, a past president of the National Therapeutic Recreation Society and a far-sighted thinker in the field, writes about the process in much broader terms. Dr. Humphrey visualizes the therapeutic recreator as a "catalyst-innovator" and "resource leader" who shares his skills and participates with park and recreation professionals in all settings, at all levels, and in all roles so that the delivery of recreation service will be truly recreative, regardless of one's physical, emotional, or social limitations; life style; age; race; and the like. He has this to say:

> As a process, therapeutic recreation is founded on the concept that the recreative experience has the potential to be therapeutic or beneficial to anyone—the child on the playground as well as the aged individual in an extended care facility. These potentials are not automatically released from a given recreation experience, nor is it always easy to bring them out. For this reason, no recreation and parks professional, whatever his special interest area, has the "option" to be therapeutic. It is, instead, an ethical responsibility. Therapeutic recreation as a process opens to the therapeutic recreator the unique opportunity—and basic responsibility—to serve the broad profession of recreation and parks as its catalytic and resource leader in adding this process dimension to the recreation experience, regardless of the circumstance in which it occurs.[17]

Conceptualizing, theorizing, and intellectualizing are integral parts of therapeutic recreation. The art and science of therapeutic recreation are integral parts of the therapeutic recreation process. Science suggests knowledge, or intellectualization; art suggests action.

A conscious awareness of one's personal philosophy and a due consideration for human values, ethics, and beliefs are essential if one wants to develop one's own concept of the therapeutic recreation process. To this end, I restate the concept that I put forth in the earlier edition. *Because of the therapeutic implications of recreative experiences, therapeutic recreation can certainly be considered a process wherein recreative experiences are used to bring about a change in the behavior of those individuals with special needs and problems. The focus of the process is on the use of recreative experiences to (1) enhance growth and development of the individual and (2) enable the individual to meet his responsibility for fulfilling his own leisure needs.*[18] The ultimate goal of the therapeutic recreation process is, therefore, to assist special population members to achieve successful daily living in the environment.

A review of the various concepts presented here suggests that the process is a unified whole; it can be described in terms of phases, but each phase is dependent on the others—none can stand alone. The elements can be distinguished for analysis and scrutiny, but for useful and practical purposes, a total concept of the process is necessary.

The process also suggests a power behind the action or a mover of the action. The key to the process or power behind the action is the therapeutic recreator who intervenes to assist the special population member in changing so that the member can eventually have a truly recreative experience and thereby be as independent as possible. To accomplish this desired goal, the therapeutic recreator proceeds in an orderly, systematic manner to determine the special population member's problem, make plans to solve it, initiate the plan or assign others to implement it. Then he evaluates the extent to which the plan was effective in resolving the problem identified. This intervention will be more fully explored and discussed in depth in a later chapter.

therapeutic recreation service

Concurrent with the foregoing discussion of therapeutic recreation and therapeutic recreation process is the issue of the place of therapeutic recreation as a service in the conceptualization of therapeutic recreation. One is inclined to say that therapeutic recreation as a service and therapeutic recreation as a process are one and the same. However, one is reminded of the millions of special population members living in the community who are yet to be fully accepted as contributing members of society. In addition, these same members are in need of recreation service and recreative experiences for a variety of reasons. Such needs are not presently met within the broad field of public parks and recreation. Likewise, there are those who are the victims of circumstances who may or may not reside in a care and treatment setting but who need services of a therapeutic, rehabilitative, supportive, or custodial nature. Until such time as the concept of therapeutic recreation as a process is deemed essential to the social realities of modern society by all park and recreation professionals, the concept of therapeutic recreation as a service will remain.

In recent years a number of definitions or statements about therapeutic recreation service have appeared. While not using the term service within the definition of therapeutic recreation, one can't help but feel that it was intended within the Public Health Service (PHS) statement: "Therapeutic recreation is the specific use of recreational activity in the care, treatment, and rehabilitation of ill, handicapped and aged persons with a direct program."[19]

Avedon, on the other hand, views therapeutic recreation as a service in the following manner:

> It becomes apparent that personnel offering therapeutic recreation service do not function with respect to the primary phenomenological concept of recreation generally operant in the entire field of professional recreation service, but that practice has developed based upon the experiential context of recreation; that is, service is not based on the need of people to re-create themselves as a

consequence of labor, but rather upon the set of potential effects derived from engaging in various experiences, effects that might influence the behavior of a person because of his current existential situation. Service is usually offered to those persons who are not members of the work force, those who do not "labor," those who have another rationale for "recreation"—some who did work and others who never will.

Generally, service is not offered in a social institution whose primary responsibility is the provision of opportunities for volitional participation in popular recreative activities. If a person can use these resources, he probably doesn't need the service of a therapeutic recreation specialist. Service is usually offered in settings that have other social functions. Social institutions identified with the field of professional recreation service are primarily viewed as "expressive" institutions in that they offer opportunities for spontaneous, emotionally meaningful, reciprocally empathic experiences. Therapeutic recreation specialists function as "expressive" elements in "instrumental" institutions—institutions that are characterized as being "task-oriented"; for example, hospitals, mental health centers, prisons, homes for the aged, and others.[20]

A somewhat different approach, although similar in nature to the one expressed by PHS, is taken by Shivers and Fait. They write:

Therapeutic recreational service is the provision of activities which are prescribed and adapted to meet an individual's limitations or restrictions imposed by some mental, emotional, social, or physical disability or disease. It is a process concerned with maintaining the mental and emotional fiber of the afflicted or handicapped, providing skills to those who cannot be discharged from an institutional setting, and assisting in the rehabilitation or recovery pattern of those who are debilitated by any affliction, injury, or permanent crippling.[21]

Kraus summarizes the views of a number of authors by stating that:

...therapeutic recreation service may be perceived as a form of professional service that provides recreational and related activities specially designed to meet the needs of individuals suffering from some significant degree of illness or disability. It seeks to help these participants help themselves through a process of referral, counseling, instruction or actual program development. It may be provided in an institutional setting, where its primary purpose is to contribute to the process of overall recovery and to facilitate successful return to the community. It may also be a continuing service intended to enrich the quality of the lives of those with permanent disability in institutional or community settings by providing important psychological, physical and social benefits.[22]

More recently, Gunn and Peterson in their excellent publication on programming describe therapeutic recreation service in this way: "Therapeutic recreation service broadly describes those processes that promote independent leisure functioning for special populations through remedial, educational, and recreational experiences that use various activity and facilitation techniques."[23] They hasten to add that the focus of services can be within any one or all three of the following settings: rehabilitation, education, or recreation. Within the concept of the definition, they suggest a therapeutic recreation service model wherein the special population member may be involved in therapy or treatment (improving functional ability), in education (acquiring leisure skills and attitudes), or in recreation (engaging in self-directed leisure) at any given time depending on the functioning level of the member and the setting in which the member is found. The model suggests the idea of a continuum whereby the member enters the therapeutic recreation service model at a specific point, for example, a rehabilitation setting, and progresses or moves to a point where the member is able to make meaningful decisions about leisure activities and where the availability of resources in the community may be found to express leisure needs upon release.[24] It would appear that Gunn and Peterson have incorporated the concepts of therapeutic recreation and therapeutic recreation process into their therapeutic recreation service model.

Since concepts of therapeutic recreation service are being presented here it seems appropriate to include the concept of therapeutic recreation service that the author suggested in his earlier edition. He wrote:

> . . .therapeutic recreation service may be defined as those professional recreation services that are specifically designed to bring about a change in behavior of a special population member as well as to assist that member to move toward achieving the fullest recreative experience possible.[25]

The author also added: "This service is usually a part of a much larger system of services offered by the agency and must be in association with the goals and objectives of that agency."[26] Furthermore, recreative experiences can be used to further treatment goals and to further general leisure activity goals.[27] Incorporated within both goals are the experiences of teaching recreative skills and assisting special population members to develop positive attitudes about the importance of leisure.[28]

While each of the above statements do not outline in specifics the types of services, kinds of settings, for whom the services are provided, and under what circumstances they are provided, they do suggest greater agreement about what therapeutic recreation service is than they did at an earlier period of time. It is interesting to note in passing that Meyer found agreement relative to the types of services that should be provided: "general recreation (activities of a leisure nature usually associated with provisions of service found in community settings), recreation therapy, and leisure education."[29]

If there is apparent confusion on the part of students regarding the discussion to this point, they are again reminded that therapeutic recreation is a new field of service. And the statements expressed here are limited to what one might consider as being specific stages of development. The need for sound concepts and theories has been expressed earlier. Basic theories and concepts can be used to pursue further theories and actions, thereby setting up a continual cycle of activity—selecting a theory or concept, using a theory or concept to determine its effectiveness in terms of benefit to the special population member, perhaps selecting a new or different theory to use, testing and reevaluating for future action. Hence, the deliberate use of therapeutic recreation actions results in qualitative therapeutic recreation service and practice.

early therapeutic recreation service models

As therapeutic recreation service gained acceptance in various settings a number of models developed. While many now have been discarded one early model of organized therapeutic recreation service found primarily in treatment settings and still very evident today in psychiatric institutions is the clinical and nonclinical approach to provide recreation services. The *clinical approach* focuses on the use of recreation in the treatment of illness or disability. The *nonclinical approach* centers on the broader conception of recreation: the subjective enjoyment and enrichment of the patient's living experience.

More recently, Martin has suggested that there may be at least four approaches employed in providing therapeutic recreation service. Further, these approaches are applicable within any medical or rehabilitation setting. Martin describes these four approaches as follows:

> In the "Fun and Games" approach, the Recreation Specialist is expected to provide the means for patients to pursue a pattern of activities which approximates their usual use of discretionary time outside of the therapeutic environment. . . .
> In what can be characterized as the "Personal Adjustment" approach, recreative activities are viewed as helping the patient adjust to the anxiety-providing situation of being in a state of illness and/or functional disability. . . .
> A third distinct approach is that which views the Recreation Service in the medical setting as an integral part of the therapeutic process itself, with recreation part of the patient's daily prescription along with his medication. . . .
> Finally, in the "Educative" approach, the Recreation Specialist seeks to assist the patient to develop a broader recreation horizon through improved utilization of his leisure both during and after his involvement with the therapeutic process. Counseling . . . and referrals to outside recreation services consistent with the amelioration of any lingering effects of the patient's medical condition are basic to this approach.[30]

It should be pointed out, however, that the four approaches suggested by Martin are included in the clinical and nonclinical approach, although they were not as clearly defined as they are today. Akerman, for example, commented in 1966, using an institutional frame of reference, that the objectives of recreation service were:

1. To help the medical staff meet specific emotional, psychiatric, and physical needs of the patient.

2. To help the patient develop a proper attitude toward the use of leisure time, and then to help him develop commensurate skills that will allow him to pursue an activity or activities of interest to him upon returning to his home community.

3. To help the patient adjust to hospitalization and to make life as enjoyable as possible.[31]

range of therapeutic recreation services

Today, the literature and discussions with therapeutic recreators reveal a wide range of therapeutic recreation services. These services are not limited to a particular health or social problem agency or to any particular model, but are found in all settings and in all models where recreation services are offered. At the same time, professional guidelines (standards) for therapeutic recreation service in clinical and residential settings have been developed as noted earlier. These guidelines incorporate philosophy and goals, administration and personnel needs, program services, facilities and equipment, and evaluation and research.[32] Likewise, similar guidelines relating to community recreation services for special populations include guidelines concerning personnel, programs, finance, and transportation by community size.[33]

When I entered the field as a "recreation therapist" in a western state psychiatric institution, the range of services was limited to administration, activity programming, leadership, and coordination of services with other professional disciplines. The use of recreative activities to assist in diagnosis and in treatment in this same institution was yet to be fully accepted or appreciated. A few years later in another psychiatric institution, I was somewhat reprimanded by the superintendent for suggesting a recreation counseling service. Recreation counseling, if time perimitted, in his opinion, was a social service responsibility, and, in addition, my role was to be in the institution, not out in the community surveying recreation resources and following up ex-patients to learn what they were doing during their nonworking hours. While some administrators still have these attitudes and believe in placing additional limits on personnel, facilities, and economics, the range of services in the various settings that offer recreation service to special populations is today extremely broad, but not all-inclusive. Others may very well be added in the future. The range of services at the present time includes the following.

Activity Programming

Foremost among the varied services offered is activity programming. Activities are the media through which the special population member is assisted in behavior changes. They have important physical, emotional, social, and intellectual applications.

It is impossible to consider all of the various kinds of programming concepts here, including those variations found in different settings. However, attention will focus on three types of activity programming found in various settings — namely, general or leisure activity programming, supportive activity programming, and treatment activity programming.

The concept of *general* or *leisure activity programming* is the same as one would find in any social or public recreation agency. It is directed toward assisting individuals in meeting their leisure needs and interests. Activities center on the subjective enjoyment for the individual, on the depth, quality, and duration of his pleasure. The specialist deals with whatever healthy functions and unimpaired capacities the individual possesses.

Just because an individual is admitted to a hospital does not mean that recreational activities are inappropriate. To expect individuals who have acquired leisure interests to adjust abruptly to no activity at the time of hospitalization is often to court failure and impede successful treatment procedures.

A *supportive activity program* is one that makes a systematic effort toward the further prevention of deterioration or is designed to maintain benefits of prior treatment. The individuals who profit most from such a program include those with chronic or organic limitations, but who are at the same time not completely limited in their physical abilities. Individuals of this type are most often found in nursing homes, extended care facilities, and the like. Theoretically, a program should be planned to ensure activity in every hour of the waking day; actually, the activity program is usually limited as a result of insufficient staff and, at times, lack of imagination and ingenuity on the part of the specialist.

Because these special population members are inclined toward isolation, group activities are utilized. Since many of these individuals are found in nursing homes that usually employ only one specialist, volunteers must assist the specialist. Activities are directed toward encouraging an interest in personal intercourse and restoring self-respect, the loss of which is frequently one of the factors in continued illness. It is important for the specialist to realize the importance of instilling faith in eventual recovery in the patient, regardless of how long or uncertain the future may be.

There is another group of chronically ill individuals for whom activity programs may provide a supportive form of treatment — namely, the neurologically disabled; epileptics; and victims of post-traumatic conditions, multiple sclerosis, and other similar conditions. A great majority of individuals with these conditions possess considerable insight into their conditions. Their need for activity is great and must not be forgotten.

In the *treatment activity program* activities are designed to correct or improve behavior and involve controlled interaction with the individual for specific therapeutic results. The goal of the treatment program is a positive change in behavior. Any enjoyment in activities is, to a degree, secondary.

The therapeutic plan in a treatment setting is set in motion and conveyed through a written prescription or through a treatment team meeting.

While the written prescription determines the role of the activity in treatment and no variation is usually tolerated without consultation first with the physician's or the treatment team's order, the choice of the activity and its direction is the role responsibility of the recreation specialist.

A prescription for therapeutic recreation generally includes such pertinent facts as the aims of treatment, precautions, and limitations. In some treatment settings a brief personal history and medical summary will also be included, as well as the attitude the specialist should assume in working with the individual.

A prescription usually requires that the recreation specialist report the progress of the individual. The type of report or progress note requested by the referral physician will vary greatly. Some physicians desire to know only how the individual is progressing, while others want detailed reports. Whatever the type of report wanted, it should be clear and to the point.

In some institutions the specialist will be in attendance at ward or chart rounds. In such instances, anything the specialist can learn about the individual, what will be done for him by other agencies, and how the patient's program fits into the overall picture will certainly enhance the recreation treatment plan. Further, this procedure offers an excellent opportunity for introducing the patient to the specialist.

Not infrequently the former interest of the individual will give valuable cues as to the therapeutic activity to be utilized. In addition, the type of treatment activity chosen may lay a foundation for the development of leisure interests for the patient after being discharged from the hospital or institution.

In correctional institutions, the treatment program is usually left entirely to the recreation director and staff. At this time recreation has yet to be identified as having a high priority in the treatment program.

While there has been greater emphasis today on recreation programs in correctional institutions than in previous years, many institutions still focus on individual and group athletic and sport activities. Likewise, many institutions use recreation as a means of inducing good behavior. Thus, the role of recreation service within these types of institutions needs to be reviewed.

Many offenders find their way into prison as a result of poor leisure habits while in their respective communities. After release, many of these offenders return to these same communities. It follows, therefore, that programs must be more diversified and considered part of the treatment program. As Carroll Hormachea, director of the Institute of Criminal Justice, Virginia Commonwealth University, comments:

[Recreation] must be viewed as one of the methods that can be employed to assist the inmate in his quest for a place in society. Through meaningful recreation programming, inmates can become more productive and interested in becoming contributing members of society. By giving them purpose, a step has been taken towards the effective rehabilitation of individuals.[34]

Leadership and Instruction.

The key to successful activity programming is leadership. Activities are the tools of the therapeutic recreator. He knows their parts as well as how and why they work the way they do. He knows the requirements and prerequisites for participation since these must be taken into consideration when a specific activity is selected to help the member meet physical, emotional, social, and/or intellectual needs. He has analyzed each activity and considers participation in terms of functional abilities, physical requirements, degree of coordination, degree of social involvement and interaction, and degree of complexity or difficulty. He must also assist the member to develop a positive attitude toward himself and the constructive use of leisure. The perspective that the professional worker has of himself, the role that he plays in treating and rehabilitating the special population member, and the perspective he has of the member may well determine the effectiveness of both the specialist and the activity.

The rapid growth of therapeutic recreation during the last two to three decades, stimulated by the interest of other rehabilitative disciplines, has led the therapeutic recreation specialist to be conscious of his deficiencies and anxious to correct them so he can be of more benefit to the treatment team. Roberts and McAndrew have summarized this feeling as follows:

. . . too many recreation specialists appear to regard themselves more in light of hospital activity service personnel, rather than professional recreation specialists who specialize in the therapeutic aspects of recreation. Too many specialists fail to recognize their own professional value. The prestige of the specialist is dependent upon the recognition of his value accorded by other persons, but his morale depends essentially upon his own ability to recognize his professional value. Failure to recognize his own worth may result in his becoming lost in the activity in which he is engaged. He may then fail to see or accomplish necessary goals in relation to treatment of the patient.[35]

Counseling

Recreation or leisure counseling is another therapeutic recreation service that aims to help the individual utilize new-found skills or new resources to enhance capacity for social function. Further, it is probably the one service that is receiving considerable attention today among recreation professionals and especially therapeutic recreators. Conferences on the topic have been held,[36] books have been written,[37] newspaper articles have discussed the topic,[38] and recently, a national forum was conducted on the subject.[39]

While there is no one accepted definition of leisure counseling, there appears to be a consensus among leisure counseling authors, therapeutic recreation educators, and members of the Past-President's Council of the NTRS, according to a recent study completed by Andrea Morris at the University of Maryland. Consensus was that leisure counseling is:

> a helping process which facilitates interpretative, affective, and/or behavioral changes in others toward the attainment of their total leisure well-being. It attempts to foster, in a person, independent responsibility for choosing and making decisions as to his leisure involvement.[40]

Some educators and practitioners have developed leisure counseling models independent of each other, while others have overlapped their models with models which have been suggested or are in use. Generally speaking, the literature reflects three approaches utilized within the concept of leisure counseling. They have been summarized by McDowell as follows:

1. leisure resource guidance (initially established by Dr. Robert Overs and his associates at the Milwaukee Curative Workshop, Milwaukee, Wisconsin) makes the assumption that no maladaptive leisure behavioral problems exist and the individual is only seeking community leisure resource information to engage in desired leisure interest;

2. therapeutic-remedial-normalization makes the assumption that the individual lacks certain leisure skills because of a specific problem and needs a more structured program of activity involvement to acquire functioning behavioral skills for independent community living;[41]

3. leisure lifestyle-development-educational makes the assumption that the individual is dissatisfied with present leisure-work life-style and attempts to bring about change in the leisure-work life-style dimensions.[42,43]

Regarding the special population member, Rusk states that leisure counseling can help a discharged psychiatric patient avoid the solitary ways that set the stage for readmission to a psychiatric institution.[44] Likewise, Acuff has commented that counseling can help the patient seek a more satisfying leisure life,[45] while Humphrey believes that a recreation counseling program is the only answer to successful social adjustment in the community for the patient.[46]

The advantages of a good recreational activity program cannot be denied; nor can it be denied that leisure counseling before discharge or release must be an integral part of the overall therapeutic program, regardless of setting.

Administration

Administration, as the word is commonly used, is understood to mean the planning, organizing, staffing, directing, coordinating, reporting, and budgeting for achieving the objectives of the organization, department, or service. Administration is not an end in itself; however, it is a means to an end. The end in therapeutic recreation service is assisting the special population member to change behavior, develop a positive personal philosophy about recreation, and develop recreative skills to participate in recreative experiences.

Administration of the provision of therapeutic recreation is a full-time responsibility, whether the department or service is administered within a residential setting or a community-based setting. However, it should be realized that in small settings, such as a nursing home, the therapeutic recreator will not only administer a program of service, but also be a leader of activities.

Facilities, Equipment, and Supplies

Objectives, primarily activity programs, cannot be met without adequate facilities, equipment, and supplies. They may either enhance or diminish the possibilities of successful service. Facilities are the means of implementing the diversified activity program as patterned by the process of planning and organizing. Likewise, few activities can be conducted without some sort of equipment and supplies. Consideration must be given to age, sex, skill of the participant, mental and physical abilities, facilities and space, and a host of other factors in determining the type of equipment and supplies.

Those who will eventually work with individuals having limited physical ability should become familiar with the American Standards Association's *Specifications for Making Buildings and Facilities Accessible to and Usable by the Physically Handicapped* (New York: the Association, 1961), Edward Lowan and Judith L. Klinger's *Aids to Independent Living* (New York: McGraw-Hill, 1969), and *Trends* (Washington, D.C.: National Recreation and Park Association, publication of the Park Practice Program, January, February, and March 1974).[47]

Consultation

The increased need to deal with the personal and social change of special populations in the environment has led naturally to a demand for professional help. As a result of the fact that special populations are requesting more recreation service, public and private municipal agencies are expanding their services to meet the requests of special populations, physicians and workers in the human service professions are accepting the concept of therapeutic recreation, and administrators in various health and correctional facilities are recognizing the shortcomings in dealing with the "whole man," the service of therapeutic recreation consultation has developed. Consultation, according to Avedon, is an interactive process between two persons—consultant and consultee.[48]

Therapeutic recreation consultation may be directed toward the special population member *(special population member-centered)*, a colleague *(colleague-centered)*, or an agency *(agency-centered)*. In the special population member-centered consultation, help is sought out by a physician, a family member, an interested friend, or perhaps an agency that feels one of its participants needs help. The therapeutic recreation specialist in private practice is new and relatively uncommon. Colleague-centered consultation is often requested by public or private municipal recreators. The consultant is often requested to assist in program development that meets special population members' needs in the community, to suggest programs of in-service training, or to assist in grant writing. In agency-centered consultation, the therapeutic recreation specialist is engaged to consult on problems, policies, or procedures that affect the total agency. The consultant may also be engaged by a national organization to provide information or assistance in overall policy and program development as it affects recreation service. In many national health organizations, recreation service is only one of the many services provided.

Consultants may be either "inside" consultants or "outside" consultants. An inside consultant is one who is already employed within a specific agency or organization and provides consultation service on a regular basis to the various units associated with the agency. The outside consultant, on the other hand, must receive a formal or appropriate request from an agency before consultation service can be provided.

Education and Training

Education and training as a service may be provided in four ways:

1. The education of special populations to assist them in developing a philosophy about the importance of leisure in their lives.
2. The education of society about the problems and needs of special populations and therapeutic recreation.
3. The education and training of students through clinical affiliation in various health, social, and correctional agencies.
4. The training of volunteers to assume responsibility for assisting special populations to participate in recreative experiences.

Today, it is recognized that leisure is important to all people, regardless of their age, sex, social status, or physical or mental condition. However, there is every evidence that too many people are not able to make good use of their leisure. Martin considers the problem of leisure to be one of the most crucial public health issues of our time. He takes serious exception to the thesis that humans will naturally know how to adapt themselves to their newly made leisure, that an evolutionary process is at work, and that society can let nature take its course.[49] Because of this rapidly evolving scope of leisure, the therapeutic recreator must assist special populations to develop an appropriate philosophy of leisure that will meet their own needs.

The therapeutic recreation specialist has a very definite responsibility to educate society about special populations and therapeutic recreation through participation on councils of social agencies, service clubs, and other like organizations. Opportunities to speak at club, lodge, church, and home neighborhood meetings should be utilized. The formal channels of community communication, when available in a society, play a very important role in educating the public. Predominant among these channels are the newpapers, radio, and television. Press articles should emphasize problems, programs, and the organization, not the therapeutic recreator. It should be kept in mind that therapeutic recreation as a service in most situations is a part of a tax-supported public agency that belongs to the people it serves. Its existence in a democracy depends in the final analysis upon the people's desire to maintain it. In the long run, this desire can be sustained only by giving the public an understanding of its value.

A clinical affiliation is a part of the total educational process for the potential therapeutic recreation specialist. It is also the responsibility of the specialist to assist in this education process.

Volunteers play an important part and are needed in the provision of recreation service. The increasing demand for more service is delegated by everyone concerned, but for maximum effectiveness, volunteers must receive training in the philosophy, theory, and technique of therapeutic recreation. In additon, volunteers can help promote a better community understanding of the part that therapeutic recreation service plays. Describing their duties to families, friends, and organizations throughout the community helps further to build the understanding that forms the basis for strong public support.

Research

No profession, particularly one as recently established as therapeutic recreation, can grow in stature unless it can give evidence that it is willing and able to keep up with other professions by evaluating its own particular contribution. Furthermore, as one of the professions engaged in promoting health and welfare, it must meet the challenge of changing concepts and practices in these areas. To this end, the critical analysis of therapeutic recreation philosophy and practices as they apply to therapeutic recreation requires disciplined research.

Therapeutic recreation is a distinct and significant discipline — not imitation occupational therapy, or counterfeit psychology, or even pseudo-psychotherapy. It must establish itself with an independent identity and a definite philosophy and purpose. Moreover, the specialist must define his role not in vague generalities or platitudes, but by a realistic analysis of the part he plays through therapeutic recreation as a service in the life of the individual.

These are but some of the service elements offered through a therapeutic recreation service. Others might very well include working on a community committee concerned with activating community resources for use by special populations, coordinating institutional recreation services with municipal recreation services, and assisting to improve the personal characteristics of special population members. Undoubtedly, these can be incorporated with those services already discussed.

SUGGESTED REFERENCES

Austin, David R. "A Humanistic Approach to Management and Motivation," *Therapeutic Recreation Journal,* 11:3 (1977), pp.. 123–127.

Avedon, E. M. "A Critical Analysis of the National Therapeutic Recreation Society," Position Statement in *Therapeutic Recreation Workshop.* Terre Haute, Id: Department of Recreation, Indiana State University, 1970, pp. 5–7.

Ball, Edith L. "The Meaning of Therapeutic Recreation," *Therapeutic Recreation Journal,* 4:1 (1970), pp. 17–18.

Barnett, Lynn A. "Research Methods for the Practitioner," in *Expanding Horizons in Therapeutic Recreation* V. Gerald Hitzhusen, ed. Columbia, Mo: Department of Recreation and Park Administration. University of Missouri, 1978, pp. 29–46.

Felix, Robert H. "Preface," *Recreation in Treatment Centers,* 1 (1962), p.3.

Gray, David E. "Exploring Inner Space," *Parks and Recreation* (December 1972), pp. 18–19, 46

Goldstein, Judith E. (Ed.) *Consultation: Enhancing Leisure Service Delivery to Handicapped Children.* Arlington, Va.: National Recreation and Park Association, 1977.

Goldstein, Judith E. "Therapeutic Recreation Consultation: A Component of the Leisure Service Delivery System," in *Expanding Horizons in Therapeutic Recreation IV.* Gerald Hitzhusen, Gerald O'Morrow, and John Oliver, eds. Columbia, Mo: Department of Recreation and Park Administration, University of Missouri, 1977, pp. 73–88.

Hayes, Gene. "Leisure Counseling II," *Therapeutic Recreation Management School: Second Year Curriculum,* Gerald S. O'Morrow and Morris W. Stewart, eds. College Park, Md: Department of Recreation, University of Maryland, 1979, pp. 23–27.

Kelley, Jerry. "Therapeutic Recreation: A Quarter Century Service to the Disabled," *Therapeutic Recreation Journal,* 7:1 (1973), pp. 3–7.

Knudson, A. B. C. and James W. Gibson. "Concepts of Recreation in Rehabilitation," in *The Doctors and Recreation in the Hospital Setting.* Raleigh, N. C.: North Carolina Recreation Commission, 1961.

Martin, Fred W. "Therapeutic Recreation Service: A Philosophic Overview," *Leisurability,* 1:1 (1974), p. 22.

McDowell, Jr., Chester F. "Emerging Leisure Counseling Concepts and Orientation," *Leisurability,* 2:4 (1975), pp. 19–26.

O'Morrow, Gerald S. (ed.) *Administration of Activity Therapy Service.* Springfield, Ill. Charles C Thomas Publisher, 1966.

O'Morrow, Gerald S. "Administration—Management by Objectives," *Therapeutic Recreation Management School: Second Year Curriculum,* Gerald S. O'Morrow and Morris W. Stewart, eds. College Park, Md.: Department of Recreation, University of Maryland, 1979, pp. 1–6.

Rathbone, Josephine L. and Carol Lucas. *Recreation in Total Rehabilitation.* Springfield, Ill.: Charles C Thomas Publisher, 1970.

Recreation Proof of Its Value in Research and Application. Raleigh, N. C.: North Carolina Recreation Commission, 1966.

Rensvold, Vera, and others. "Therapeutic Recreation," *Annals of the Academy of Political and Social Science,* 313 (September 1957), pp. 87–91.

Rule, Warren R. and Morris W. Stewart. "Enhancing Leisure Counseling Using an Adlerian Technique," *Therapeutic Recreation Journal,* 11:3 (1977), pp. 94–102.

Rusalem, Herbert. "An Alternative to the Therapeutic Model in Therapeutic Recreation," *Therapeutic Recreation Journal,* 7:1 (1973), pp. 8–15.

Shivers, Jay S. "One Concept of Therapeutic Recreation Service," *Therapeutic Recreation Journal,* 5:2 (1971), pp. 51–53.

Shivers, Jay S. "Why Not Recreational Therapy," *Leisurability,* 4:4 (1977), pp. 4–10.

Smith, Debby A. and Ronald P. Reynolds, "Integrating Leisure Counseling and Psychological Services," *Therapeutic Recreation Journal,* 12:3 (1978), pp. 25–30.

Terry, Luther K. "A Message from the Surgeon General," *Recreation in Treatment Centers,* 4 (September 1965), p. 3.

Therapeutic Recreation: Dialogues with Doctors. Raleigh, N. C.: North Carolina Recreation Commission, 1961.

chapter 6
therapeutic recreation activities and leadership

This chapter is designed to provide the student with basic information about human needs, activities, and leadership skills which are essential to the success of the therapeutic recreation process. Nearly all students who enter this professional field of service will probably begin their initial employment at a level where activities and leadership are their prime responsibility.

Activity programs are the backbone of the therapeutic recreation service, whether such programs are offered in community or institutional settings. Activity programs are influenced, as noted earlier, by agency philosophy, facilities, supplies and equipment and, as we will now read, by leadership and people to be served. Activities can be considered the major media through which special populations are assisted to change behavior; in essence, activities are constructive tools used as a means to an end. The end point is desired change in behavior so that individuals with physical, emotional, social, and/or intellectual problems can live fuller, more satisfying and productive lives. Furthermore, a limitless variety of activities is available to therapeutic recreation specialists to assist special populations to improve the quality of their daily living experiences or to assist in their restoration or adjustment.

Equally as important as activities is leadership. While much remains to be learned about the art and science of leadership and the many types of leadership roles, the key to the success of any therapeutic recreation experience, or for that matter any therapeutic recreation service, is in large measure the quality of leadership. There is no substitute for good leadership.

Leadership has a marked effect upon any individual or group effort. Every person has influence on others; with practice and use, this influence grows. Leadership requires the active use of a person's ability and talent toward influencing others in the achievement of their respective goal.

Effective leadership in therapeutic recreation is rapidly becoming significant. The increased emphasis on the individualistic human element in therapeutic recreation practice has stressed the importance of leadership as a necessary ingredient to bring about a change in behavior through activities. Therapeutic recreation experiences can and should be dynamic, purposeful, and richly satisfying. They can be so because of proper leadership. A leader does not offer activity just for activity's sake. Rather, the leader should select activities that are in accordance with the needs and objectives of people regardless of setting.

As we begin our discussion, it is important to reemphasize that this chapter does not attempt an expansive treatment of any one of the topics or subtopics under consideration. This should be provided in other recreation core and social-behavioral courses in a more comprehensive manner. Likewise; the Suggested References at the close of the chapter offers additional readings. The chapter is provided to highlight the importance of activities and leadership in recreation service to special populations. It has been my experience that students take lightly these two service elements. Activities and leadership are like football; you win by proper execution and use of basic fundamentals.

human needs

Therapeutic recreation programs of activity have but one vital basis—the needs and interests of special populations. To meet individual as well as group needs and interests, programs must be varied and flexible. But to offer such a program, the specialist must be acquainted with some of the physical, emotional, and social needs of human beings.

The study of personality is basically the study of behavior patterns. Because behavior is motivated by needs, these elements provide valuable insights into individual personalities, thereby assisting the specialist to meet special population needs.

The late Abraham Maslow organized human needs into a scheme that both categorizes and classifies them according to the degree of personality growth they indicate. He believed that while basic human needs are innate, they tend to emerge in an orderly manner during the normal course of development and that this process follows a relatively predictable sequence. In other words, according to Maslow's scheme, needs move from meeting physical necessities toward self-actualization, representing freedom from self-concerns and full involvement with satisfying tasks.[1] A more detailed description and discussion of Maslow's scheme follows.

Physical Needs

Food, water, air, and sexual expression comprise the principal physical needs. Maslow felt that these must be reasonably satisfied before the individual can concern himself with the next level or other types of needs. The specialist might consider here the disadvantaged youth. His actions might very well be determined mainly by his biological need for food and shelter and the closely related needs for physical safety and security. The need for self-esteem in his case might be a luxury that he can ill afford during the course of his development.

Safety Needs

The infant shows little concern for his safety beyond a natural dislike for loud noise and sudden falls; he generally shows no distress until he is actually hungry or hurt in some manner; however, young children soon begin to "cry before they are hurt," that is, to be fearful. This new class of needs obviously serves a protective function, but the individual now becomes vulnerable to the trauma and anxiety that physical threats can produce. People who live in continued fear for their physical security commonly develop personality problems or emotional disturbances.

Love and Affiliation Needs

During the normal course of personality development each person displays a need for a feeling of belonging to his family, social group, and perhaps vocational group. The urge to be together is one of the strongest motivations of humans. However, they also need a deeper, affectional relationship with one or more specific persons.

"Love is the only satisfactory answer to the problems of human existence," says Dr. Erich Fromm in *The Art of Loving*. He has succinctly described the need for love:

Man is gifted with reason; he is life being aware of itself; he has awareness of himself, of his fellow man, of his past and of the possibilities of his future. This awareness of himself, of his own short life span, of the fact that without his will he is born and against his will he dies, that he will die before those whom he loves, or they before him, the awareness of his aloneness and separateness, of his helplessness before the forces of nature and of society, all this makes his separate, disunited existence unbearable prison. He would become insane could he not liberate himself from his prison and reach out, unite himself in some form or other with men, with the world outside.[2]

Man commonly attempts to overcome his aloneness by establishing lasting interpersonal relationships with others. The importance of such relationships is indicated by the fact that most suicides stem from their failure.[3]

Esteem Needs

When the individual has achieved a reasonable degree of fulfillment for his needs in the lower categories, then he is in a position to respond to certain standards of conduct and achievement that produce the need for rather specific types of behavior. Also within this category is the need for the recognition and respect of other significant persons in one's environment. For most people it is not enough merely to be accepted, to belong; one must feel respect as a person of worth or consequence. Even more vital is the individual's own self-assessment of his real worth or importance.

Until self-esteem is developed, one is boggled, and happiness lies out of reach. Before one can proceed, self-confidence must be developed, and one must begin to like and respect oneself, according to contemporary psychiatrists. In his book, *The Psychology of Self-Esteem,* Nathaniel Branden states:

Man needs self-respect because he has to act to achieve values—and in order to act, he needs the beneficiary of his action. In order to seek values, man must consider himself worthy of enjoying them. In order for his happiness, he must consider himself worthy of happiness.[4]

Self-esteem deficiency is a very serious disease, producing unhappiness, dependency, and physical disease. It motivates many kinds of human behavior. The businessman deficient in self-esteem may turn to alcohol. A child who hates himself may withdraw and become schizophrenic. A housewife who lacks self-esteem may turn to drugs.

Need for Self-Actualization

Maslow's concept of self-actualization refers to a process rather than a need in any technical sense. It is something that happens to a person when he succeeds in committing himself to some cause whose importance appears to extend well beyond his selfish concerns. The real "need" here seems to be for involvement, commitment, and a wholehearted effort rather than for accomplishment of any specific goal. The therapeutic recreation specialist, as an example, would be acting in a self-actualizing way to the degree that he focused his concern on affairs related to the welfare of his special population participants and the advancement of therapeutic recreation for their own value rather than as a means to increase his own status and professional gain.

activities

range of activities

Before a specialist can intelligently plan a program of activities, he must have a knowledge of the great variety of activities that are available to him and suitable for his use. As he eventually finds out, the range of activities is as varied as humanity itself.

The types of activity that can be used to meet physical, emotional, social, and intellectual needs of special populations are limitless. There are any number of publications which deal solely or partially with activities as they relate to special population members. Students are encouraged to review these publications. Likewise, students are encouraged to initiate on their own, adaptations and modifications of activities.

The task of adapting a leisure skill however, must not be taken lightly. there are several important principles to consider when doing so. Activities should not be altered as to make the participant stand out as different, especially in community settings. The extent of the adaptation should be enough to increase participation, success and enjoyment. Adaptations should always be viewed as a temporary change as the participant must work toward engagement in the original activity. Adaptations should be made on an individual basis meeting individual needs as opposed to modifications for an entire group when only one participant needs activity simplification.

Activities may be classified in various ways, such as by type, season, age, sex, space required, number taking part, place, skill required, time involved, cost, and method of organization. Hopefully, the student recognizes that any classification cannot be completely adequate because the range of activities is endless and also because the interrelationship of one activity to another is so pronounced. Moreover, no complete rigid classification is practicable.

The following classification incorporates some important activity areas for special populations.

Arts and Crafts

These activities offer an outlet for persons who seek an opportunity for creative expression. Because arts and crafts take a wide variety of forms that appeal to persons of all ages, skills, occupations, and interests, they have a large place in any program. The specialist must realize that many children and adults who do not enjoy or excel in other activity areas find great satisfaction in this area. Activities in this area are extememly adaptable and are well suited for either ambulatory or non-ambulatory individuals.

Clinical observation of psychotic behavior reveals that the tendency to create, for some patients, is not just a sporadic impulse, but a deep and absorbing preoccupation. It has been suggested by some investigators that this urge to create is an attempt by the patient to bring himself into contact with the world of reality at a time when contact is in danger of being completely lost.

The following are only a few typical examples of arts and craft activities: oil and water painting, sketching, ceramics, woodworking, sculpturing, weaving, needlepoint, model construction, whittling, leather work, basketry, rug-making, quilt-making, and jewelry-making.

Dance

One or more forms of dance is found in practically all programs and has an enthusiastic appeal to every age level and every condition and impairment. Dancing is frequently used in combination with other activity forms. It can serve as an individual or a group experience, and through its many forms can bring pleasure and satisfaction as a social and creative activity. It can also be used as a treatment tool. According to movement therapist Claire Schmais, movement can sublimate potentially destructive tension or aggression. She writes: "The act of moving together literally mobilizes people. The energy released tends to reduce fragmentation, to diminish defenses, and to permit integration of feelings, thoughts and actions."[5]

Dance forms include modern, social, folk, square, country, and interpretive.

Drama

The universal tendency for people of all ages to imitate what they see or hear indicates the fundamental importance of this activity form. Through drama the child enters the land of make-believe, and the adult often most fully utilizes powers of self-expression while playing the part of another. Drama affords many channels for human emotional expression and is a widely accepted means in treating those with emotional and social problems. Creative dramatics and psychodrama have become established, recognized forms of psychotherapy.

Aside from acting there are opportunities for using color in costumes and stage design, for developing lighting effects, and for building sets.

Drama activities include the following: writing and/or performing plays, skits, musical dramas, charades, pantomines, puppetry, marionettes, and story telling.

Entertainment

All of us like to be entertained and would prefer, at times, to be a spectator at an activity rather than a participant in an activity. Much can be gained emotionally and socially by being entertained. For some individuals, being entertained is the only activity in which they can participate. However, the beginning specialist is cautioned about developing a total program around entertainment.

A few of the many entertainment activities include attendance at concerts, plays, and sport events; listening to records and radio; and watching films and television.

Hobbies or Special Interests

A hobby is a recreation activity joyously pursued with intense interest over a sustained period of time with little outside stimulation to sustain this interest. An individual may pursue a hobby as a youngster and continue to excel in and utilize those skills with increasing degrees of sophistication throughout his/her lifetime. Hobbies are as varied as the field of human interest and experience. They contain the element of exploration that gives the hobbyist a chance to discover himself and the world. The same hobby activity will often satisfy different needs for different people. Participation in a hobby is usually of a solitary nature, and therefore, noncompetitive; here the concepts of "win and lose" are nonexistent. Hobbies may be the only activity for shut-ins and nonambulatory individuals. In this regard, I recall a specialist working in a physical rehabilitation center commenting that they encouraged severely nonambulatory patients (but with adequate speech patterns) to develop an interest in ham-radio operation. The center had a ham-radio club as an on-going activity program which had been in existence for years.

Hobbies may be categorized into collecting, learning, constructing, creating, and performing, and may include some of the following: coin, stamp, and doll collecting; ornithology; model building, soap sculpturing, and radio set construction; designing, block printing, and sewing; and archery, shooting, and cooking.

Literary Activities

Closely associated with hobbies and special interests are literary activities. Reading, writing, and speaking have a definite place in a well-rounded program because they appeal to all ages and to every economic group, and are inexpensive to the individual and the therapeutic recreation program: reading, because it is the easiest to do and can be either an individual or a group effort; writing, because it involves the process of creation; and speech, because of the almost universal urge on the part of all people to be seen, heard, and understood.

Literary activities include writing book reviews, poetry writing, holding writing classes, debating, storytelling, and working on agency–institution newspapers.

Music

Music is a means of expression found in all ages and among all peoples. Music exerts a strong influence upon the human emotions and makes a valuable contribution to many other forms of activity. Whether employed passively or actively, music is probably the one activity that appeals to all people. It can be expensive, time-consuming, and complex; it can also be inexpensive and simple. It is one activity to which everyone can be exposed.

Active participation has many psychological values. It gives an opportunity for creative effort, it may increase self-respect through accomplishment and success, it may increase personal happiness by the ability to please others, it may be used as a form of energy release, and most important, it can be a socializing agent.

Passive participation or listening can be on one of several levels. There are those who listen intently because of habit, training, or professional or amateur interest. Some prefer music in the air as a background to work, play, eating, or just daydreaming. Listening can be the basis for group therapy discussion. Music can also be used by groups in an educational appreciation hour.

Nature and Outdoor Recreation Activities

Nature and outdoor activities often receive less consideration than do some of the other activities, but they merit serious consideration in every activity program. Such activities help children and adults gain a knowledge of the world about them and thereby stimulate their interest in their physical and social environment and contribute to their understanding of it. Nature and outdoor recreation include, in general, those experiences that involve being in, using, enjoying, or interpreting the natural environment. Many forget that outdoor recreation is as old as the human race. In an earlier period of time, outdoor skills were essential to survival. With few exceptions, investigators strongly support the contribution nature and outdoor recreation activities make to physical, emotional, and social well-being. A few of these many activities are hiking and exploration, day and residential camping, gardening, canoeing, swimming, and fishing.

Outing Activities

Closely associated with outdoor recreation activities are outing activities or excursions. This type of activity is certainly an important aspect of any program because of the opportunities it offers to the individual who has been out of contact with society for a period of time as a result of a serious impairment. Because of the custodial nature of some institutions, it is important that individuals in such institutions have contact with the physical and social environment before being released. Among outing activities we find excursions to art galleries, industrial plants, museums, parks, places of historic and scenic interest, and zoos and aquariums.

Physical Activities

Physical activities rank very high in popularity among all ages, sexes, and special populations. Participation by members of special populations in the endless activities of a physical nature have been shown to have many values over and above the obvious benefits of therapy. The urge to play and participate for enjoyment, satisfaction, accomplishment, and fellowship accounts for the strong interest in physical activities, especially for the special population member. There is no need to even suggest activities, for they are endless.

This activity category also includes both individual and team sports. Sports, as opposed to games of a physical nature, have more sophisticated rules and equipment with greater emphasis placed on the competitive aspects of the activity. Sport activities for special population members are becoming extremely popular as can be observed by the increased interest in the Special Olympics and in wheelchair sports.[6]

Social Activities

Social activities include those activities and experiences in which the central purpose is sociability. Social activities provide opportunities through which the individual can learn to adjust to the social demands of our society. Unlike some other needs that appear only during a given age period, social needs must be met throughout a lifetime. The response today of persons of all ages to opportunities for social life is an additional indication of the importance of social experience in daily living.

Such social events as birthday parties, dances, and picnics can promote a general air of friendliness, sociability, and happy cooperation, whether it be among a group of notable asocial patients in a psychiatric institution, a group of blind persons cut off from many normal contacts, people in wheelchairs and on crutches, residents in a home for the aged, or a ward full of children in casts, frames, and braces.

A few of the widely used social activities include parties for holidays and birthdays, teas, and the like based on all kinds of themes and events; barbecues and picnics; hay rides; and table games. Included here would also be the electronic games which have become so popular and appeal to all ages.[7]

Special Events

Activities associated with social activities that are held from time to time and that supplement regular activities are referred to as special events. These activities add variety and interest to the program. Special event activities usually are highly organized, have a uniqueness about them, involve many persons, and serve as a stimulus for individual and group accomplishment. I am willing to venture that nearly all institutions for the mentally ill or residential school and training centers for the mentally retarded in the United States have a July 4 program involving the entire hospital.

The following are some special event activities: amateur nights, costume shows, handicraft exhibitions, treasure hunts, tournaments, and contests.

Voluntary Service or Community Service Projects

One of the highest forms of recreation is to use part of one's leisure to do something for someone else. Such uses of one's leisure return to the individual the same satisfactions that others receive from participation in other types of activities. A volunteer is a person who performs necessary services without remuneration. Such services may include making scrap books for children at hospitals, working with patients in hospitals or drug treatment centers, entertaining residents of the county home, preparing toys and favors for hospitals, raising plants for distribution to the sick and shut-ins at Easter, and sewing for orphan homes. For example, one only needs to read *Prime Times,* a publication of Action, to know how some senior citizens use their leisure.[8]

Games

Within a majority of the activity areas above, games are found. A game may involve competition and/or cooperation of participants and usually involves more than one person. The players must learn to take turns and abide by the rules. In games, the concept of winning and losing is introduced. For many special population members this is an important factor. Games are the purest form of recreation in that they are played because the participants enjoy playing that particular game; sheer pleasure is the primary motivating factor.

The range of activities that may be used in therapeutic recreation service is, therefore, as broad as the needs and interests of the special population members being served and the ingenuity, the versatility, and the initiative of the individual therapeutic recreation specialist. Furthermore, the specialist who is familiar with the wide range of activities, who understands their therapeutic value, who can adapt and modify them to meet the needs and interests of special populations, and who can combine them into a well-balanced program has achieved one of the most important qualifications for offering successful therapeutic recreation.

activity analysis

In recent years considerable attention has been given to the concept of activity analysis. It is not the intent here to discuss in detail the concept and procedures of activity analysis since a number of excellent resources are available. However, within the limitations of space, it is important to briefly highlight the characteristics of this process since it is very much a part of the therapeutic recreation process which will be discussed in some detail shortly.

Many individuals, including therapeutic recreation specialists, have been involved in systematic research on the effects and contribution of recreative experiences to further the growth and development, achievement, and adjustment of individuals with limiting conditions and impairment. As these research efforts relate to activity analysis, special note is made regarding the work of Drs. Elliott Avedon,[9] Carol Peterson,[10] and Doris Berryman[11] in the development of various activity analysis models.[12]

When I started working in this field, little attention if any was given to analyzing an activity by breaking it down into all of its component parts. In some instances, activities were selected randomly for the patient with little consideration given to the physical, mental, emotional, or social demands that the activity put upon the patient. As Hayes has commented: "Few therapeutic recreation 'professionals' first analyze their activities for inherent values these activities possess for the individuals participating in the activities . . ."[13] Today, more so than ever before, therapeutic recreators are expected to have a sophisticated approach to the use of activities to bring about changes in behavior. As the result of Medicaid and Medicare, PL 94–142, hospital/institution accreditation standards, and third-party payment all requiring some sort of an individual treatment plan (ITP) or individual education plan (IEP), therapeutic recreators must show more validity and reliability in the application of activities for specific behavior change.

While there are a number of methods or approaches to analyzing activities, the following definition by Peterson appears to explain its aim:

> Activity analysis is a process which involves the systematic application of selected sets of constructs and variables to break down and examine a given activity to determine the behavioral requirements inherent for successful participation.[14]

What Peterson is saying is that activity analysis is the breaking down of an activity into small behaviors. These behaviors can then be taught individually and later chained together as the individual becomes more proficient in the activity. This allows for part learning instead of whole learning; learning in small chunks reduces strain on the learner and facilitates acquisition of new materials. It also provides for the selection of the appropriate entry skill for training since it minimizes the likelihood of offering activities or teaching skills which are too simplistic or too advanced. Activity analysis is also a more systematic means of evaluating the effectiveness of a program as it allows for an objective measure of how many steps were taught and learned once instruction began. In general, the application of activity analysis leads to the following:

1. A better comprehension of the expected outcomes of participations.
2. A greater understanding of the complexity of activity components, which can then be compared to the functional level of an individual or group to determine the appropriateness of the activity.
3. Information about whether the activity will contribute to the desired behavioral outcome when specific behavioral goals or objectives are being used.
4. Direction for the modification or adaptation of the activity for individuals with limitations.
5. Useful information for selecting an interventional, instructional, or leadership technique.
6. A rationale or explanation for the therapeutic benefits of activity involvement.[15]

As indicated, there are a number of approaches to the concept of activity analysis. One approach considers the three behavioral domains—cognitive, affective, and sensory-motor as well as the social interaction skills needed to participate.[16,17] Another considers the elements of an activity. For example:

- Purpose of the activity; its intent, aim or goal. Example: To capture the opponent's flag in the game of Strategy.
- Procedure for action; series of specific operations or required courses of action. Example: Players draw letters which must be combined to form words appropriate for the spaces on the board in Scrabble.
- Rules governing action; fixed principles which determine conduct and standards of behavior in the activity. Example: Go back to where you were, you did not say, "May I?" in Giant Step.
- Number of participants; fixed or stated minimum or maximum number needed for action. Example: Nine individuals needed for each team in baseball.
- Role of participants; specific functions or status. Example: Goalie, forward, others in soccer.
- Results of play-off; value assigned to outcome of action. Example: a medal for winning a relay race.
- Physical setting and environmental requirements and required equipment are two additional elements but are not necessarily associated with all activities.[18]

Another activity analysis model is that developed by the Patient Activities Center for Education (PACE) in Harrisburg, Pennsylvania.[19] In this model the characteristics of the activity are classified on a four-level continuum from basic to complex. The activity characteristics include: group interaction, learning required, components of activity, decisions required, environmental stimuli, control or limits, direction involved, and motor requirements (upper extremities and total body). Still others use various psycho-social and perceptual motor dimensions to arrive at suitable models.

At present, considerable information is known about the sensory-motor or physical dimensions of an activity. On the other hand, additional information is needed about the cognitive and emotional behavioral areas. As an example, individuals bring past experiences and various emotional responses to an activity. One individual may respond with considerable excitement while another reacts with frustration to the same activity. As Berryman comments: "It is apparent. . . that basic information on possible models and methods of activity analysis exists; however, there is a definite need to coalesce and refine this information in order to develop a practical model for comprehensive activity analysis which can be used by recreation practitioners."[20] Just because there is work yet to be done, it does not mean that therapeutic recreators should take a 'wait and see' attitude. Rather, it is hoped that students and practitioners will explore and use some of the concepts of activity analysis in both the classroom and in practice.

Further consideration of analyzing activities and other factors necessary for program development and meeting special population members' goals and objectives will be discussed in Chapter 8.

aims and objectives of activities

Every therapeutic recreation experience, as stated before, should in some way contribute to the growth and development and meet the needs of the individual. If the therapeutic recreation opportunity and service pattern in the community and institutional setting is to be justifiable, it must provide for the growth and development needs and interests of special populations at all levels of life. Emphasis and areas of concentration in therapeutic activities vary according to the settings and in the light of pressing needs of special population individuals and groups as they are affected by their specific limitations, social progress, and social conditions. Avedon, for example, suggests that activities are used in relation to five objectives, namely: diagnosis and evaluation; treatment and care plans; altered life situation; predischarge counseling; and sheltered experience.[21]

Present-day therapeutic recreation specialists emphasize the concept that the "whole person" is involved. It is not an original concept. Yet it is perhaps the most succinct and arresting of those many expressions that have gained currency within recent years, emphasizing the essential "individualness" characteristic of each human being. Further, since the individual does come or is referred to the specialist as a "whole," it is difficult to chop him up and work on him in parts and reassemble him at the end of the day or at the time of release or discharge and send him home as a "whole" person again. According to the psychologist Wiener, the whole is greater than the sum of its parts, and if we follow this thinking, we understand that we must deal with this whole person.[22] Consequently, the aim of any activity is to promote the physical, emotional, social, and intellectual growth and development of special population individuals. However, the specialist must also realize that while he works with the whole person and will promote the above aims, each individual is different with his own unique problems. Thus, at times, it will be necessary for him to consider the parts so as to eventually promote the "whole."

activity values

The focus in any activity will be determined by the objectives that have been formulated to meet the therapeutic needs of special population members. In some situations the focus of the activity will be on meeting and promoting all of the objectives that have been formulated. In others, however, the focus may be directed toward only one of the objectives. Regardless of whether the focus is directed toward general or specific objectives, it appears, as indicated earlier, that objectives promote or have implication for the physical, emotional, social, and intellectual growth and development of special population individuals.

Since the value of activities has been noted in the literature,[23] we will just highlight here some general values.[24] The order in which the values are presented is not intended as an evaluation of the importance of these qualities, nor is it implied that every activity must incorporate all of these values to be therapeutic.

To Assist in Diagnosis and Evaluation

The specialist is in an advantageous position for discovering significant diagnostic material and making it available for the treatment team. Activities provide numerous opportunities to view the individual in a "normal" situation. The spontaneities of the individual in activity enable the observer to formulate a diagnostic portrait of behavior.

Activity may reveal conflict that gives clues to the underlying causes of difficulty. The hostile child often finds outlets for his destructive and sadistic tendencies and thus reveals factors underlying his difficulties in the course of working with finger paints or papier-mâché, or in the process of knocking down blocks and rebuilding. Thus, the attitude of the patient and his expressed mental and physical interests and capabilities, as demonstrated through participation in activities, may be noted and later utilized in planning for the patient's total rehabilitation.

To Assist the Individual to Adjust to Hospital or Institution Routine

Whether the individual is to be under medical care or incarcerated for a short or a long time, activities can help in adjustment. Children, for example, coming from a sheltered home into a hospital are likely to suffer from homesickness. Others who have never been in a hospital or who have distorted impressions of hospitals may be quite apprehensive. (Since the patient is often subjected to a series of laboratory and other tests, to X-rays, and to special examinations that usually require several days, weeks may elapse before actual treatment begins.) Activities planned to direct attention from the illness and to stimulate interest can do much to help the individual adjust to life in a new environment. Furthermore, as Haun has commented: "Having an established place in the community, [recreation's] extension into the hospital environment acts as a potential normalizer that effectively dispels some of the inevitable threat of cultural isolation and social rejection."[25]

To Increase Growth and Development

A physically efficient person enjoys sound functioning of bodily processes and is free of physical and emotional defects in general. It may be
generally stated that an activity directed toward this specific objective can
elevate and maintain the total bodily fitness for vigorous living. It is not the
intent of this objective to make every child and adult an athlete. Rather,
the objective must be stated in terms of helping each person to develop to
his fullest individual potential.

Physical objectives are closely related to the emotional, mental, and
social aspects of personality. The relationship of the body and the soul are
almost as old as human thought. As Aristotle commented:

> Probably all the affections of the soul are associated with the body: anger,
> fear, pity, courage and joy and gentleness, as well as loving and hating: for
> when they appear, the body is affected. . . . There are times when men show all
> symptoms of fear without any of the soul being present. If this is the case then
> clearly the affections of the soul are ideas expressed in matter.[26]

To Increase Socialization Through Interpersonal Relationships

One of the first signs of an emotional disturbance is withdrawal from
the physical and social environment. The social offender has trouble interacting positively with the social world. The mentally retarded youth has
problems in society because he lacks specific social skills. Many physically
disabled and aged persons experience loneliness. It is believed that many
problems associated with individuals in any type of institution would be
solved if greater emphasis were placed on preparation for discharge,
release, or parole and on more extensive guidance thereafter, with particular emphasis on social rehabilitation. Every minute of the individual's
institutionalization should be used as preparation for his return to the community. The extent to which the individual is resocialized determines
whether or not the individual may be completely rehabilitated.

A large segment of therapeutic recreation activity programming is
based on social interaction. It is usually the foundation of all group activities. Its therapeutic value is in improving social relationships between
one another and in improving one's attitude by instilling self-respect, self-
reliance, self-control, and self-responsibility.

To Provide Opportunities for Creativeness, To Develop New Skills and In-
terests, and To Utilize Existing Skills

All individuals have the need to create and feel significant. As
creative beings humans must find creative outlets, else they are doomed to
the life of a robot. What cannot be secured in one area of life activity must

be sought elsewhere. Approbation may be important, but it is secondary. The individual works for the pleasure his own creation affords. Because the special population individual in many instances has never previously achieved, or believed that he could achieve, that which in his eyes is good, he gains self-respect. If others praise the work, he gains self-confidence.

Many special population individuals do not have skills to develop interests, or never have had the opportunity to develop skills or interests. Thus, the specialist has the responsibility to assist such individuals to develop skills and interests to meet their needs. The value of developing skills and interests is enhanced when the activity can be useful after the period of hospitalization or incarceration by meeting leisure needs in society. On the other hand, it may be necessary for the individual only to retain or expand the interest and to preserve his ambitions and regain self-confidence while he is building up normal habits again.

To Improve Attitude Toward Self and Toward the Future

All of us want to succeed. Self-attitudes of inferiority and insecurity that plague many special population individuals may undergo changes if the individual is given the opportunity to experience success. By observing achievement and progress, the individual may be helped toward a better self-image through knowledge of his real capabilities. Likewise, the experience of successful participation with others in an activity in a non-threatening situation may help build the self-reliance and self-esteem necessary for the future.

To Bring One into Contact with Reality

While this specific value is associated more with those considered mentally ill, there are others who because of age or physical disease live in a world of fantasy and defeat. The activities utilized in such a program must be carefully chosen; they must be simple, yet not on so low a level that they would emphasize the feeling of inferiority usually present in these individuals. Effort is directed toward encouraging the individual to cope with the social order through appeals to his various senses that reality, however difficult, is better than unreality. Any remnant of interest or spontaneous expression of normal behavior is used as a basis on which socially accepted forms of behavior may be reconstructed. The first reactions may be passive, but much can be accomplished if the activities have a strong inherent interest arising from childhood experiences, which one recalls through association of constructive thoughts and ideals.

It is evident that many regressed individuals require a simplified medium for communication. They cannot ordinarily be motivated through words for they have withdrawn to a level lower than the verbal. Sight, sound, touch, and movement become the major areas of contact in which the specialist can organize activity approaches. This therapeutic medium becomes uniquely effective in working with the more difficult individual as activity becomes a language of the individual.

To Provide Approved Outlets for Hostility, Aggression, and Other Emotions

Every society with its particular cultural patterns produces tension in varying degrees in all individuals. The ability of the individual to allay this tension and to find socially acceptable ways of discharging it is one of the basic characteristics of a healthy personality. Play and recreation represent a major source for resolving, or at least releasing, the inevitable tensions of living that develop throughout the lifetime of the individual.

Another concept in the process of adaptation is the fulfillment of infantile yearnings that follow the individual into adulthood. In many activities the individual, keeping within the controls established by the rules of the game, can live vicariously by identifying with the exploits of some other heroic individual. In other activities, the individual can find fun, excitement, pleasurable sensations, and the feeling of fulfillment that all serve to relieve tension and anxiety.

To Promote Healthy Personal Habits

An activity program may have for its primary purpose the re-establishment of personal habits that have been lost through disuse or disease. To a varying degree, an outstanding characteristic of mentally ill and retarded patients, aged, and others is a disregard for personal self. This constitutes a major problem in hospitals, institutions, and nursing homes as well as in one's personal home. Restoration or development of good habits through a program of constructive, normal activities results in the improved social status of the individual by restoring or developing self-respect and interest in the world. The re-establishment of personal hygiene habits and of interest in personal appearance is sought through participation in carefully chosen and presented activities.

To Prepare the Individual for Activities of Daily Living

This value has great significance if recreation is to be part of everyone's daily living experience. If recreation is a fundamental part of realization of the abundant life, it necessarily follows that the specialist must strive to educate individuals in the worthy use of leisure. Education for leisure begins with the first purposeful contact with the individual. The readiness on the part of the individual to respond is dependent on the condition of the individual. If the individual is in a treatment setting where he is limited in his activity because of a physical or an emotional problem, then the specialist must wait until conditions are more favorable. If, on the other hand, the individual is already in the community or in a training school, education for leisure could possibly begin immediately.

Other values might include the following: to assist the individual to adjust to his physical disability or restricted activity; to supplement education; to supplement various treatment procedures; and to aid in vocational rehabilitation.

leadership

There are any number of leadership roles in the profession of therapeutic recreation—administrator, supervisor, educator, and the like. However, for our purposes here, I will direct my discussion to the type of leader or specialist who works directly with special population members as they participate in recreative experiences—the rationale being that most potential specialists will more than likely be involved initially, regardless of setting, in offering and directing activities more than in any of the other forms of service. Further, extensive consideration of the role played by the specialist as he attempts to bring about a change in behavior through recreative experiences will be covered in Chapter 8. We are only concerned here with highlighting those functions which make for an effective leader.

leadership functions

Leadership is the activity of influencing the activities of people in their effort toward goal achievement. In other words, the specialist exercises his function primarily in relation to people. The specialist's efforts become meaningful to the extent that he participates with people in determining and meeting their present needs and in attempting to forecast future needs in a program of long-range planning.

The effective leader tends to follow certain practices that appear to bring out satisfactory results. First, he understands people, including their individual characteristics and what qualities will elicit their best efforts. The specialist realizes that special population members have different basic needs, and he tries through his leadership to help them satisfy their needs. The effective leader accepts his members as they are and influences them by skillful application of their individual interests and skills so that their respect and best achievement are obtained. He has an ability to awaken emotional, as well as rational, powers of the member. The objective is explained clearly and in terms that show it is to the special population member's best interest for this goal to be achieved.

The effective leader is also aware of social and behavioral interactional skills necessary for success to take place in an activity. In this regard, Avedon has indentified eight interactive processes which he says limit, influence, or regulate the behavior of persons involved in the process. He continues by stating that it appears individuals master a particular pattern, incorporate the pattern in their behavioral lifestyle, and move on to attempt mastering another pattern. These interactive processes are as follows:

> *Intraindividual.* Action taking place within the mind of a person or action involving the mind and a part of the body, but requiring no contact with another person or external object.
>
> *Extraindividual.* Action directed by a person toward an object in the environment, requiring no contact with another person.
>
> *Aggregate.* Action directed by a person toward an object in the environment while in the company of other persons who are also directing action toward objects in the environment. Action is not directed toward one another, and no interaction between participants is required or necessary.
>
> *Interindividual.* Action of a competitive nature directed by one person toward another. This is the first of the true dyadic relationships.
>
> *Unilateral.* Action of a competitive nature among three or more persons, one of whom is an antagonist or *it*. Interaction is in simultaneous competitive dyadic relationships.
>
> *Multilateral.* Action of a competitive nature among three or more persons, with no one person as an antagonist.
>
> *Intragroup.* Action of a cooperative nature by two or more persons intent upon reaching a mutual goal. Action requires positive verbal and nonverbal interaction.
>
> *Intergroup.* Action of a competitive nature between two or more intragroups. This process is inherent in team games such as basketball or bridge.[27]

Helping members to achieve their respective maximum potentialities so as to enrich their living experiences is the key in effective leadership. The specialist is a developer of his members. The consequence and satisfaction to the members are of prime importance. The specialist serves at the same time he leads.

How effective the specialist is in an activity leadership role of assisting the special population member toward goal achievement is dependent upon a number of factors—namely, the specialist's skills, the goals and objectives of the activity, and the specialist's knowledge about the special population member's impairment or problem, physical characteristics, socioeconomic status, skills, abilities, and needs. Further, the type of leadership role assumed by the leader may shift with a particular individual or group on a daily, weekly, or monthly basis. This is the result of each individual's being unique and having his own personality.

Other factors the leader must be concerned with in assisting special population members to achieve their needs will include some of the following, if not all of them, although this list is not all-inclusive:

- Planning ways and means to assist special population members to achieve their goals.
- Teaching basic skills so as to achieve a variety of skills.
- Encouraging the qualities of teamwork, cooperation, tolerance, self-discipline, and respect for the rights of others.
- Providing information that the member or group needs for intelligent action.
- Assisting the member to accept common or community goals so that the member can realize and understand the job of life and the art of living.
- Securing supplies and equipment and, if need be, facilities.
- Assisting the special population member, above all else, to find success.

It would appear that the specialist is active in making things happen; he has a capacity for accomplishment. The specialist is creative; goals are visualized long before others clearly see where they are going. There is an old saying that some people make things happen, others watch what happens, and still others have no idea of what is happening. The leader—specialist belongs in the first group—he makes things happen.

leadership styles or roles

Some of the problems felt by leaders today are due to the fact that our concepts of leadership have changed significantly. At the beginning of the twentieth century there was widespread acceptance of the notion that leaders are born, not made. Later, leadership focused largely on the personality of the leader. Still later, styles of leadership became the center of attention. In the late 1960s researchers focused on the functions of leadership. Today, there appears to be general agreement that there is not one "best" leadership style, type, or role.[28] Today, the leader must be aware of those factors or elements that indicate a specific style or role should be used.

According to Danford and Shirley, those factors which the leader must be aware of are the group as a whole; the individual group members; the situation; the problems, goals, and needs of the group individually and collectively; and the interaction among the group members themselves and the members with the leader. This is no simple task when one is in a face-to-face leadership role with patients. It takes time and effort to sort out all of the factors, but contemporary researchers tell us that any other approach will meet with failure.[29]

Generally speaking, therapeutic recreation research or theories relating to nearly all of the above factors appear to be lacking. Leadership roles as a function of the situation, however, have been identified by Avedon. According to the situation, a specialist selects a role "...based upon the patient or client's *relative level of maturity* — that is, *how much internal control over his own behavior a patient or client manifests,* and *how much external control is needed in order to function effectively in social situations.*"[30] The eight leadership roles which Avedon has identified for any particular situation include:

> *Controller.* Makes all decisions regarding action.
> *Director.* Actively leads, but does not make all the decisions. He allows the participant some personal latitude.
> *Instigator.* Starts action, gets participants involved, and then moves out of a direct leadership role. He sets minimal limits and expects some degree of participant control.
> *Stimulator.* Generates positive interest in activity and stands by to encourage and assist participation when necessary.
> *Educator.* Teaches skills which the participant wishes to learn so that he may become more active and more socially involved.
> *Advisor.* Makes suggestions to participants concerning involvement and behavior. He also makes recommendations regarding decisions or courses of action. He may counsel or give guidance and information.
> *Observer.* Watches the participant as he engages in activity. He takes notice of behavior, and recognizes the underlying meaning of various actions.
> *Enabler.* Assists the participant when asked. He provides the kind of assistance the participant wishes when the participant wishes it.[31]

In addition to the leadership roles identified above, Tannenbaum and Schmidt have described five patterns of leadership behavior which progress from a leader-centered approach to a group-centered one. The reader might find these helpful in working with special population members.[32]

Since therapeutic recreation specialists are primarily in face-to-face leadership roles, it is important to examine what are considered the more traditional styles of leadership — authoritarian, democratic, paternalistic, and laissez-faire — which focus on the effects of leadership behavior on those being led. These styles are not mutually exclusive. They may be used effectively depending on the situation. They represent styles of leadership in which certain characteristics are emphasized.

Authoritarian leadership is based on the premise that leadership is a right and is vested in the degree to which an individual has authority. The authoritarian specialist believes that because of his position, he can decide best for the member. Special population members are assigned to specific activities with little consideration to their needs. It is basically a one-way edict, a this-is-the-way-it-is-going-to-be type of function. Fundamentally, rigid control by the specialist is featured.

Authoritarian leadership is useful in certain situations. However, even when conditions warrant such leadership, it has serious shortcomings for it does not develop a pride of accomplishment, personal development, or satisfaction in the member. Leadership exercised in an authoritarian manner is likely to antagonize the member, and the needed cooperation is probably not achieved.

Democratic leadership is characterized by participation of the special population member and utilization of his opinion. Initiative by the member is encouraged. The specialist suggests possible actions but awaits consideration or approval of the member before putting them into effect. Democratic leadership emphasizes the member's interests and strives to satisfy them.

Paternalistic leadership is characterized by a paternal or fatherly influence in the relationship between the specialist and the member, and is manifest in a watchful care for the comfort and welfare of the individual member. It aims to protect and guide. On the other hand, however, the approach may be too sentimental. While the intentions are good in this form of leadership, self-reliance and independence of the special population member in some instances have yet to develop. Thus, the member fails to achieve the first step toward independence. For the most part, when paternalistic leadership is practiced, success is common—but future success usually depends upon continuation of the paternalistic specialist's services.

Laissez-faire leadership, as the name implies, offers no direct leadership. Little direction, if any, is provided or offered to the member. Each special population member is permitted considerable freedom. Laissez-faire leadership usually does not yield positive results because the intimate influence of the specialist upon the member as well as the dynamic interaction between the specialist and the member are lacking.

As already stated, the foregoing types of leadership are not mutually exclusive. A specialist may employ, for example, democratic leadership in a particular activity or situation and authoritarian leadership in another activity. The particular conditions determine the type of leadership to be used. To illustrate, for a member who is withdrawn, feels insecure, and has participated little in any type of recreative experiences, a paternalistic type of leadership probably will bring the best results initially. This should be followed by a democratic form as the member becomes more stable and socially aware. Evaluation among the different types is confusing and leads to difficulty because it is not a question of the best type but of the proper type to employ for a given situation. Techniques are shifted to fit changing conditions.

Before bringing this chapter to a close, it is worthwhile to comment about the price that leadership demands at this level within most settings that offer a service of therapeutic recreation. There are sacrifices to be made and skills to be developed if the specialist is to become a truly effective leader. Contrary to the popular notion, a specialist must accept certain obligations that are a part and parcel of his job. Frequently the best interests of the agency or institution come before his own personal interests. Seldom can the specialist make the position exactly as he personally wishes. For example, in many institutions the specialist may work one or two evenings a week plus a weekend day or evening. Health and social rehabilitation agencies are usually open 24 hours a day, 7 days a week.

Of particular significance is what the specialist truly believes. A specialist must have convictions and confidence about fundamental truths and natural laws. The specialist needs a basic philosophy of life and a positive interest in special population members as benchmarks in his leadership efforts. In other words, the specialist must have a purpose in life and give full cognizance to what he is trying to achieve. The formation of such a plan crystallizes the specialist's thinking on what the setting is trying to accomplish and his decision on the objectives for this important segment of the population.

In summary, the range of activities is necessarily broad in order to meet the various growth and development patterns and basic needs of special population members. Further, activities can be of greatest service only when there is effective leadership and the special population member is considered as a whole individual.

activity value references*

Anderson, R. D. "Application of Educational Rhythmics to Therapeutic Recreation Service," *Therapeutic Recreation Journal,* 5:2 (1971), pp. 75–78, 94.

Archambeau, M. Kathleen, and David J. Szymanski. "Dance Therapy and the Autistic Child," in *Expanding Horizons in Therapeutic Recreation V,"* ed. Gerald Hitzhusen. Columbia, Mo.: Department of Recreation and Park Administration, University of Missouri, 1977, pp. 141–147.

Asher, J. "The Learning Strategy of the Total Physical Response: A Review," *Modern Language Journal,* 50:2 (1966), pp. 79–84.

Autex, D., E. Zahar, and L. Ferrini. "Body Image Development of Emotionally Disturbed Children," *American Corrective Therapy Journal,* 21:5 (1967), pp. 154–155.

---

* Reference listing developed primarily by Thomas R. Collingwood, "Therapeutic Recreation's Relevance to the Rehabilitation Process," *Therapeutic Recreation Annual,* 8 (1971), pp. 32–33.

Bigelow, G. W. "A Comparison of Active and Passive Recreational Activities for Psychotic Patients," *Therapeutic Recreation Journal,* 5:4 (1971), pp. 145–151.

Boyd, N. L. "Play As a Means of Social Adjustment," *Therapeutic Recreation* 1:2:4 (1967), pp. 18–24.

Buchan, S. C. "Camping for the Handicapped in Selected Camps in California," *Therapeutic Recreation Journal,* 9:1 (1975), pp. 38–41.

Burmeister, Julie G., "Leisure Services and the Cultural Arts as Therapy for Mentally Retarded Persons," *Therapeutic Recreation Journal,* 10:4 (1976), pp. 139–142.

Campbell, D., and J. Davis. "Report of Research and Experimentation in Exercise and Recreational Therapy," *American Journal of Psychiatry,* 96 (1940), pp. 915–933.

Carr, A., C. Swinyard, and T. Mihalov. "A Therapeutic Recreational Program for Children with Spina Bifida and Myelomeningocela," *Recreation for the Ill and Handicaped,* 8:2 (1964), pp. 8–9, 15–16.

Cobb, Michael D. "Skiing Is For Everyone!," *Therapeutic Recreation Journal,* 9:1 (1975), pp. 18–20.

Cohen, P. H. "A Compilation of Recreation Activities Which May Aid in the Reduction of Hostility in Psychiatric Patients," *Therapeutic Recreation Journal,* 8:1 (1974), pp. 47–49.

Collingwood, T. R. and M. Engelsgjerd. "Physical Fitness, Physical Activity, and Juvenile Delinquency," *Journal of Physical Education and Recreation,* 48 (1977).

Collingwood, T. R. "The Effects of Physical Training upon Self-Concept and Body Attitude," *Journal of Clinical Psychology,* 27:3 (1971), pp. 411–412.

Corder, O. "Effects of Physical Education on the Intellectual, Physical and Social Development of EMR Boys," *Exceptional Children,* 33 (1969), pp. 357–363.

Costonis, Maureen. "Dance Therapy for Mentally Retarded Children," in *Expanding Horizons in Therapeutic Recreation II,"* ed. Jerry D. Kelley. Champaign, Ill.: Office of Recreation and Park Resources, University of Illinois, 1973, pp. 79–90.

DeMunck, Charles R. "Wilderness Experiential Learning Programs an Alternative to Incarceration, "in *Expanding Horizons in Therapeutic Recreation IV,"* eds. Gerald Hitzhusen, Gerald O'Morrow, and John Oliver. Columbia, Mo: Department of Recreation and Park Administration, University of Missouri, 1976, pp. 69–72.

Endres, R. "Northern Minnesota Therapeutic Camp," *Journal of Health, Physical Education and Recreation.* 42 (1971).

Fischer, J. "Helping to Solve Social and Psychological Adjustment Problems of the Handicapped," *Journal of Health, Physical Education, and Recreation,* 35 (1960), p. 75.

Flavell, J. *The Developmental Psychology of Jean Piaget.* Princeton, N.J.: Van Nostrand, 1967.

Freeberg, W. "Recreational Camping for the Retarded," *Recreation in Treatment Centers,* 5 (1966), pp. 8–11.

Gonzales, M. "Organized Camping: A Therapeutic Tool for the Juvenile Delinquent," *Therapeutic Recreation Journal,* 6:2 (1972), pp.86–92.

Hammontree, Jan. "A Case for Day Camps for the Emotionally Disturbed Child," in *Expanding Horizons in Therapeutic Recreation I,* ed. Jerry D. Kelley. Champaign, Ill.: Office of Recreation and Park Resources, University of Illinois, 1971, pp. 59–63.

Heaps, R. A. and C. T. Thorstenson. "Self-Concept Changes Immediately and One Year After Survival Training," *Therapeutic Recreation Journal,* 8:2 (1974), pp. 60–63.

Hefley, Paula D., and Arnold Sperling, "Therapeutic Recreation Through Horticulture," *Therapeutic Recreation Journal,* 7:3 (1973), pp. 31–34.

Hein, F., and A. Ryan. "The Contributions of Physical Activity to Physical Health," *The Research Quarterly,* 312:2 (1960), pp. 263–285.

Helsendager, D., D. H. Jack, and L. Mann. "The Buttonwood Farms Project," *Journal of Health, Physical Education, and Recreation* (March 1968), pp. 46–56.

Holzworth, W., J. Grot, and N. Hippensteel. "Effects of Day Camp on Adult Psychiatric Inpatients," *Therapeutic Recreation Journal,* 7:1 (1973), pp. 37–40.

Hourcade, Jack, "Effects of a Summer Camp Program on Self-Concept of Mentally Retarded Young Adults," *Therapeutic Recreation Journal,* 11:4 (1977), pp. 178–183.

Howard, Gordon K. "Recreation for Deaf-Blind," in *Expanding Horizons in Therapeutic Recreation III,"* eds. Gary Robb and Gerald Hitzhusen. Columbia, Mo: Department of Recreation and Park Administration, University of Missouri, 1975, pp. 53–60.

Jacobs, E. "Social Dance: An Aid to Rehabilitation," *Recreation* (December 1965), pp. 494–496.

Jarman, Phillip H., and Dennis H. Reid, "The Importance of Recreational Activities on Attendance to a Leisure Program for Multihandicapped Retarded Persons," *Therapeutic Recreation Journal,* 11:1 (1977), pp. 28–32.

Joseph, L. "Skiing. . .Is Believing," *Woman Sports* (January 1976), pp. 28–29.

Kramer, E. *Art as Therapy With Children.* New York: Schocken, 1971.

Larche, Harry, and others. "Music the Connecting Link for the Mentally Retarded and Developmentally Disabled," in *Expanding Horizons in Therapeutic Recreation III,"* eds. Gary Robb and Gerald Hitzhusen. Columbia, Mo: Department of Recreation and Park Administration, University of Missouri, 1975, pp. 67–72.

Lederer, William. "Senior Adults Get Physically Fit," *Parks and Recreation* (October, 1978), pp. 40–42.

Lemieux, Charles, "Therapeutic Recreation in Alcoholics," *Therapeutic Recreation Journal,* 5:1 (1971), pp. 19–21.

Lipton, B. H. "Wheelchair Sports: Its Role in the Rehabilitation of the Physically Disabled," *Therapeutic Recreation Journal,* 4:4 (1970).

Lovelace, Betty M. "The Use of Puppetry with the Hospitalized Child in Pediatric Recreation," *Therapeutic Recreation Journal,* 6:1 (1972), pp. 20–21.

Marshall, P. "A Coordinated Summer Program of Therapeutic Recreation and Academic Instruction for Emotionally Disturbed Children," *Therapeutic Recreation Journal,* 3:4 (1969), 1, pp. 46–47.

Maynard, Marianne, "The Value of Creative Arts for the Developmentally Disabled Child: Implications for Recreation Specialists in Community Day Service Programs," *Therapeutic Recreation Journal,* 10:1 (1976), pp. 10–13.

McCloy, C. "Physical Reconditioning of the Ill," in *Science and Medicine of Exercise and Sports,* ed. W. Johnson. New York: Harper and Row Publishers, 1960.

McCormick, J."The Role of Perceptual—Motor Training in Therapeutic Recreation Programs for the Mentally Retarded," *Therapeutic Recreation Journal,* 5:2 (1971), pp. 63–66.

McGinnis, Rozanne W. "Dance as a Therapeutic Process," *Therapeutic Recreation Journal,* 8:4 (1974), pp. 181–186.

Meyers, R., and C. Williams. *Operation Recreation.* Sacramento, Ca.: California Youth Authority, 1970.

Morgan, W. "Psychological Considerations in Exercise Somato-therapy." Paper presented at the Twelfth Annual Tri-Organizational Scientific and Clinical Rehabilitation Conference, Little Rock, Ark. 1968.

Narwold, S. J. "Coping with Hospitalization through Play," in *Leisure Today: Selected Reading,* ed. Larry Neal, Washington, D.C.: American Association for Leisure and Recreation, 1975.

Navar, N. and J. A. Nordoff. "Recreation as a Change Agent for the Alcoholic," *Journal of Physical Education and Recreation,* 46 (1975), pp. 36–37.

Nees, R. A. "Weight Training for Severely Mentally Retarded Persons," *Journal of Health, Physical Education and Recreation* 45 (1974), pp. 87–88.

Plant, J. "Recreation and the Social Integration of the Individual," *Recreation,* 3 (1937), p. 7.

Rathbone, J. *Teaching Yourself to Relax.* Englewood Cliffs, N.J.: Prentice-Hall, Inc., 1957.

Retondo, T. "The Male Heroin Addict's Participation in Recreation Activities," *Therapeutic Recreation Journal,* 6:4 (1972), pp. 162–163, 177.

Robb, G. "A Correlation Between Socialization and Self-Concept in a Summer Camp Program," *Therapeutic Recreation Journal,* 5:1 (1971), pp. 25–29.

Rosen, E. "The Selection of Activities for Therapeutic Use," *Recreation in Treatment Centers,* 1 (1962), pp. 29–32.

Sheridan, Paul M., "Therapeutic Recreation and the Alcoholic," *Therapeutic Recreation Journal,* 10:1 (1976), pp. 14–17.

Shoemaker, F., and H. Kaplan. "Observation on Physical Fitness and Development Skills of Emotionally Disturbed Boys," *Therapeutic Recreation Journal,* 6:1 (1972), pp. 28–30, 35.

Stein, J. "Motor Function and Physical Fitness of the Mentally Retarded," *Rehabilitation Literature,* 24:8 (1963), pp. 230–242.

———. "The Importance of Physical Activity for the Mentally Retarded," pp. 25–26. Paper presented at the National Conference of the American Association for Health, Physical Education, and Recreation, Washington, D.C., 1968.

Therapeutic Recreation Journal (special research issue), 5:4 (1971), pp. 145–173.

Thompson, M. "Anchor: A Community Recreation for Handicapped Children," *Therapeutic Recreation Journal,* 6:4 (1972), pp. 167–171.

Thorstenson, C. T., and R. A. Heaps. "Outdoor Survival and Its Implications for Rehabilitation," *Therapeutic Recreation Journal,* 7:1 (1973), pp. 31–33.

Weishahn, M., and L. F. Neal. "Therapeutic Recreation Programming for the Visually Disabled," *Therapeutic Recreation Journal,* 5:2 (1971) pp. 69–71, 94.

Zumberg, Cathy and Marshall Zumberg. "A Body Movement Program for the Emotionally Impaired," in *Expanding Horizons in Therapeutic Recreation V."* ed. Gerald Hitzhusen. Columbia, Mo: Department of Recreation and Park Administration, University of Missouri, 1977, pp. 123–134.

SUGGESTED REFERENCES

Adams, Ronald C., Alfred N. Daniel, and Lee Rullman. *Games, Sports and Exercise for the Physically Handicapped* (2nd ed.). Philadelphia: Lee and Febiger, 1974.

Anderson, Marian H., Margaret E. Elliot, and Jeanne La Berge. *Play With A Purpose.* New York: Harper and Row Publishers, 1972.

Avedon, Elliott M. "The Structural Elements of Games," in *The Study of Games,* eds. E. M. Avedon and Brian Sutton-Smith. New York: John Wiley and Sons, Inc., 1971, pp. 419–426.

Bull, Edith L. and Robert E. Cipriano. *Leisure Preparation.* Englewood Cliffs, N.J.: Prentice-Hall, Inc., 1978, pp. 29–96, 116–141, 169–207.

Beal, George M., Joe M. Bohlen, and J. Neil Raudabaugh. *Leadership and Dynamic Group Action.* Ames, Iowa: The Iowa University Press, 1962.

Berne, Eric. *The Structure and Dynamics of Organizations and Groups.* New York: Grove Press, Inc., 1963.

Buist, Charlotte A. and Jerome L. Schulman. *Toys and Games for Educationally Handicapped Children.* Springfield, Ill.: Charles C Thomas Publisher, 1969.

Caillois, Roger. "The Structure and Classification of Games," *Diogenses,* 110 (1955), pp. 62–75.

Chapman, Frederick M. *Recreation Activities for the Handicapped.* New York: The Ronald Press Company, 1960.

Check, Neil H., and William R. Burch, Jr. The *Social Organization of Leisure in Human Society.* New York: Harper and Row Publishers, 1976.

Cratty, Bryant J. *Social Dimensions of Physical Activity.* Englewood Cliffs, N.J.: Prentice-Hall, Inc., 1967.

Erikson, Erik H. *Childhood and Society* (2nd ed.). New York: W. W. Norton and Company, 1963.

Hunt, Valerie V. *Recreation for the Handicapped.* Englewood Cliffs, N.J.: Prentice-Hall, Inc., 1955.

Kenyon, Gerald S. "A Conceptual Model for Characterizing Physical Activity" (unpublished research paper, University of Wisconsin, 1966) as cited in Gunn and Peterson, *Therapeutic Recreation Service,* p. 193.

Kraus, Richard G., and Barbara Bates. *Recreation Leadership and Supervision: Guidelines for Professional Development.* Philadelphia: W. B. Saunders Company, 1975.

Mager, R. E. and P. Pipe. *Analyzing Performance Problems.* Belmont, Ca.: Feason Publishers, Lea Seigler, Inc., 1970.

Maslow, Abraham H. *Toward a Psychology of Being.* New York: Van Nostrand Reinhold Company, 1968.

McIntosh, Peter. *Sport and Society.* London: C. A. Watts and Company, Ltd., 1963.

Napier, R. and M. Gershenfeld. *Groups: Theory and Experience.* Boston: Houghton Mifflin Company, 1973.

Overs, Robert P. and Ann R. Trotter. *Guide to Avocational Activities* (Vols. 1, 2, 3). Milwaukee: Curative Workshop of Milwaukee, Wisconsin, 1972.

Petrie, Brian M. "Physical Activity, Games and Sports: A System of Classification and an Investigation of Social Influences Among Students of Michigan State University" (Doctoral dissertation, Michigan State University, 1970).

Shivers, Jay S. *Leadership in Recreation Service.* New York: The Macmillan Company, 1963.

Tillman, Albert. *The Program Book for Recreation Professionals.* Los Angeles: National Press Books, 1973.

Ulrich, Celeste. *The Social Matrix of Physical Education.* Englewood Cliffs, N.J.: Prentice-Hall, Inc., 1968.

Warren, Johnson, and E. R. Buskirk, eds. *Science and Medicine of Exercise and Sport.* New York: Harper and Row Publishers, 1974.

chapter 7
therapeutic recreation and human service models

In Chapter 3, we considered those agencies and institutions that offer health, social, and correctional rehabilitation service. We also noted that therapeutic recreation as a service usually does not function or operate independently—outside an agency or organization. It is found most often within a system that provides a specific kind of care or service. These *human service models,* as I prefer to think of them, differ in historical development, in orientation, in their mode of intervention, and in the professional groups that dominate the various service models. While there is specialization of function in these models, there is also overlapping. For the most part, these models provide treatment (therapy), rehabilitation, counseling, training and/or re-education, and a social service. Since there are a number of different models with many variations, we shall limit the discussion to the more prominent ones and the provisions of therapeutic recreation within them. It is anticipated that further exploration of these models including the provisions of therapeutic recreation will occur in a therapeutic recreation programming course.

While it may come as a shock to some potential therapeutic recreation specialists, it should be stated "out front" that therapeutic recreation service is not one of the primary services within some of the models which will be discussed herein. The goal of any medical care system is to organize for the provision and distribution of health services to those who need them, and to use the resources, knowledge, and technologies available to prevent and alleviate disease, disability, and suffering to the extent possible under prevailing conditions. Further, the form health institutions take to provide service is related to the form of other societal institutions and to the economics, organizational, and value context that society puts upon a particular service. In some models, therapeutic recreation service is considered an important service. In other models, the extreme is found wherein the service is only tolerated.

Even with these harsh words, it is important to point out that the largest percentage of therapeutic recreation specialists are found working in health care and treatment settings. It has been so traditionally and I suspect will continue to be so. In a recent study conducted by Fain, he found that in a small random sample of 147 registered therapeutic recreation specialists, nearly 92 percent were employed in hospital/institutions.[1] While the role of therapeutic recreation service and therapeutic recreation specialists may be somewhat unclear in light of my above comments, I support the concept of striving for a certain level of autonomy in relationship to physicians and other health workers as well as seeking recognition for our unique role in care and treatment.

medical-clinical model

This traditional model, for the most part, is found today in general medical and surgical hospitals and medically oriented physical rehabilitation institutes and centers. However, it has not been too many years ago that this model was also the only one found in psychiatric institutions and centers as well as in other kinds of health facilities. Within this model, it is important to recognize that medicine dominates the other health professionals found here. To a large extent this dominance is supported by political and legal factors.

The model is characterized by a doctor-centered, illness-oriented approach to patient care and treatment. Treatment is directed at just the disease rather than the "whole" person. Professional disciplines involved in the treatment process carry out the physician's orders within the goals and objectives as determined by the orders.

The provision of therapeutic recreation within this model is limited by the treatment prescribed by the physician. The therapeutic recreation specialist, along with other professional personnel, performs a supportive role in the treatment process, unable to make decisions in many instances without the approval of the physician. As Haun writes:

> Hospitals are complex sociological structures. Their staffs are made up of scores of people, each with specialized individual skills. Within their fields of particular competence, the efforts of all must be coordinated by the physician for one purpose and one purpose only—the welfare of the patient.[2,3]

That therapeutic recreation specialists are caught up in this traditional medical model is reflected by Humphrey in discussing the interpretation of therapeutic recreation with other professional disciplines. He comments:

> It seems to me the greatest obstacle to role analysis and definition [of therapeutic recreation] has been, and still is, [the therapeutic recreation profession's] immature professional need to copy the medical role model.[4]

However, he goes on to say shortly thereafter:

> I sincerely trust we have matured—professionally and personally—to the point where our professional and personal role needs and resources offer the participant, our disciplinary associates and the total clinical and rehabilitation process . . . the potential for therapeutic experiences which far exceed those possible within the framework of the pure medical model.[5]

In the past, few therapeutic recreators were found working in this specific model. If they were, they usually were assigned to the occupational therapy department within the physical medicine and rehabilitation service. Their responsibility for the most part consisted of providing diversional recreation service although at times they might have worked under the direction of an occupational therapist in a diagnostic-prescriptive-treatment program. The only deviance to this approach would have been if the hospital offered psychiatric services. Here the therapeutic recreator would have functioned somewhat independently and been restricted to that specific service.

In more recent years there has not only been an increase in the number of therapeutic recreators found in the model, but also in the establishment of therapeutic recreation or recreation therapy departments responsible for services throughout the hospital. Today, therapeutic recreators are found working in physical medicine and rehabilitation, in inpatient and out-patient psychiatric services, and in pediatric, orthopedic, cancer, cardiac, kidney, and burn units. Their responsibilities include providing diversional recreation services as well as treatment or remedial recreation services.

The recreation treatment program in this model may be directed toward any disease aspect—physical, emotional, social, or intellectual. It is more likely, however, to be directed toward the physical since this model is characterized by individuals having short-term physical problems, although in centers of a physical rehabilitational nature, the length of stay is usually longer.

Taking into consideration the services available within a general medical and surgical hospital, the recreation treatment program for a recent unilateral below-knee amputee might involve the development of as nearly normal a range of motion as possible in the affected extremity. The program might consist of playing shuffleboard. As the individual progresses, additional activities can be used to assist the individual to develop strength in the stump and security in movement. Thereafter, the program includes utilization of community resources to increase skill confidence and enhance acceptance of the prosthesis. Incorporated within the use of community resources might be a program of leisure education or counseling.

Diversional programs in this model are many and varied. Some may consist of audio-visual programs on a pediatrics ward, closed-circuit bingo, arts and crafts projects brought to the bedside, and even a babysitting service so parents can leave their children during an examination. Hopefully, in the latter example, the program would be staffed by volunteers. Recently a former graduate of our program called and asked assistance in developing a program for patients who must spend three to four hours on a dialysis machine. The request came from the physician in charge of the service.

custodial model

While this model functions little today in its pure definition, shades of it still exist in some settings. As the term indicates, the custodial model refers to "maintaining" or "guardianship" of special populations in specialized facilities — institutions for the mentally ill and mentally retarded, nursing homes, homes for the aged, and correctional institutions. The model is characterized by conformity, order, subordination of individual needs to the institutional routine, and even punishment for deviating from these routines. In this model there is little or no treatment; physical care and control are emphasized.[6,7]

This model, as it relates to the care and treatment of the mentally ill, is unfortunately the result of a very good model called *moral treatment,* (late nineteenth century to early twentieth century) which had as its important features: (1) staff optimism reflected in the strong belief of curability that produced a favorable reputation for hospitals in the eyes of the surrounding communities and of its patients, and (2) a belief that a favorable environment could repair the damage due to the impacts and stresses of life.[8,9] This favorable environment was created through devoted care; presumption that the dignity of the person continued despite his disorder; and preservation of human rights, including those of privacy, self-determination, and attention to personal comfort. Deliberate attention to the physical and psychological environment was shown in the lack of coercion; the encouragement of useful interpersonal relations in work, play, and social functions; and the development of an atmosphere of maximum liberty, initiative, and useful activity. Deutsch quotes a statement concerning this philosophy from the writings of a doctor in New York State in 1911. Moral treatment, he explains:

> consists in removing patients from their residence to some proper asylum; and for this purpose a calm retreat in the country is to be preferred: for it is found that continuance at home aggravates the disease, as the improper association of ideas cannot be destroyed . . . .have humane attendants, who shall act as servants to them; never threaten but execute; offer no indignities to them, as they have a high sense of honour. . . .let their fears and resentments be soothed without unnecessary opposition; adopt a system of regularity; make them rise, take exercise and food at stated times. The diet ought to be light, and easy of digestion, but never too low. When convalescing, allow limited liberty; introduce entertaining books and conversation.[10]

One important reason given for the abandonment of moral treatment as a model was the lack of a supporting theoretical context. Another was industrialization and urban growth.[11] Other observers noted that hospitals increased in size and lost their earlier intimate characteristics with the increase in public pressure for more facilities for care of chronic cases. Operating budgets that were inadequate for the greater patient loads, institutions that were isolated from urban areas and that acquired unsavory reputations, and, finally, preoccupation with cellular pathology and romantic causation all converged to replace the concept of curability with the concept of pessimism.[12,13]

In writing of the doctrine of moral treatment and the custodial model, Greenblatt and others state:

> Thus, fertile beginnings in the use of interpersonal relationships and a pleasing physical environment were replaced by custodial attendants, by prison-like wards devoid of an appearance either of comfort or culture, and often by provisions for use of physical restraints.[14]

Provision of recreation service in the custodial model (if any at all) was limited: an evening of games, an occasional dance, and motion pictures for those who were ambulatory and somewhat active. Social interaction was possible only for the more "oriented" patient. For the most part, activities were of diversional nature to keep the patient busy, quiet, and out of trouble.

Our nursing home programs, as an example, still reflect to a large degree unfortunately the provision of recreation service just mentioned. Because we have a tendency to stereotype the elderly, we plan our programs based upon these stereotypes and we respond to those who do conform. The main purposes of the program are keeping the resident occupied and having pleasant experiences. Further, only those residents who are ambulatory need to come to the activity room. This kind of situation exists in far too many nursing homes. The residents, according to Halberg, should be helped to utilize their ability, no matter how limited, for meaning and satisfaction, as well as for fun. This suggests an activity program which has as its purpose as many kinds of opportunities as possible with as few limitations as possible.[15]

In many correctional institutions that still abide by the concept of punishment rather than rehabilitation, the recreation programs consist of sports and athletic events to reduce tension and boredom. As noted in the previous chapter, it is not unusual to find that recreation activities are used as a reward for good behavior. The findings reported by Decker in a recreation study completed for the Oregon State Division of Corrections in 1969 can still be applied today to many correctional institutions in the United States. He reported:

1. The role and values of recreation are not emphasized.
2. There is no professional staff member trained in recreation.
3. The emphasis is on custodial care and security.
4. Professional guidance and assistance in recreational services are not readily available to the staff.
5. Where recreation programs do exist, they often are instituted with little planning and few long-range objectives in mind.
6. The administrative climate is not conducive to evaluation and change.
7. The professional recreator's efforts have not been directed toward explaining and increasing the role of recreation in the institutional setting.[16]

therapeutic community or therapeutic milieu model

This model is the result of the shift away from a custodial to a humanitarian orientation in psychiatric care and treatment. Institutionalization is viewed not as a means of removing the individual from society, but rather as an opportunity to give him a sheltered milieu in which specific therapeutic experiences can be provided. In some respects, it is a return to *moral treatment*. Generally speaking, the model suggests that individuals are affected and even changed by their relationship with others and their environment.[17] Treatment is focused on as many aspects of the patient as possible and on a wide range of patients' relationships, and no longer exclusively on physiological disease or psychological conflict.[18]

Variations of the model have been applied in nearly all, if not all, settings that offer some kind of health or social service to people. In the main, it dominates psychiatric hospital/institution practice in the large state psychiatric institutions, the Veterans Administration psychiatric hospitals, the small private psychiatric institutions, the in-patient and out-patient psychiatric units of general hospitals, and the community mental health clinics or centers. It must be recognized, however, according to Norris and others, that although the model remains the same, the application of the model will vary and be unique to the type of setting in which one implements it: whether it has many or few patients, whether the staff-patient ratio is high or low, by what kinds of patients are admitted, whether the institution has a long history of a custodial orientation or is a new one with a reformist base, and so on.[19]

The therapeutic milieu model can be defined as the means of organizing a community treatment environment so that every human interaction and every treatment technique can be systematically utilized to further the patient's aims of controlling symptomatic behaviors and learning approaches to psychosocial skills. Moreover, the therapeutic milieu involves the entire setting—utilizing both staff and patients in the treatment process. Everyone taking part in the activities of the therapeutic community—whether he be patient, physician, nurse, social worker, or attendant—shares in the commitment to the institution's effectiveness as a therapeutic agent. Only if all individuals, regardless of their particular roles, contribute as much as they can to the therapeutic effectiveness of the setting can each person receive maximum benefits. It is the responsibility of all individuals who make up the therapeutic community to make sure that the hospital/institution functions as closely as possible in accordance with its ideal goals and to see that the social structure is organized to facilitate optimal participation, interaction, and involvement.[20]

The therapeutic community is not without its problems. Those patients who need protection from the intensity of group interaction and involvement do not always benefit from this type of environment. The large state psychiatric hospital at times cannot allow the community to make decisions since trial and error are often involved. Poorly trained personnel who use patients to satisfy their immature unconscious attitudes frequently present problems. Administrative officials who are responsible for efficient maintenance and low budgets are usually appalled at the efforts of patients to deal with their own problems. Lastly, patients often wish to be cared for by an omnipotent parent who will indulge and/or punish them.[21]

The role of the therapeutic recreation department or service in this model is to focus on every aspect of the patient's life. The therapeutic milieu model provides a climate most favorable to the use of recreative experiences as a socializing therapy. These experiences may range from basic socializing activities to reality-oriented social functions that are a part of everyday living. As Edelson points out,". . . an individual's approach to playtime accurately reflects the organization of his drives and controls."[22] Thus, therapeutic recreative experiences can serve as a means of helping the individual regain social competence, confidence, and acceptance. An example of a change in psychosocial skills that I recall follows:

> A middle-aged farmer's wife entered with a retarded depression. After a favorable response to drug therapy, she indicated some disappointment with the lonely, grim quality of her life. She was on beck-and-call to feed the men whenever they came in from work and she never went into town except with her family. In fact, she had forgotten how to drive. The remainder of her hospitalization was used to teach her to drive, to play cards, and to bowl; to schedule these activities into her life; and to enlist the family's cooperation in her regular involvement in church social functions, card clubs, and family group activities.

Thus, the therapeutic environment consists of the patient, the therapeutic recreation specialist, the activity (or service), and the physical environment. All of these elements combined in accordance with the treatment plan constitute a milieu therapy approach for therapeutic recreation.

As noted in the medical model, the responsibility for the treatment plan rests with the physician. But in milieu-oriented settings this responsibility often rests with all personnel concerned with a given patient who meet together and arrive at a consensus about the treatment for the patient. The goal is open and easy communication. The traditional hierarchical and authoritarian professional roles and relationships are minimized. The therapeutic recreation specialist is a member of this treatment team. As such, the specialist is not only responsible in particular for bringing into focus the importance and use of recreative experiences as a therapeutic tool as well as the use of such experiences for diagnostic and evaluative purposes, but also becomes involved with other professional workers in determining the total therapeutic plan. Further, treatment team meetings allow the specialist to educate and consult with others about therapeutic recreation. Thus, the base of the specialist's therapeutic relevancy is broader.

A trend which has helped this model to develop in recent years has been the decentralizations of authority in hospitals/institutions. This decentralization has occurred most frequently in hospitals/institutions for the mentally ill and mentally retarded. The hospital/institution is divided into several autonomous sections, each responsible to a unit director who may be from any of the professional disciplines found in the institution. (Personally, I know a large number of therapeutic recreation specialists who function in this position today.) A 1000-bed institution may thus function as four 250-bed units, each with its own treatment, eating, and sleeping facilities. Each unit may also have its own recreation facilities and utilize a central facility (activity building) for large group or mass programs.

In some institutions, the patients in the units are further divided into sections under a leader who represents any professional discipline. One can well imagine the close therapeutic relationship and attention to patient needs and interests that can occur in such a structure.

In addition, the unit system encourages closer relations with the community. Each unit is usually responsible to a specific segment of a community or a state. The particular unit becomes the institution for this geographical area. Out-patient diagnostic and therapeutic services are provided for the same population by the same unit. In some instances follow-up care is carried out in the same manner.

We have noted earlier the consequences of this model in an institution. The model also has its implication for therapeutic recreation. Since all personnel concerned with the patient have input relative to his treatment plan, they may decide that the direction of recreation experiences, in some circumstances, should be delegated to another person allied with another professional discipline. While the literature and personal experience indicate that those administering the plan usually function according to their specializations, there is the possibility of role alterations.

education and training model

This model cuts across all kinds of settings, residential and nonresidential. It is found within the models just discussed. It is found in special schools and training centers for the mentally retarded, in settings that provide health services to those with specific sensory and nonsensory disabilities, and in prisons and training schools for juvenile and young adult offenders. The model is also applied in sheltered workshop-like settings and can be utilized on a temporary basis, if not on a permanent basis in some situations, with the homebound.

The model focuses on (1) formal or informal academic educational programs; (2) prevocational or vocational preparation programs or work-study programs; and (3) socialization training. The importance of these areas is justified by the belief that the special population member will view himself and will be viewed by others in a more positive way if he has developed some academic and vocational skills and is capable of socializing. If, on the other hand, the member lacks skills in these areas, he will probably be a relatively less happy and less adjusted person, have little or no social status within his family or community, be an economic burden to others, and be susceptible to patterns of social and personal misbehavior. Moreover, the economic consequences of a member's being unable to work and requiring care in some kind of setting are substantial in our present-day society.

The role of the therapeutic recreation department or service in this model is dependent to a large degree on the setting wherein the model is found. But regardless of setting, stress will be placed on the use of recreative experiences to develop a positive self-concept, social skills and activity skills that can be used in leisure pursuits following release or discharge, and leisure counseling to include the importance of developing a personal philosophy about leisure.

One's concept of self develops, to a large extent, on the basis of direct comparison of one's performance with the performance of others. Secondly, self-concept is formed according to how the member believes others view him. Thus, if activities are either too difficult to realize or improper, and modifications in them do not occur, the special population member will perpetually fail and lose faith in himself and in his ability to subsequently perform in a reasonably satisfactory way.

Chapter 1 noted the importance of recreative experiences as a contributor to social skills, and this will be discussed further in Chapter 8. However, it seems important to mention that a large majority of special population members have not experienced a wide range of social situations that offer opportunities to practice appropriate responses or what constitutes a proper manner of behavior. Indeed, for many, attempting to behave in socially proper ways has not always been a rewarding experience because of clumsy, imperfect performances. It is especially important, therefore, that activities focus on social skill competencies that are reasonable to achieve and are consistent with the character, needs, situation, and prognosis of each person.

There are few publications today that concern themselves with special populations that do not mention the importance of leisure activities for these individuals following release or discharge. It has been said that one of the major problems in the area of health, social, and correctional service is not the person who *is* institutionalized, but the person who *has been* institutionalized—the former patient or offender. The period immediately following release or discharge appears to be extremely crucial with respect to whether a person remains in the community or returns to the institution.

Some administrators of rehabilitation programs have noted that successful vocational training often is followed by failure to keep a job because an individual either lacked the social skills necessary to get along well with others on the job or did not have the activity skills necessary to participate in leisure activities after a full day of work.[23] As a result, according to Haun, individuals often engage in seemingly delinquent acts, or in self-created games of a bizarre nature, or return to play patterns found in an early development period while losing interest in more highly developed activities.[24]

It is unfortunate that our society places an individual in an aggregate whose identity is dependent not only on his behavior but on the response of community members to the way he acts. Thus, therapeutic recreation specialists must be exceedingly sensitive to the environment to which the patient returns. Services must be directed toward greater conformity to the normative demands of the larger community. At times, I can't help but feel that therapeutic recreators place too much emphasis on "low expectations" of patients as they leave the setting. In other words, the recreative skills that a particular patient takes with him when he leaves the setting simply support the performance expected and reinforce the patient's failure to perform in ways defined by the larger community. Therapeutic recreation specialists, therefore, must become more involved in offering activities that develop activity skills. Moreover, they must become more concerned with offering a leisure counseling service to meet the post-discharge needs of the special population member prior to discharge or release.

community model

The community, as the term is used here, means those people as a whole found in a specific geographic area — i.e., a town or city — who share or are linked together as a group and individually by common needs and interests. This does not mean a community in which all norms, beliefs, values, drives, motives, and ways of life are standardized. But it does suggest that community means that there is a "common life" of some kind, and that there is value in identifying oneself with, and sharing in, this common life. Implicit in this definition is that individuals whom we have identified as special population members are members of this community. As indicated, the vast majority of these members are found in the community, not in an institution or special school or rehabilitation center. They have as much right to be associated with and feel "part of" this common life as the individual with no physical, emotional, and/or social problems.

As noted in an earlier chapter, recreation service to special population members has been provided since the early 1900s. Such services, however, were found primarily in larger communities; in addition, the services were limited and restricted to special population types, i.e. cerebral palsied, mentally retarded, and the like. Since the early 1950s, we have witnessed a gradual movement toward integrated programming which has met with varying degrees of success depending upon the attitude of the community and sponsoring agency toward special population members, as well as the type of services being provided. In more recent years, municipal recreation programming settled into a threefold approach: sheltered, semisheltered, and nonsheltered (integrated).[25,26,27,28] In some instances, voluntary service organizations and public park and recreation departments combined to provide the recreation services, and in other instances, each provided separate services, often in duplication.

Since 1970 several major legislative acts (for example, Rehabilitation Act of 1973 and Education for All Handicapped Children Act of 1975) are affecting or should ultimately have positive effects on community recreation services for special population members. Likewise, in recent years, advocacy groups at national, state, and local levels are requesting more recreation services. The President's Committee on Employment of the Handicapped has had for several years a subcommittee on recreation and leisure. This same President's Committee and the NRPA co-sponsored in 1974 a National Forum in Park and Recreation Needs of the Handicapped. In 1975, the National Institute of New Models for Community and Leisure for Handicapped Children and Youth was established at the University of Iowa under the direction of Dr. John Nesbitt through a grant from the U.S. Bureau of Education for the Handicapped.

One of the studies undertaken by the National Institute of New Models was to identify various types of recreation delivery systems found in the community. They identified some distinct delivery system models. These models are as follows:

Leisure Consumer Models. Programs organized and conducted by people who are handicapped (Wheelchair Athletic Association).

Consumer Leisure Competency Models. Programs which help the handicapped become aware of recreation and leisure opportunities (Educational and counseling programs).

Leisure for Handicapped Advocacy Group Models. Organizations that advocate for handicapped rights with respect to leisure needs of the handicapped (National Therapeutic Recreation Society).

Special Recreation for Handicapped Facility and Service Models. Recreation programs and facilities specifically designed for use by the handicapped (San Francisco Recreation Center for the Handicapped).

Commercial Recreation for Handicapped Models. Travel agencies, equipment manufacturers, private facilities (theaters, bowling establishments, etc.) and transportation agencies which serve the handicapped.

Community Service and Civic Organization Models. (Toastmaster, Chamber of Commerce, PTA, political parties).

Creative and Performing Arts Models. Organizations and clubs that offer programs in the area of dance, music, art, and the like at both a spectator and participation level (Theater of the Deaf).

Education and School Models. Preschool through post secondary education.

Park and Recreation Departments. The full range of leisure services to the handicapped at all levels (national, state, local, urban, and rural).

Rehabilitation, Health, Social and Welfare Models. Federal, state, and some private funding for specific services to the physically, emotionally, socially, and mentally handicapped.

Support Service Models. Services of consultation, planning, in-service training, information research which are provided by national or state organizations to both participants and practitioner (National Consortium on Physical Education and Recreation for the Handicapped; U.S. Bureau of Education for the Handicapped; Information and Research Utilization Center in Physical Education and Recreation for the Handicapped [IRUC]; Cooperative Extension Service in Therapeutic Recreation).

Voluntary Health Agency Models. Agencies serving specific impairments or disabilities.

Youth Service Models. (Boy Scouts, Girl Scouts, 4-H, YMCA).[29,30]

A general conclusion drawn by Nesbitt regarding the three-year period of the National Institute involving a review of the literature, research and demonstration grants; conducting field site case studies on programs; conducting a national survey of community recreation and park departments; providing program/service consultation; conducting training institutes; and other like functions was:

At the local level, recreation programs for handicapped are starting and expanding every year. Wheelchair athletes number some 15,000. There are as many as 750,000 participants, parents and volunteers involved in the Special Olympics each year. The range of recreational activities in which handicapped are making breakthroughs to participation is inspiring and limitless. . . .

Special recreation, that is, recreation of, by and for the handicapped, is moving so rapidly that the volunteers, advocates and professionals are hard pressed to keep abreast.

Anyone—consumer, parent, advocate or professional—interested in people who are handicapped can take satisfaction in the fact that we have entered into an era in which thousands and millions of people who are handicapped will take "first class citizen" roles in recreation yielding personal accomplishment, personal equality and personal joy in living.[31]

While the remarks of Nesbitt are quite stimulating to read, there were some disconcerting facts in the National Institute report relative to the limited role nationwide that park and recreation agencies have played at all levels of government in providing recreation services to special population members. This limited role or lack of action has been noted by other investigators and authors.[32,33]

In the national survey of community-based recreation and leisure programs conducted by the National Institute it was found that out of 61 responding communities representing a total population of 14 million people, only 31,306 (3 percent) of the handicapped population were receiving leisure services.[34] Of this number, 37 percent were mentally retarded, 24 percent physically disabled, and all remaining disabilities (deaf and hard of hearing, aged with impairments, blind and visually impaired, learning disabilities) less than 10 percent each.[35]

Relative to personnel, it was found (using a full-time equivalency ratio—FTE) that of the 61 agencies reporting, the total FTE (full-time and part-time) number of personnel utilized for delivery of leisure services to the handicapped was 366; non-paid FTE personnel (volunteers, students, interns) was 212. An analysis of this data by the Institute showed that larger communities with larger programs tend to employ full-time personnel while smaller communities and programs employ part-time personnel to provide leisure services to the handicapped. Also, regardless of community size, it was presumed that volunteer and part-time personnel and aides provide the vast majority of services.[36]

The number of personnel found employed in the National Institute study does not differ greatly from what the NRPA found in a larger survey study. Of 1,862 public, tax supported, municipal, county, special district, and state park systems responding, 302 or slightly over 16 percent employ one or more personnel in service to the handicapped. Further, out of 43,103 total persons employed within these systems, 910 or 2.1 percent are employed in service to the handicapped.[37]

The implications of the National Institute study and that of the NRPA would seem to support the opinion of Stein, who writes:

> Perhaps one of the most frustrating and discouraging commentaries that can be made of organized community recreation in America is its failure to serve large segments of citizens. It seems paradoxical that on the one hand it is generally agreed by recreation professionals that opportunities for meaningful recreation experiences are a universal need and that programming should be designed to meet the needs of all of the people. This is particularly true in the public sector or in governmentally sponsored community recreation. Yet, such opportunities are not being offered to some members of our communities except in limited instances.[38]

The question as to why public park and recreation departments are not offering more recreation services to special population members is difficult to answer. Any number of reasons have been given—lack of funding, lack of transportation, lack of accessible facilities, lack of specialized leadership, lack of awareness of needs of special population members, lack of proper attitude toward special population members, lack of cooperative attitude between municipal recreators and therapeutic recreators.[39] Regardless of the various reasons given, few reasons are going to be acceptable today and in the future as the result of federal legislation. While federal guidelines as they might affect provision of recreation service for special population members have yet to be completely worked out, they will be as time passes.

The role of the therapeutic recreator in the community now and for the foreseeable future will be, as Humphrey has indicated, that of a "catalytic and resource leader."[40] In this leadership role the specialist will function as a consultant, public relations expert, advocate, community planner, educator–teacher, supervisor, and/or leader. The specialist might also serve as coordinator of a recreation service referral or on a coordinating council responsible for offering assistance and advice to recently discharged or released patients and offenders in locating recreative resources in the community.

As noted, leisure service agencies are giving more attention to offering recreation opportunities to special populations. Likewise, other community agencies are initiating leisure services. The therapeutic recreation specialist by virtue of his specialized knowledge and experience can add, when requested, to the competence of the central administration by assisting and participating in leisure service program development and in production and direction of in-service workshops; by serving on committees; by working on experimental or pilot projects; and by providing fieldwork supervision to students in schools offering course-work in therapeutic recreation.

The playground leader is a key person in any leisure service program. Leader and specialist may work together, for example, in exploring the scope of a physically disabled child's difficulty in participating in a playground program. Growing out of this mutual exploration, a plan will be developed and the method of its implementation determined.

In these days of rapid social changes, the specialist might very well work with an anti-poverty program in helping local community representatives determine what kind of recreative services are wanted, what they think about current services, what really is available, and why so many people are not making use of the services they obviously need. The specialist will help communities involved in such programs to do something for themselves, not do it for them, creating the ability to move toward independence rather than dependence.

Increasingly we are observing that therapeutic recreation specialists are employed in various youth-serving agencies either helping juvenile delinquents find their way into positive recreation opportunities through referrals to public recreation agencies or participating in specifically designed activities directed by a specialist. Similar procedures and programs have been developed for the adult offender who is either on probation or parole.

One approach used to meet the increasing community social problem is the formation of an interagency council that would usually meet monthly to share information and discuss problems of common interest in the community. Here the specialist can offer unique assistance in helping community agencies implement leisure services to meet leisure needs.

Where the size of the community and the funds available permit it, therapeutic recreation specialists have been employed by leisure service organizations, most often the municipal recreation agency. The specialist's role is usually that of supervisor of special services, although funds may make necessary a delimitation as to the number and kind of special population members actively served, as well as the geographic area.

This last point concerning the employment of therapeutic recreation specialists in municipal recreation agencies is an issue that is being discussed more and more among specialists and municipal recreators independently and collectively. The issues center primarily around the matter of training or education for service to special population members and professionalism. There are those within the profession who feel very strongly that it does not take a "trained therapist" to provide recreation services to special population members living in the community, that this is a responsibility of any municipal educated recreator. On the other hand, there are those who feel just as strongly that since trained therapists have the knowledge and understanding of special population members, they should be employed by municipal recreation agencies to provide the recreation services to these members.

The other issue concerns professionalism. According to Robb, who has addressed this issue,". . . are we therapists first and recreators second, or . . . are we recreators first and therapists second?"[41] As noted earlier, most specialists are found working in hospitals/institutions and not in community settings; however, this may change as federal guidelines (P.L. 94–142) are implemented and more recreation services provided. For the present, specialists are found in institutional or rehabilitational settings and the type of involvement and interaction in this type of setting is much different from what occurs in the community settings.

The implications of these issues could have a tremendous effect upon our profession in the future. One implication could be a separate organization, not associated with NRPA. Students, therefore, are encouraged to review the literature concerning these issues and discuss them in the classroom.[42,43,44]

We cannot leave this community model without indicating that complications exist within the model relative to the development of recreation services for special populations. It takes time, effort, and a considerable amount of human service development to initiate recreation services. It takes planning, administration, community organization, consultation, coordination, and citizen participation. In the planning process alone, for example, it requires problem assessment, problem clarification, goal setting, objective setting, examination and decision among alternates, and determination of strategy, as well as steps to take concerning the implementation of strategy, monitoring, and evaluation. In the end, provision of recreation service to special populations requires a commitment to the listening, sharing, and compromising inherent in the process of working with others, and the requisite skills—communication skills, group process skills, and orchestral skills—necessary for meeting such a commitment.

SUGGESTED REFERENCES

The suggested references are brief and limited primarily to the various human service models. The student is urged to consult and read the many fine articles appearing in therapeutic recreation, recreation, health, and social journals that are concerned with provision of therapeutic recreation within the various human service models.

Avedon, Elliot M., and others. *Activating Community Resources for Therapeutic Recreation Service.* New York: Comeback, Inc., 1966.

Bannon, Joseph J. *Leisure Resources: Its Comprehensive Planning.* Englewood Cliffs, N.J.: Prentice-Hall, Inc., 1976.

Bassuk, Ellen L., and Samuel Gerson. "Deinstitutionalization and Mental Health Services," *Scientific American* 238 (February 1978), pp. 46–53.

Bockoven, J. Sanbourne. *Moral Treatment in Community Mental Health.* New York: Springer Publishing Company, 1972.

Brown, Esther L. *Newer Dimensions of Patient Care, Part I: The Use of the Physical and Social Environment of the General Hospital for Therapeutic Purposes.* New York: Russell Sage Foundation, 1961.

———. *Newer Dimensions of Patient Care, Part II: Improving Staff Motivation and Competence in the General Hospital.* New York: Russell Sage Foundation, 1962.

———. *Newer Dimensions of Patient Care, Part III: Patients as People.* New York: Russell Sage Foundation, 1964.

Cressey, Donald R. *The Prison: Studies in Institutional Organization and Change.* New York: Holt, Rinehart and Winston, Inc., 1961.

Cumming, John, and Elaine Cumming. *Ego and Milieu: Theory and Practices of Environmental Therapy.* New York: Atherton Press, 1962.

Fairchild, Effie, and Larry Neal. *Common-Unity in the Community.* Eugene, Or.: Center of Leisure Studies, University of Oregon, 1975.

Freidson, Eliot. *Professional Dominance: The Social Structure of Medical Care.* New York: Atherton Press, 1970.

Glaser, Daniel, ed. *Crime in the City.* New York: Harper and Row, 1970.

Godbey, Geoffrey. *Recreation, Park and Leisure Services: Foundations Organization, and Administration.* Philadelphia: W.B. Saunders Company, 1978.

Goffman, Erving. *Asylums.* New York: Anchor Books, 1961.

———.*Stigma.* Englewood Cliffs, N.J.: Prentice-Hall, Inc., 1963.

Hjelte, George, and Jay S. Shivers. *Public Administration of Recreational Services* (2nd ed). Philadelphia: Lea and Febiger, 1978.

Huey, Karen. "Alternates to Mental Hospital Treatment," *Hospital and Community Psychiatry,* 27 (March 1976), pp. 186–192.

Hutchison, Ira J., David C. Park, and Milton L. Tearn. "Recreation for Everyone," in *Managing Municipal Leisure Services,* pp. 138–152, eds. Sidney G. Lutzen and Edward H. Storey. Washington, D.C.: International City Management Association, 1973.

Irwin, John. *The Felon.* Englewood Cliffs, N.J.: Prentice-Hall, Inc., 1970.

Michaux, Louis A. *The Physically Handicapped and the Community.* Springfield, Ill.: Charles C Thomas, Publisher, 1970.

Murphy, James F., and Dennis R. Howard. *Delivery of Community Services: An Holistic Approach.* Philadelphia: Lea and Febiger, 1977.

O'Morrow, Gerald S. ed. *Administration of Activity Therapy Service.* Springfield, Ill.: Charles C. Thomas Publishers, 1966.

Park, David C. "Therapeutic Recreation: A Community Responsibility," *Parks and Recreation* (July 1970), pp. 25–26, 66.

Roemer, Milton I., and Jay W. Friedman. *Doctors in Hospitals: Medical Staff Organization and Hospital Performance.* Baltimore: Johns Hopkins Press, 1971.

Rosenhan, David L. "On Being Sane in Insane Places," *Science.* 179 (January 19, 1973), pp. 250–257.

Rothman, Theodore, ed. *Changing Patterns in Psychiatric Care.* New York: Crown Publishers, Inc., 1970.

Schwartz, Morris S., and Charlotte G. Schwartz. *Social Approaches to Mental Patient Care.* New York: Columbia University Press, 1964.

Stanton, Alfred H., and Morris S. Schwartz. *The Mental Hospital.* New York: Basic Books, 1954.

Stotsky, Bernard. *The Nursing Home and the Aged Psychiatric Patient.* New York: Appleton-Century-Crofts, 1970.

Stracke, Richard. "The Role of the Therapeutic Recreation in Relation to the Community Recreator," *Therapeutic Recreation Journal,* 3:1 (1969), pp. 25–28.

Thomas, Herbert E. "The Dynamics of the Interdisciplinary Team in the Adult Correctional Process," *The Prison Journal,* 44 (1964).

Wallace, Samuel E. *Total Institutions.* Washington, D.C.: Transactions, Inc., 1971.

Yablonsky, Lewis. *The Violent Gang.* New York: Penguin Books, 1972.

chapter 8
the
therapeutic recreation
process

The therapeutic recreation process is central to all recreation functions; it is the very essence of recreation, potentially beneficial to every individual, applicable in any setting — community, hospital, institution, center, or other agency/institution — in any frame of reference, and within any philosophical discussion of therapeutic recreation.

process models

The term *therapeutic recreation process* will be used herein to describe the series of steps the therapeutic recreation specialist takes to meet the needs and problems of special population members through recreative experiences. This view implies that the therapeutic recreation process is concerned with moving the member from a particular point in the environment, wherein the member is involved in activity as a result of unconscious needs or interests or is unable to participate because of a variety of circumstances, to a point where the member is able to fulfill his responsibility for meeting his own recreation needs and interests at a conscious level — or short of this, participating in recreative experiences to the extent possible within the limitations imposed by the circumstances. The latter, in most instances, refers to those members who are impaired severely by developmental defeats, physical injury or illness, or psychological and social disabilities.

Since the late 1960s, several authors have expressed thoughts similar to the above, and it is appropriate that we briefly review some of them. Of particular interest are those process or continuum models suggested by Berryman, Ball, Frye and Peters, and Gunn and Peterson.

Berryman contributes a model wherein recreational activities become "experiential bonds," joining the member with his environment.[1] Initially, the specialist presents activities that hopefully will have a positive effect on the special population member, thereby establishing the first link or bond between the member and his environment. As new recreative experiences are introduced by the specialist, new bonds are created. Eventually, the member no longer needs the assistance of the specialist and pursues recreative experiences on his own, establishing new bonds between himself and the environment. Moreover, according to Berryman:

> The self actualization process continues ad infinitum with recreative experiences creating ever new bonds between the self and his environment and Self and Environment continue to establish new relationships and additional expansions.[2]

Ball, in her continuum model, outlines a series of four progressive stages that a member may move through until such time as the member reaches a "true recreative experience" (Table 8.1).[3] Moreover, Ball

TABLE 8.1   RECREATIVE PROGRESSION

Experience	Type of Time	Major Motivation
1 Activity for sake of activity	Obligated time	Drive is outer directed
2 Recreation education	Obligated time	Drive is outer directed
3 Therapeutic recreation	Unobligated time	Motivation is inner directed but choice of experiences is limited
4 Recreation	Unobligated time	Motivation is inner directed

Source: Edith L. Ball, "The Meaning of Therapeutic Recreation," *Therapeutic Recreation Journal,* 4:1 (1970), 18.

visualizes that the member may also function simultaneously in all four stages. She comments thusly:

> An individual might have a work experience (typing copy for the newspaper), a recreation education experience (learning the skills and knowledge about volley ball, and developing attitudes towards participating), a therapeutic recreation experience (participating in a party) and a recreation experience (listening to music). No one of these experiences negates the other and in fact, they probably complement each other and help the individual to gain or regain a balance in living.[4]

A clinical model that appeared in Frye and Peters' *Therapeutic Recreation* has also precipitated thought and discussion among therapeutic recreation specialists. This model identified five stages:

1. Recreator administers highly structured program under medical orders.
2. Recreator "sells" program to patient, motivates patient to participate.
3. Recreator and patient construct program together.
4. Recreator advises patient and community.
5. Patient is free to participate in any activity available to him.[5]

The model proposed by Gunn and Peterson is not that much different from what has been discussed by the previous writers and the author. Generally speaking, it promotes independent leisure functioning in special population members through the use of various activities, facilitation techniques and programs within various settings. Their approach, however, to arrive at independent functioning for special populations is a systems approach. This approach incorporates determining purposes, goals, and objectives; designing a program based on purposes; determining a delivery system; implementing the program; monitoring; evaluating; and revising the program, if needed, with appropriate feedback at each step in the sequence. They further suggest that the systems approach not only has value in individual and group program planning, but can be used to develop a total therapeutic recreation service within a specific setting.[6]

process rationale

Before we proceed with a discussion of the therapeutic recreation process it is well for us to consider briefly the rationale for such a process. As noted earlier, therapeutic (hospital) recreators often provided recreation service without too much consideration as to how these services would bring about a change in the behavior of special population members. Activities, which were the main service, were provided to appeal to large numbers of members, and fun was the major concern. The recreators were referred to as "jocks" or "play people," or some other name was used which did not have a very good professional connotation. While their activities were generally accepted, the acceptance more often than not was because patients were kept busy, not because activities made a major contribution to treatment or a particular goal. In recent years, our approach to programming has become more sophisticated, and our image as recreators has become more therapeutic, more professional. Today we are considered a professional discipline with professional procedures and services. However, if we are to continue to develop as a professional discipline and to be accepted by other professionals, especially in health settings, and to make contributions in a professional manner, we must continue to improve our procedures in offering recreation services. Other professional disciplines utilize a standardized procedure in providing their services; we cannot do otherwise. Today, we are expected to act and provide recreation service in a very professional manner.

There are two factors, in my opinion, which have had a profound effect upon the development of a standardized procedure in the delivery of recreation services to special population members in health settings. One factor is the "right-to-treatment" litigation; the other is the economic recession which occurred during the mid-1970s and led eventually to the concept of "accountablity."

The right-to-treatment litigation relates to civil commitment procedures and is associated with the mentally ill, the mentally retarded, the aged, and a variety of other unfortunates who have been committed to hospitals/institutions. Although there were some early precedents in right-to-treatment decisions, the breakthrough came in *Wyatt v. Stickney* (December 1971) in which the U.S. Supreme Court held that involuntarily committed patients "unquestionably have a constitutional right to receive such individual treatment as will give each of them a realistic opportunity to be cured or to improve his or her mental condition."[7] The court found that the defendant's treatment program was deficient because it failed to provide a human psychological and physical environment and a qualified staff in sufficient number to administer adequate treatment and individualized treatment plans. The court proposed detailed standards, which it defined as "medical and constitutional minimums."[8]

As a result of this litigation, various state courts and legislative bodies established standards mandating changes in staffing, physical resources, and treatment process. (Various accrediting bodies also tightened up their standards.) Moreover, these standards affected both voluntarily and involuntarily committed patients. Within the concept of the treatment process were included guidelines relative to procedures for planning the program, implementing the program, and evaluating the program. While the standards or guidelines which have been developed tend to reinforce a medical model of treatment (which has used a systematic standardized procedure approach for many years), they have promoted a more effective delivery of recreation services.

The concept of accountability as it relates to recreation services is of more recent origin. In the past, beginning with our growth following World War II and until the economic recession which began about 1974, programs were justified on a philosophy of the importance of recreation. The programs in those days were operational through dollar appropriations. Today, it is a different story.

It is a conservative estimate that more than 100-billion dollars are spent annually on the practice of health care. Costs have skyrocketed. The name of the game today is cost containment; a cost-benefit evaluation is being placed on all health care services. Therapeutic recreation service will continue to receive direct appropriations and probably always will to some degree, particularly in governmental agencies, but more and more funds will be coming from third-party carriers—commercial insurance companies and in large measure, those federal programs such as Medicare, Medicaid, and the like—and it is anticipated that these types of programs will not only increase dramatically in the future but will dominate the entire health industry. However, you cannot talk about third-party insurance helping a person forever. Some independence must be achieved in some way by most people because premiums or appropriations must at least match the outlay. Therefore, a host of controls are being placed on all health care services.

One of the controls is that every patient must have an individual treatment plan (ITP). Further, this plan must be written into the medical record of the patient. In the medical record will be a statement of the problem, followed by a treatment plan that includes who provides the services to meet the plan, and how long will it take to bring about a change in the behavior of the patient including projected discharge or release. Generally speaking, the therapeutic recreator will be involved in all aspects of developing and carrying this plan, to the extent deemed necessary by the specific agency.[9]

Another control is that all treatment plans will be monitored. A peer committee verifies that the treatment provided is consistent with the state of the art or with established successful procedures. For years physicians reviewed procedures used by other physicians. Accrediting bodies (JCHA) have used a monitoring procedure for some years to determine whether a hospital or institution should be accredited. I have written elsewhere that our services may eventually be required to establish peer review committees.[10] The federal government has already initiated committees which regularly monitor services provided through Medicare. And Medicare is found in nearly all types of health settings. In short, our profession like other professions is now expected to document our plans, procedures, goals, objectives, and the like. You will be required to document your results. Those who are knowledgeable and skillful in working in this type of atmosphere will thrive and the profession will prosper. Those who cannot adjust or cope will either resign or be forced to resign.

More recently, as a result of PL 94–142, therapeutic recreators who provide recreation services in association with special education to special population children in local education agencies will be expected to participate in the individualized education plan (IEP) for each child. This is so whether the specialist is employed directly by the educational agency or is a staff member of the local municipal park and recreation department which has been contracted to provide recreation services. The IEP is similar in nature to the ITP wherein a study is made of leisure needs, a plan developed, evaluation occurs, and each step is recorded. In addition, therapeutic recreators working in public and voluntary recreation agencies which provide recreation service to special population members, both children and adults, are expected to establish programs based on sound principles of program development and use adequate and proper evaluation tools. Such procedures are recorded so as to provide for better accountability.

process goals

It would appear from the various models presented that there are several steps through which the specialist proceeds to effect change in the special population member. However, all have one aspect in common—helping the special population member respond in a more rewarding manner. It is a form of assistance to bring more happiness to the individual, to permit the member to function better, and, in general, to give him a more satisfactory way of life.

Webster's Third International Dictionary defines *process* as an action of moving forward, progressing from one point to another on the way to a goal, or to completion; it is the continuous movement through a succession of developmental stages; it is the method by which something is produced, something is accomplished, or a specific result is attained.[11]

To perceive a process as an action suggests a power behind the action or a mover of the action, hence control and/or systematic movement. Conscious and deliberate effort must be exerted to arrive at a desired goal.

The therapeutic recreation process is oriented toward the future. Both specialist and special population member have come together to help the member function more effectively in the future. The specialist, however, must focus on the past, present, and future. The primary goal of the specialist is to assist the member to achieve those goals that lead to more rewarding behavior. However, in order to attain this long-range goal, it may be necessary to first attain certain more immediate goals. This requires a systematic and complex planning process. Adequate planning involves not only a knowledge of humans, of their specific problems, and of their adaptive behavior, but also a means of applying that knowledge to the promotion and maintenance of the special population member as he responds in a holistic manner to his environment. Thus, the essential characteristics of the therapeutic recreation process are that it is planned, it is person-centered, and it is goal-directed.

components of the therapeutic recreation process

Dividing the process into phases is an artificial separation of actions that, in actual practice, cannot be separated since the basic concept of the process suggests it is a unified whole. The whole process is dynamic since data from one phase can alter or support the other phases. However, to ensure a deliberateness and thoughtfulness in proceeding through the process and to facilitate the discussion, the therapeutic recreation process is here divided into the following phases or steps:

1. An *assessment* of the special population member's therapeutic recreation needs (including the collection of information about the members).
2. The *development (planning)* of goals for therapeutic recreation action.
3. The *implementation* of therapeutic recreation action to meet goals.
4. An *evaluation* of the effectiveness of therapeutic recreation action.

To summarize, the therapeutic recreation process is a designated series of actions intended to fulfill the purposes of therapeutic recreation—to maintain the special population member's "wellness" (i.e., health wellness or social wellness), and, if this state changes, to provide the amount and quality of therapeutic recreation experiences his situation demands to direct him back to wellness, and, if wellness cannot be achieved, to contribute to his quality of life, maximizing his resources within his limitations.

The therapeutic recreation specialist and special population member are viewed as partners in the therapeutic recreation process. It is this "complex interaction," according to Collingwood, that provides "the sources of gain for clients."[12] Each member is viewed also as a unique member in units of a social system. The specialist draws heavily on perception, communication, and decision making as well as his knowledge of activities in his use of the process. The member also utilizes these skills in his role by participating in assessing, planning, implementing, and evaluating. Thus, there is a cyclical nature to the therapeutic recreation process, and the movement is constant between and among the components (Figure 8.1).

The skills the specialist must have to use the therapeutic recreation process are intellectual, interpersonal, and technical. Intellectual skills entail solving problems, thinking critically, making judgments, and analyzing activities. Interpersonal skills relate to the abilities to communicate; listen; convey interest, knowledge, and information; establish rapport; and obtain needed data in a manner that enhances the individuality of the special population member as a person. These skills foster relationships with the member, his family, co-workers, colleagues, and the community in general.

Interpersonal skills cannot be overemphasized regardless of the problem or setting. In dealing with members having physical problems such

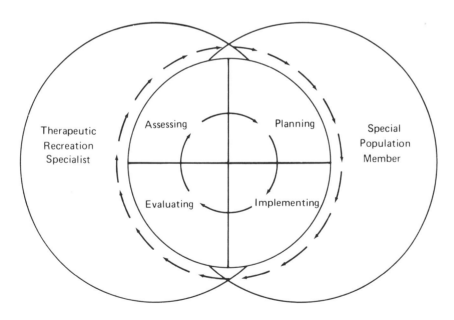

FIGURE 8.1   CYCLIC NATURE OF THE THERAPEUTIC RECREATION PROCESS

skills are extremely important in supplementing one's technical knowledge in the treatment of a member as an individual. When dealing with members having emotional problems it becomes preponderantly so. In fact, it has been suggested by some psychiatrists that a proper relationship with the member may, in certain cases, be of greater importance than the activity media itself. This concept is offered because some therapeutic recreation specialists are so action oriented that feelings of guilt develop if they are not providing direct leadership to special population members all the time.

Technical skills relate to methods, procedures, and the ability to direct and conduct activities to bring about the desired results or behavior responses of the member. However, students are cautioned that leadership behavior changes from setting to setting. While these skills are always necessary, the emphasis may vary with the special population member and the agency involved.

For the therapeutic recreation specialist to engage successfully in the process, it is important to state the following premises about the special population member:

1. A special population member is a human being endowed with worth and dignity.

2. A member has basic human needs.

3. Problems result when needs are partially met or unmet.

4. Inability to fulfill one's basic needs may entail the intervention of another individual who can help a member meet his needs or fill the need directly until such time as the member can resume that responsibility for himself.

5. The therapeutic recreation specialist is interested in rendering high quality service to special population members, no matter what their problem or disability, life-style, economic status, culture, or beliefs might be.

6. To utilize the therapeutic recreation process and to develop goal-directed recreative experiences, the specialist must have knowledge of theories from the biological, emotional, and social and behavioral sciences, and must have knowledge of the concepts of therapeutic recreation and recreative activities as well.

7. The heart of the specialist-member interaction is the development of a helping relationship in which the specialist fosters the member's personal growth and development. Thus, the leader is in reality a therapeutic agent.

8. The practice of therapeutic recreation involves the ability to focus on a member and requires the full attention and energy of the

specialist when he is engaged in the practice of therapeutic recreation. Bridges tells us that

... we must approach patients as human beings, use our awareness and our perceptiveness; but most important, we must approach patients with an aliveness, with feeling, and with the urge to communicate our whole selves. Only in this manner can we genuinely confront the patients' false solutions constructively and transmit a vision of what life could be.[13]

9. The specialist strives to meet his own self-development through the practice of therapeutic recreation.

10. Every member has the right to enjoy quality leisure and park and recreation programming, and to participate in such.

11. Therapeutic recreation specialists need to focus on preventing illness, maintaining wellness, and rendering services to those who have physical, emotional, social, and intellectual problems through leisure and recreative experiences.

assessing

Assessment is the first phase in the therapeutic recreation process. It is the act of reviewing a situation for the purpose of determining the member's problem. It consists of identifying and obtaining data about the member from many sources; these data are then classified, analyzed, and summarized to determine problems or needs.

Data Collection

Data collection is time consuming but is an absolutely essential part of problem identification. Data can be collected from many sources. The member's past history, his health and social history, and his past and present leisure and recreative experiences are all areas that contribute to the assessment.

Past and present practices in play and recreation cannot be considered apart from other influences experienced by the individual. Thus, to understand the influence that play and recreation exert upon the individual, there is a need for some knowledge of the setting within which these influences were experienced. Home influences, parental relationships, presence or absence of brothers and sisters, emotional or physical maladjustments or deficiencies, social problems, housing conditions, opportunity to use varied and extensive play materials, presence or absence of adult leadership, and extent and quality of neighborhood and school resources favorable to the development of recreation habits all have a telling effect upon the character of recreation needs and interests. Environment, whether urban or rural, also contributes to foundational recreation needs and interests. Data collection involves astute observation, purposeful listening, a broad knowledge of human behavior, and an understanding of what needs to be known and where to obtain that information.

Verbal Communication

If a formal interview is used to collect data, the format will vary according to the setting and services rendered and the role of the specialist. While core data about the member will always be needed, specific areas of information will differ if the member, for example, is being admitted into a mental health center, or is being interviewed or observed in a long-term health care facility or in a correctional institution.

Personal interviews must be carefully used lest they become too formalized. Thus, group interviews are often more successful as the initial application of the interview method. A subsequent interview with the individual appears to be a more logical outcome. In fact, the individual may be pleased or flattered that the specialist has taken an interest in him as an individual.

An attitude of real friendliness without suspicion is needed. Accept the person as he is. Don't criticize. Don't attempt to act as moralist or judge and don't be disturbed by the hostility or resentment the individual may show. It is difficult to think clearly when hostility is being shown, and it may be necessary to postpone consideration of the action until it can be regarded more objectively. Prolonged reactions of disgust, irritability, or resentment toward members are indications of a lack of emotional maturity and integration on the part of the specialist.

The special population member should feel that the specialist is interested in him as a person and that the specialist has communicated—both verbally and nonverbally—that he views the member with respect and dignity. The fact that the specialist calls the member by name, listens with full attention, anticipates questions, and speaks *with* the member rather than *to* the member, conveys respect. The specialist should refrain from using language unfamiliar to the member and guard against responding to questions in a condescending manner. Finally, the specialist should tell the member how the information being requested will be used, as well as the plan for continuing the interaction into the planning, implementing, and evaluating phase, Hopefully, such an interview begins a relationship based on trust, respect, concern, and interest.

In some instances, checklists and questionnaires are used for the convenience of staff and to save time. Often these can be used routinely and contribute a negative factor because only items on the form are used. At times, it may be appropriate for the member to fill out recreative information sheets. This, of course, is only appropriate if the member can read and write, is oriented and aware, and has the strength to do so. If possible, in any case, a personal verification should follow.

Frequently the former recreational interests of the individual will give valuable clues as to the therapeutic activities to be utilized; not infrequently the type of activity chosen may lay a foundation for the development of a future hobby for the individual.

Observation

Up to this point, verbal interaction between specialist and member has been emphasized. Intelligent observation is important to sound therapeutic recreation practice; it should be both systematic and scientific. It is just as important as the interview to the identification of the problem and the subsequent planning and evaluating of therapeutic recreation. In interacting with some special population members, observation is the only technique available. With other members, verbalization may be at such a low level that observation is the only method that will provide cues for behavior change. The specialist's skillful observation also aids other members of the treatment team in determining a total approach to the member's problems.

Although the specialist's observations may intentionally be made to appear casual in order not to arouse anxiety in the member, in actual fact, the specialist's observations are always systematic; the specialist is aware of what to look for and differentiates the normal from the abnormal. It is only through a knowledge of normal behavior that digressions from the normal are recognized. The specialist's observations are scientific in that they are objective and are based on his knowledge of the sciences.

The specialist can consciously develop his skill in observing. It is not possible to note everything that comes within one's range of vision; therefore, the specialist must learn to be selective in his observations. He learns what to look for, and his eyes and ears become trained to observe significant factors in the member's appearance and behavior and in the environment. Observations should be as objective as possible and described in terms of a factual record.

The specialist must recognize that there are times, however, when people will be unable to determine their needs because of their specific problem or circumstances in their physical environment. In most instances these will be of a short-term nature; however, there will be other situations that will last for months or even years. In such situations it is difficult to suggest guidelines to follow since each situation is unique. However, it does call for a systematic approach, working closely with other disciplines in exploring avenues that might be taken to overcome the present problem.

In other situations the specialist must be aware that some special population members may resist change even after they have participated in service. This is usually the result of emotional dependence on the specialist; general opposition to any kind of change; clinging to existing satisfactions; financial cost of change; inability of other individuals, groups, or the environment to change; and the like. When such occurs, the specialist must step back and re-evaluate the total situation. It is of interest that many resistance forces can be converted into change. Resistance comes into being originally in response to certain needs. If the member is saying, in effect, that the status quo must be maintained because it is the best way to meet leisure needs, the specialist might be able to show that the same need would be met even more satisfactorily in a different set of circumstances. Then the very energy that the member once used to maintain the status quo may shift direction and give impetus to change.

Techniques

It is impossible here to discuss in any detail the personal approach and observation techniques to use with special population individuals having specific problems. However, it does seem important that we consider a few in a broad general way.

Most persons with physical injuries, whether obvious ones or not, suffer from *fears*. The most common fear is that of pain and disfigurement. However, the focus of the person's attention on pain changes when they become absorbed in an activity. The fear of disfigurement is frequent, and many persons are embarrassed because of a disabled part and may try to hide it. Until the individual realizes that this reaction tends to draw more attention to the condition, it is often difficult to gain full cooperation. Fear of permanent disability is also a problem in the satisfactory recovery of an individual. When a condition is permanent, the patient must adjust to it and learn to live with it.

The potential specialist with an active, open mind and a will to learn will be rewarded by acquisition of the ability to adjust and to work effectively with emotionally ill patients. The attitude toward mental illness and the approach to the patient determine to a great extent the quality of the care and treatment that is provided. Persons suffer from emotional problems that are the result of an accumulation of unsuccessful efforts on the part of the individual to adjust to his environment, as we have noted earlier. Whether the mental problem is organic, functional, or toxic in origin, the individual is hospitalized because he has been unable to cope with the social order.

A tactful approach is of importance in working with the emotionally disturbed. As a result of emotional difficulties, a patient's standard of ethics may be momentarily submerged beneath the drive of more powerful instinctive tendencies, rendering him incapable of temper control or of regard for the niceties of life. The ability to become identified with the member is important, but at the same time an objective attitude must be maintained. The value of being a good listener cannot be overemphasized. However, suspicion should not be aroused in the individual that his personal affairs have been discussed. Frequently the individual regards the specialist as he would a member of his family. The importance of keeping this relationship within normal limits cannot be overstressed; it should be restricted to personal interests.

In approaching the newly blinded person tact and resourcefulness are essential, and there must be knowledge of the special techniques used. It is important to help the person to think of himself as an individual, rather than as one of a group apart. Being treated differently causes many a blind person to feel he is different. The effort must be made to help the blinded person realize that in spite of his disability, his individuality is not lost and that if he is otherwise physically and mentally capable, he is able to lead a normal, active life. It must be recognized that although the shock of blindness has its emotional effect on the individual, the reaction is not the same in all persons, and the needs of the individual must always be foremost in planning the approach. To most blinded persons, the loss of sight is not so disturbing as the loss of freedom of motion and the dependence upon others.

The first contact with a geriatric resident in a nursing home should be made in the individual's room, if possible, since it is the resident's homeground, and the first step is to gain his confidence. Old age robs people of confidence; they feel helpless, useless, and unwanted. Other attributes of old age must also be taken into consideration: reduced physical mobility, poor eyesight, diminished hearing, cosmetic changes, less ability to concentrate for long periods of time, and lack of finer movements, to name a few. In addition, Peters and Verhoven point out that unfortunately many recreational programs are designed for the ambulatory resident.[14]

The specialist must recognize that it is difficult to motivate some geriatric residents to participate because of fear of ridicule and failure, childish activities, and lack of confidence.[15] However, once involved their energy and enthusiasm become remarkable. Also, it is extremely important for the resident to become involved in activities as soon after entering the nursing home as his medical condition permits. One of the most important aspects of geriatric therapeutic recreation is its preventive side. Many of the long-term degenerative diseases of the aged, both physical and mental, can be postponed, almost indefinitely in many cases, if the individual remains active.

Instruments

Assessment of an individual is both subjective and objective. It is not uncommon for the specialist to be unable at times to determine the functioning level of a special population member even after observation in an activity. The specialist, therefore, may want to use an instrument to obtain more meaningful data on the functioning of the member. Assessment instruments are being used with increasing frequency and prevent guessing at the performance level of the member, as well as eliminating any biases the specialist might have toward gathered information. Using such instruments is comparable to the physician's scheduling laboratory tests so as to obtain additional information prior to the diagnosis or the psychiatrist's ordering a series of psychological tests to better determine the individual's capacity to interact intellectually and emotionally with his environment. Naturally, the usefulness of any test depends to a great extent on the ability of the specialist to administer the test and iterpret the results. Some tests are extremely simple to administer and interpret while others are complex and quite involved.

Assessment instruments cover a broad range of factors concerned with cognitive, affective, and psychomotor skills; self-help and everyday community living skills; leisure or recreational skill preference; and so on as they relate to a specific special population type or special populations as a group. Assessing favorite leisure activities of a special population member is an important step in the initial stages of leisure counseling. Identifying fine motor or gross motor ability for object manipulation with the develpmentally disabled is another example of the use of an assessment instrument. Assessment instruments are also a valuable tool in determining goals and objectives in planning and for evaluative purposes.[16]

A word of caution, however, is needed about the use of assessment instruments. No matter how carefully obtained, the results may not do justice to the breadth of a member's behavior. No one person is exactly the same as any other person and this includes special population members. Test results are at best a limited description of capabilities that may be useful when considered with other collected data that describe the behavior of the member.

It would appear, therefore, that personal approaches to and observation of special population members would include:

1. *General appearance.* The general appearance of a member can give clues to physical and emotional health. The depressed member, for example, may stand with a stooped defeated posture.

2. *Interpersonal interaction.* Observing the member's interpersonal behavior tells the specialist about patterns of socialization, anxiety level, acceptance or rejection of the problem, and ability to cope with the present situation.

3. *Motor activity.* The member's agility, range of motion, and ability to manage himself are all indications of his place on the dependence–independence continuum.

4. *Body language.* By definition, body language means the behavioral patterns the member uses to communicate nonverbal messages.[17] Stance, distance relationship, facial expression, and posture tell much about how the member thinks and feels. Body language is particularly significant when the member is or becomes mute. For although the member does not verbally communicate, he does not stop communication altogether. The real value of body language, however, remains in its blending with the spoken word to convey thoughts, ideas, and feelings.

Other members of the treatment team contribute to the specialist's understanding of the member and his problems. Observation and interpretation may be communicated by the physician, social worker, nurse, security officer, and vocational therapist, to name only a few, through written notes on the member's record if in a health or correctional facility and through consultation with another specialist or in a team meeting, and by significant members of the community.

In the rehabilitation of any special population member no one discipline or method by itself can assume the total responsibility for member management if optimal results are to be achieved. A comprehensive rehabilitation program can be compared to a symphony orchestra. If one were to listen to a single instrument individually, the tones produced would be meaningless and ineffective in most cases. It is only in the total harmonious well-integrated and properly conducted efforts of all the necessary instruments that the really beautiful and meaningful harmony of the musical theme is created. On the other hand, occasionally, and at an appropriate time, a single musical instrument is selected to play a solo. Similarly it is in a well-integrated and properly directed team approach that the rehabilitation of the member is best accomplished. At times selected methods or disciplines may play the predominant role in helping the member find his proper place in society. Also, the emphasis on a particular type of therapeutic approach may be different at the beginning of a member's problem than during the period of convalescence when the major responsibility changes from one group of the therapeutic team to another.[18]

Problem Identification

For a number of years, *diagnosis* was a forbidden word in therapeutic recreation. A literal definition of the word, with no qualifier proceding it, suggests it is a good word to use when conveying the idea that one is seeking knowledge or information about what needs to be improved, or what is causing the difficulty, or what is interfering with normal functioning. With this in mind, therapeutic recreators can use the word *diagnosis* as effectively as can the physician, or any person who is trying to discover where his efforts must be applied to perform his service for the benefit of the member.

After the data are collected and sorted, it is possible to identify the member's problem. Problem identification begins with an identification of the member's needs. The word *need* is used in many ways, sometimes as a noun and sometimes as a verb. It is used to denote a lack of something or to mean a requisite for bodily, psychic, or social functioning. It is used frequently in everyday conversation. A need is not necessarily a problem, but a special population member can develop a problem when a basic human need is not filled, or filled only partially.

By definition, a problem is an interruption in the member's ability to meet a need. According to some investigators, problems exist when there is no straight-line action possible.[19] This means a progression of events toward need gratification has been interrupted, altered, or disturbed; in some way, need gratification is not clearly or discernibly evident.

The therapeutic recreation specialist's function is to assess the problem and the extent of the problem. In contrast to goals of some professions, the specialist does involve himself with basic human needs that affect the total person rather than just one aspect. To focus on one aspect, such as a physical problem, to the exclusion of other aspects is to assess the member's problem in a limited manner. The limited perspective could create problems rather than solve problems for the member.

The objective is to meet all basic human needs. Thus, the specialist will try to satisfy the needs of each member. His effectiveness in assessing these needs depends upon his knowledge of basic needs relative to age and sex—i.e., needs, roles, expectations, and behaviors relating to infancy, childhood, adolescence, adulthood, and senescence for male and female members. The specialist may use a variety of theoretic models to designate basic human needs. I have earlier referred to Maslow's Hierarchy of Needs.[20] Two more such models are Erikson's Eight Ages of Man[21] and Duvall's Family Development.[22] All are popular and useful models in determining basic human needs.

When assessing factors relating to the needs of special population members from different racial groups, the specialist needs to know their customs, rites, rituals, roles, traditions, expectations, and views. Likewise, religion, formal or informal education, and socioeconomic status affect each member's needs. It is also important to assess the member's perception of this status. It has always been a source of amazement why some specialists offer recreative activities or assist a member to develop skills in a particular activity when the member does not have the economic status to afford those activities after release or discharge.

To assess biological, physical, emotional, and social status, the specialist needs a model of wellness to serve as a base. The model must incorporate such factors as age, sex, socioeconomic status, and culture. Knowing what is expected or normal for bodily and psychosocial functions provides the framework within which the status of each can be assessed for a special population member.

The specialist must have a knowledge of pathological and psychopathological problems important to the member at various age levels, for each sex, for the major racial and cultural groups, and for specific geographic areas of certain environments. The specialist who works with the social offender likewise must have a knowledge of the social problems that result in incarceration.

With a knowledge of normal human function and a working knowledge of major pathophysiological, psychopathological, and sociological problems, the specialist is prepared to begin the assessment phase of the therapeutic recreation process.

Assessment takes place through either verbal communication or observation, or both. There is no specific personal approach that can be used with all individuals. Each participant is a unique individual with his own needs and interests. The individual must be considered as a human being with a problem, not as a number, a case, or a nobody. As Frye and Peters so well state:

> Human characteristics are so complex that no two individuals are alike. Those qualities of behavior, emotional tendencies, habit patterns, character traits, attitudes, and so on which characterize an individual considered collectively, make up his personality, and each individual has a distinct and different personality.[23]

The selection of techniques and their appropriate use are based upon how well they facilitate obtaining information. A technique is not good or bad within itself. How appropriately it can be used and the outcome will designate its value.

Conclusions

The specialist sorts, organizes, groups, categorizes, compares, analyzes, and synthesizes the data about the member obtained up to this point. Decision making and judgment now come into play and are inherent in every phase of the therapeutic recreation process. The specialist summarizes all available data, and then makes one or more of the following judgments:

1. No change in behavior is needed.

2. No behavior problem exists, but there is a potential problem that may be offset by giving the member information—for example, through leisure counseling.

3. A behavior problem exists but is being adequately handled by the member and/or his family. Plans for a reassessment may be formulated, and a scheduled reassessment in time is set for the future.

4. A behavior problem exists that the member needs help in handling. Intervention is needed.

5. A behavior problem exists, but additional study is needed to resolve it.

planning

The planning phase begins when the specialist determines that a problem exists and terminates with the development of the plan; it involves setting goals, designing methods for implementing the plan, and providing the framework for evaluation. Said in another way, the specialist determines goals and articulates them in plans. Plans are formulated from decisions. Decisions guide action because they are selected choices that actions follow.

Goal Setting

Judicious, careful, and deliberate goal setting is vital to this phase of the therapeutic recreation process. The specialist considers possible actions and their consequences in order to determine the best actions. The goals should be realistic and attainable in terms of both the potentialities of the member and the ability of the specialist to help the member meet the goals. However, the student should keep in mind that other factors, such as specific physical and/or emotional limitations or incarceration, as well as the function of the agency and its administrative polices and directives, influence goal setting.

When dealing with individuals who have recently acquired a physical disability, for example, it is extremely important to fully understand the problem before activities are selected and initiated. In other words, the choice of activity may be governed by the extent of the injury. In some cases, special equipment may be needed to adapt the activity to the individual's need. However, the use of special equipment is justified only when it accommodates a permanent disability or is a necessary temporary expedient. The obvious danger is, of course, fostering too great a dependence on adaptations that may not be practical beyond the period necessary.

Other influencing factors would include the time needed to resolve the behavioral problem, particularly from the member's point of view; the attitude of society and other professionals; the cost to the member as well as one's own service funding; and the availability of resources.

Objectives are stated in terms of the special population member's goals, rather than the specialist's goals or activities; then the specialist's action is planned to help the member achieve these goals. Without goals or objectives, the plan has lost its therapeutic value. Also, depending upon the setting, goals and objectives usually are complementary to the facility's treatment goals.

Therapeutic recreation specialists with experience realize that if activities are offered for activities' sake, they lose their value and may detract from rather than contribute to the optimal growth and develpment of special population individuals. For this reason specialists must exercise great care in the proper selection of activities. The specialist is not so much concerned with what the individual accomplishes in the activity as with what the activity does to the individual; not so much with how the individual plays the game as with how the game plays upon the emotional, physical, and social state of the individual.

The goals describe the behavior the member is expected to attain. Behavioral objectives are usually written in sentence form and include the subject (special population member), an action verb that describes the desired behavior, the conditions under which the activity is to take place, and a criterion or standard for judging the action.[24] The advantages of the behavioral approach, according to Musgrove and others, are as follows:

1. Instead of using a "hit or miss" method, the problem of programming is solved by a comprehensive view of the entire program and recognition of all the subelements and their relationships to the overall program.

2. By stating the objectives in terms of behavioral performances to be accomplished by the client, the emphasis is taken off the person leading the activities and put on the person for whom the program is designed.

3. The statement of objectives in behavioral terms forces the provider of the activities to take a critical look at the program he is offering to determine if individual needs are being met.

4. The systematic process of behavioral objectives is an efficient method for programming and should eliminate waste of time and effort.

5. The designer of the objectives should continually evaluate and revise the objectives. This should keep the objectives relevant in addition to avoiding inflexible and highly structured programming.[25]

Another method of goal setting is the utilization of standards. While the profession of therapeutic recreation is directing its efforts toward developing standards of service, these standards as they relate to programs are at present broadly stated. Most standards are stated in terms of a general systematic, goal-directed, problem-solving approach. For the most part, they do not differ that much from the behavioral objective approach discussed above.[26]

Yet another approach used quite frequently in larger hospitals/institutions is placing the member in activities which have their own goals and objectives. In other words, goals and objectives have been developed for a specific activity and the member is referred to that activity. While goals and objectives have been established for the member they are usually very general and on going evaluation is limited. Only after a considerable period of time in the activity can any sort of evaluation be made, if any. The specialist is never quite sure whether goals are being reached. Evaluation is unfortunately sketchy and based strictly on subjective impressions.

Activities

Once goals have been identified by the member and the specialist, an ordering or priority is established. The specialist should designate possible activities for each behavioral problem; however, activities offered by the member should also be considered. The possible success of each activity in solving a behavioral problem is estimated, based on scientific principles and/or sound research. Variables such as age, sex, life-style, education, socioeconomic status, and cultural background of the member and his physiologic and emotional status, as they relate to and affect suggested solutions, should be considered. To do this the specialist must know the member well enough to know the usual effect a given activity has on the member and what this specific activity is likely to mean to the member. He must also know the level of participation and involvement and the meaning of participation and involvement (for example, the interactive processes as suggested by Avedon and discussed in Chapter 6). The specialist predicts as accurately as possible the consequences of each activity. This requires that the specialist know which activities are appropriate for a dependent, a semidependent, or an independent member; which are appropriate for an acutely ill, a chronically ill, a convalescent, or an aged member; and lastly, which are appropriate for those with a disability who might be living in the community. Then he selects the activities most likely to be successful in resolving or diminishing the behavioral problem (activity analysis).

Resolving the behavioral problem may be a multifaceted process, with immediate, intermediate, and long-range implications. An immediate goal is one that can be accomplished in a short span of time. An intermediate goal can be attained over a period of time, while a long-range goal is oriented toward the future. The most urgent goal, or the one that should be achieved first, is determined before long-range or more distant goals are set. Goals for the member will include preventive and reha- bilitative aspects as well as the immediate aspects.

Behavioral problems that can be resolved by the intervention of the therapeutic recreation specialist must be differentiated from those that re- quire assistance from other members of the health team or correctional team or from members in the community. A well-designed and well- developed referral system should be established so that appropriate per- sons can be involved. In some settings, methods and forms are generally available for referral use.

When the appropriate activities or services most likely to be suc- cessful are selected, specific action on the part of the specialist to achieve the immediate, intermediate, and long-range goals must be delineated. Such action must be clear, purposeful, capable of being accomplished, and adapted to the particular life style, beliefs, and expectations of the special population member. Since therapeutic recreation action is designed to solve the behavior problem, the outcomes expected as a result of that ac- tion should be stated in terms of the member's behavior. Only by recording the member's behaviors can the therapeutic recreation specialist judge the impact of his action. If the effectiveness of the services rendered is to be evaluated, expected outcomes must be stated in terms of member's behaviors.

The quality and quantity of therapeutic recreation actions delineated to solve a member's problem and effect a behavioral change will be deter- mined by the specialist's knowledge and experience. His knowledge of biological, physical, and social and behavioral sciences, as well as his therapeutic recreation knowledge, his experience (clinical and/or nonclinical), and his knowledge of resources, broadens the options, the variations in actions, and the applications of and expectations from the actions.

The Plan

During the entire planning phase, activity is directed toward the quality and quantity of therapeutic recreation actions that will be needed to resolve or minimize problems. This activity effects specified behavioral change within the context of immediate, intermediate, and long-range goals, and culminates in the formulation of the therapeutic recreation plan.

The format for this plan should flow from the goals set. A well- devised plan provides a description of the member and his problems and a plan of action to solve them. The development of the therapeutic recrea- tion plan is, therefore, a creative, intellectual activity. It is an expression of a specialist's knowledge, ability, and focuses on the member. A clearly stated plan is the most effective means of assuring the member his problems will be solved and his basic human needs fulfilled.

Sharing the plan with appropriate health, correctional, and community team members fosters a better understanding of the member, and the efforts of all are more likely to complement each other. Each team member will find that he or she can function in his or her specific role more effectively and successfully when the roles of associates are clarified. Other team members should be encouraged to utilize the therapeutic recreation plan as a resource.

Evaluation Criteria

As the specialist plans for the delivery of services, it becomes evident that some means of evaluating the services is also necessary. If the therapeutic recreation actions are designed to help the member meet a need or solve a problem, than an evaluation plan to determine if the expected outcomes of the actions are forthcoming must be developed.

When planning evaluation criteria for therapeutic recreation action, it is important to include insofar as is possible a precise idea or description of the expected outcomes. The terminal expectations should be described in unambiguous terms so that all those concerned will know what to expect. Again, they should be written in behavioral terms.

The therapeutic recreation planning culminates in the therapeutic recreation plan. The plan details the member's problems and needs, the goals or priorities that have been set, the activity approaches that have been selected, and the evaluative criteria that will measure the actions. It reflects the objectives or goals and is not merely a listing of therapeutic recreation activities. In reality, the therapeutic recreation plan has many purposes. It provides for:

1. *Individualization.* A plan that meets the member's needs, problems, and priorities.
2. *Continuity.* A plan that provides for short-term and long-term goals; information about the member's desires, preferences, and expectations; and information about the member's problems and the proposed activity approaches.
3. *Communication.* A plan that provides data about the past and present problems and becomes a resource to refer to at any one time.
4. *Evaluation.* If the specialist or other members of the team consistently keep the total plan current, it provides a means of evaluating the process. Evaluation is an ongoing process that occurs each time someone writes down a goal, an approach, and a response to that approach.

5. *Comprehensive treatment.* A plan that involves the whole person. The member's psychic, social, physical, emotional, and intellectual needs are considered.

6 *Team spirit.* The member is usually the recipient of the cooperative effort of several persons. Working together the health, correctional, or community team shares its ideas, observations, and suggestions about the member and participates in selecting therapeutic recreation approaches. This participation creates a sense of responsibility in the team for they all share in the process of planning. The essence of effective and successful activities is a planned, well-organized program carried out in close coordination with the team's findings.

In light of these purposes, it is well to offer some program guidelines or qualities desirable in recreation programming since the therapeutic recrea- . tion plan becomes the program. Since it is impossible in this introductory text to consider all of the various programming concepts including the variations found in different settings, I have incorporated only those guidelines suggested by Frye and Peters. They are as follows:

1. Considering the range in age, sex, cultural background, and areas of interest of the prospective participants in a given setting, the program should offer recreation opportunities for everyone.

2. There should be provisions for a wide variety of types of activities, including the following:

    a. physical activities, such as games and sports, dancing, camping

    b. intellectual activities, such as reading, studying, writing

    c. esthetic activities, such as music, dramatics, art

    d. social activities, such as parties, group games, discussions

    e. creativity, such as crafts, hobbies, photography, art

    f. competition, in games, sports, contests, tournaments

    g. adventure and new experience, such as trips, camping

    h. spectator activities and entertainment.

3. There should be variety in the duration of activities. There should be some activites intended for immediate and momentary enjoyment, while others should be provided for long term and continuing interest.

4. There should be variety in the location of activities. There should be outdoor as well as indoor events.

5. There should be variety in group size, with activities provided for the individual, and for small informal groups as well as for large groups.

6. There should be some variety in the degree of assistance and organization provided by the professional staff. The participants should have opportunity for individual expression and initiative, and for participation in the planning and operation of the program.

7. The program should be sustained throughout the year, avoiding letdowns on weekends and following holidays.

8. The program should be flexible, capable of responding to sudden needs for change.

9. There should be provisions for instruction in new skills. The program should provide opportunities for participants to extend the range of their leisure pursuits and gain new recreation experiences.

In the treatment center:

10. There should be provision in the program for degrees of ambulation. The bed patients, as well as the semiambulatory and fully ambulatory, should be provided with opportunities for recreation activity.

11. The program should be geared to a tempo and noise level appropriate in a hospital.

12. There should be provision for making adjustments and adaptations of the patient's usual recreation activities necessitated by physical and medical limitations.

13. In adaptations, the components of the activity should be analyzed, and those components preserved that represent the true recreative essence of the activity.

14. The program should be broad, varied, and flexible enough to provide for selection of activities to serve therapeutic goals.

15. The program should be coordinated with other medical and paramedical services.

16. The program should provide for some contact with the community outside the hospital.

17. The program should provide a bridge between the hospital and the community, and/or between the disabled and the able-bodied.

18. The program should have carryover value. It should promote long-range interests that extend into community recreation activities.

19. One of the aims of the program should be to make the patients recreationally independent.[27]

In sum, taking the time to collect data, to develop objectives, and to develop a plan with evaluative criteria is time well spent. Failure to take the time before implementation contributes to the misuse of time and wasted efforts and talents of therapeutic recreation specialists and other personnel. The cost in economic, physical, and emotional terms can hardly be estimated. Economically and morally, the profession of therapeutic recreation cannot permit this misuse of human and material resources.

implementing

Once the therapeutic recreation plan has been developed, the implementation phase begins. Depending upon the nature of the behavioral problem and the condition, ability, and resources of the special population member, as well as the nature of the therapeutic recreation action planned, the member, the member and specialist, the specialist alone, or the therapeutic recreation team members who might function under the primary specialist's supervision may implement the plan. Implementation also may be accomplished by the specialist, assisted by other therapeutic recreation specialists, or in cooperation with other types of recreation specialists and health, correctional, or community team members. All or any combination of these situations may prevail.

The Specialist's Role

The implementation phase draws heavily upon the intellectual, interpersonal, and technical skills of the specialist. Decision making, observation, and communication are significant skills, enhancing the success of action.

Just as the specialist's philosophy, education, and experience influenced the type and character of the plan designed to meet the problem of the member, so will these significantly affect implementing the plan. The specialist's emphasis, focus, and creativity will be affected by his strengths, limitations, prejudices, stereotypes, his knowledge of human behavior, the strength of his convictions, his ability to handle human closeness, and his ability to use himself therapeutically. His willingness to give of himself, as well as his knowledge of himself, will influence what the specialist will do, can do, and knows enough not to do.

In order to be successful in implementing the plan, the specialist must command respect, admiration, and confidence. If the specialist's thinking is muddled and confused relative to the task before him, these traits are reflected in individual contact; if dislike, jealousy, and self-pity are harbored, similar feelings are aroused in the member by their projection upon him. The specialist's personal inhibitions should be understood and an effort made to correct them if effective assistance is to be given in meeting the individual member's needs.

With the therapeutic recreation plan as the blueprint and the immediate, intermediate, and long-range goals in focus, the plan is put into practice. The plan is not carried out blindly, with all thinking and decision making accomplished during the previous two phases. The specialist continues to collect data about the member as a person, his problems, his reactions, and his feelings. Additional information is obtained from other team members and the community. At the same time the specialist records the reaction of the member to the plan. While brevity and clarity are characteristics of recording progress, the record's use will be diminished considerably if brevity becomes the exclusive goal.

The success or failure of the plan depends upon the specialist's intellectual, interpersonal, and technical ability. This includes the ability to judge the value of new information that becomes available during implementation and the innovative and creative ability to make adaptations. The specialist must have the ability to react to verbal and nonverbal cues, validating inferences based on observation. Paramount during the interaction is the specialist's confidence in his ability to perform the independent functions inherent in the therapeutic recreation plan.

The amount of time spent with the individual special population member or group varies significantly, ranging from short to prolonged interaction. This encounter could range from minutes to hours or from days to weeks, or be yearly, either continuing or intermittent. Interaction should be planned precisely with allowances made for the unexpected.

It is essential that each interaction be goal-directed and purposeful. The interaction demands alert, observant, attentive behavior by the specialist. Likewise, the specialist must be fully aware of the need to communicate with the member who does not respond in the usual and expected manner.

Continuing Evaluation

In each contact with the member, the specialist not only focuses on the purpose or goal of the interaction but also continually expands his perceptual ability to obtain data about the member that would indicate that the planned action is correct. The specialist also seeks data that would indicate other problems due to unmet or poorly met basic human needs. He continually reviews the member's reaction.

As the specialist implements the therapeutic recreation plan, he learns more about the member, his reactions, his feelings, his strengths, his limitations, his coping ability, his preferences, his satisfactions, and his dissatisfactions. He learns the member's response to planned therapeutic recreation action, additional ways available to him and to the specialist to perform actions, the need for additional actions, and any untoward response to the planned action. These data are synthesized and utilized to further develop the therapeutic recreation plan and are the basis for recording data about the member on appropriate progress note forms.

Once the member has invested something of himself in the activity, the danger of destruction is minimized for he will undoubtedly guard against it. The more time, thought, and energy the member expends in an activity, the more interested he becomes and the more he guards it. Thus, the specialist must be shrewd in discouraging activities that are rather obviously below or above the functioning ability of the member.

Due to the member's response during the implementation, priorities may have to be reassigned, and reassessing and replanning will then be required. Judgment is needed to know what to do with the information obtained, what information is needed, what the information means, whether a new plan is needed, and what the plan of action should be.

Thus, the implementation process, while it does have an action focus, includes assessing, planning, and evaluating activities by the specialist. In summary, implementation is an action-oriented phase of the therapeutic recreation process in which the specialist is responsible for implementing the therapeutic recreation plan that was developed. The intellectual, interpersonal, and technical actions employed during this phase are based on the plan designed for the special population member according to the member's assessed problems.

evaluating

Criteria

Evaluation, the fourth and last component of the therapeutic recreation process, follows the implementation of actions. It implies measurement against predetermined criteria that are stated in terms of how the member is expected to respond to the planned action. Further, if the specialist has used the logical, goal/objective directed problem solving approach, evaluation should have a high level of success.

While elements of evaluation, like those of assessment and planning, are concurrent with and recurrent in other components, evaluating the effect of actions during and after the implementation phase determines the member's response and the extent to which immediate, intermediate, and long-range goals are achieved. The evaluation must continue in a purposeful, goal-directed manner.

Evaluation is the natural intellectual activity completing the process phase because it indicates the degree to which the therapeutic recreation diagnosis and actions have been correct. Evaluation will also pinpoint omissions during the assessment, planning, and implementation phases. In any given situation, it is possible that some problems may be resolved within different time intervals. Since evaluation will be in terms of immediate, intermediate, and long-range goals, the evaluation process is continued until all these goals are realized.

The specialist and special population member are the agents of evaluation. Other persons, such as the member's family and other facility or community personnel, may also be involved. Based upon the behavioral expectations of the member relative to the immediate, intermediate, and long-range goals, measurement data are collected so that value judgments can be made. At present there is a paucity of tools whereby the specialist can evaluate his actions with a high degree of objectivity. However, various tools are beginning to appear more frequently.[28] For the immediate future, subjectivity will enter into much of our evaluation procedures. Thus, the specialist uses his senses to collect data, utilizes communication techniques to elicit subjective responses, utilizes those objective tests available, makes inferences and validates them, and makes a decision about the member's behavioral response. Data collected from the member about what has occurred and how it was interpreted tells the specialist whether behavior change has taken place.[29]

The use of measurable criteria for evaluation of therapeutic recreation action gives predictability to the action and reliability to the evaluation. When the performance criteria are stated in behavioral terms, evaluation is relatively simple. Criteria stated in behavioral terms describe the desired outcome of the action, the conditions under which the desired outcome will occur, and the acceptable performance. A number of persons can recognize the desired behavior, thereby providing objectivity to the evaluation, when it is stated in behavioral terms. The more measurable and objective the criteria, the more reliable the evaluation will be; and the more clearly the criteria are stated in behavioral terms, the more probable it is that the specialist will be able to evaluate the therapeutic recreation action.[30]

Results

The outcome of evaluation may be any one or a combination of the following:

1. The member responded as he had been expected to and his problem is resolved.
2. Behavioral manifestations indicate the problem has not been resolved; evidence demonstrates that immediate (but not intermediate and long-range) goals have not been achieved. Re-evaluation will continue.

3. Behavioral manifestations are similar to those evidenced during the assessment phase. There is little or no evidence that the problem has been resolved. Reassessment with replanning is needed.

4. Behavioral manifestations indicate new problems. Assessment, planning, and implementation of a plan of action to resolve these problems are in order.

Reasons for Failure

Sources for reasons why predicted behavior outcomes were not realized include the member, the specialist, other persons of importance to the member, and other team members.

Concerning the member, possible causes for failure to realize goals can include an increase in pathophysiology, psychopathology, and/or social problems; loss of self-esteem; loss of job; lack of interest in and attention to problems; and withholding important data about self and situation.

If the specialist is the source, reasons the member's problem has not been resolved may include overlooked data; failure to validate information; lack of knowledge about the member's situation; failure to recognize the member's strengths and his need for independence within the limits of his problems; inappropriate activity program; failure to consider the value of input from others; and failure to recognize one's own intellectual, interpersonal, and technical limitations.

Concerning the others significant to the member, goals may not be achieved because these others are not available or not interested in the member; the member's problem, the solution, and expected behavioral change are not understood; fears and anxieties exist between the member and others; there is a lack of transportation; and moral, cultural, and religious influences may interfere.

Reasons for the failure to achieve the goals planned for the member in relation to other team members include conflict of goals for the member, failure to see the impact of the focus upon the whole member, inability to function as a team member, failure to see value in the therapeutic recreation plan, and acts that depersonalize the member.

The fourth component of the therapeutic recreation process, evaluation, the framework for which has been prescribed, stems from the therapeutic recreation process. Evaluation is always expressed in terms of achieving expected behavior change. The entire focus of the process is goal-directed. It is systematically geared to solve the special population member's diagnosed problems by prescribing specific therapeutic recreation actions that would successfully induce a specific behavioral effect denoting that the member's problem has been resolved.

Evaluation aids the specialist to determine problems that have been resolved, those that need to be reprocessed, and new problems that have arisen.

reports and record keeping

Before bringing this chapter to a close, a few brief comments are needed relative to reports and records since documentation is now a reality. Progress reports keep the treatment team informed about the progress of the patient. How detailed these reports should be depends upon the type of care and the circumstances. The type of record kept would differ greatly from that for a research project. There may also be a marked difference between the type of record made for a patient whose disability is neither serious nor permanently disabling and that made for a badly disabled individual. In all reports the materials should be factual and not an expression of opinion.

The quality of the recording about the member and what the specialist chooses to document give direct evidence of the status of goal-achievement and individual member reactions, and designates the status of and the direction for continued problem solving. Placing a low value on recording, or insufficient or inappropriate recordings, is an affront to the member and demonstrates the specialist's limitations. Automatic notations or general statements give little or no indication of the member's individuality, his problem, and his reaction to the planned action. The recordings are related to the problem; they describe the specialist's actions and the results, and include additional data. The written report of therapeutic recreation service given serves to direct continuing action.

Recordings should reflect the member's unique situation and should be identified easily by the quality of their content. The recording should contain the information needed to give a profile of the member. Rules that set limits on what and how much should be recorded—supposedly to save time—can be a waste of time. The specialist must decide what to write, how much to write, when to write, and what is important. Writing associated with the development of the plan and recordings about member performance is a professional, not a clerical activity.

Recordings are more frequent when the member's behavior changes rapidly. If these changes occur slowly and are infrequent, there will be less to record but the information will not lose its significance. When recordings become copious or their use is minimized because one does not have the time to review them, the information should be summarized periodically in coordination and in conjunction with the therapeutic recreation plan.

To assist the student in report and progress note writing, a progress note terminology guide is provided in Appendix C.

relationship: process and models

The relationship of the therapeutic recreation process to human service models discussed earlier is fairly obvious. The process is flexible and adaptable, adjustable to a number of variables, yet sufficiently structured so as to provide a base from which many therapeutic recreation actions can proceed. In the traditional human health service models, a systematic approach as described herein is used and member's progress is noted and recorded. While the approach is not as systematic in the correctional settings which promote rehabilitation, it still exists. In the community setting, one is hard pressed to say that a consistent systematic, goal-directed approach is used to meet the leisure needs of special population members. Various community models exist; however, information of a sufficient quantity and quality to suggest a particular approach is lacking. The use of the individual educational plan and its association with leisure education and services is just beginning to be implemented. How aggressive will be either the educational system in seeing that special population members participate in leisure experiences or the municipal recreation department in delivering recreation services to such members is yet to be determined. But the key to the quality of the recreation services provided in the community and in the future will be, in my opinion, through the therapeutic recreation process.

In retrospect, this chapter has attempted to inform the student about a process which is central to therapeutic recreation functioning. A selective, though not exhaustive review of the literature related to, as well as concepts and ideas about, the therapeutic recreation process which are of value to the beginning specialist in therapeutic recreation were presented. Admittedly, the approach to the process was more clinical than nonclinical (community) in nature. However, I feel confident that the process presented here is not limited to any environment—clinic, hospital, institution, community, or other agency. Instead, I suggest the use of the process in any setting in which there are special population members.

This chapter also has been quite "meaty" from the standpoint of what is involved in using the therapeutic recreation process. Thus, I suggest that the chapter be reread incorporating those articles referred to in footnotes and in the Suggested References. Only a limited amount of material or references can be made within an introductory text.

SUGGESTED REFERENCES

Ackoff, Richard. "Towards a Behavioral Theory of Communication," in *Modern Systems Research for the Behavioral Scientist,* ed. W. Buckley. Chicago: Aldine Press, 1968, pp. 209–218.

Adair, Bill. "The Role of Recreation in Assessing the Needs of Emotionally Disturbed Youth," *Leisurability,* 1:4 (1974), pp. 27–31.

Ball, Edith L., and Robert E. Cipriano. *Leisure Service Preparation.* Englewood Cliffs, N.J.: Prentice-Hall, Inc., 1978, pp. 116–153, 208–227.

Bogan, Marty. "Diagonosing Groups and Planning from Where They're At," in *Expanding Horizons in Therapeutic Recreation II,* ed. Jerry Kelley. Champaign, Ill.: Office of Recreation and Park Resources, University of Illinois, 1974, pp. 71–75.

Collingwood, Thomas R. "The Recreation Leader as a Therapeutic Agent," *Therapeutic Recreation Journal,* 6:4 (1972), pp. 147–152.

Compton, David M., and William A. Touchstone. "Individualizing Therapeutic Recreation Service for the Profoundly Handicapped," in *Expanding Horizons in Therapeutic Recreation IV,* eds. Gerald Hitzhusen, Gerald O'Morrow, and John Oliver. Columbia. Mo.: Department of Recreation and Park Administration, University of Missouri, 1977, p. 17–28.

———, and others. "Special Population Involvement (SPI): A Model for Community Based Recreation," in *Expanding Horizons in Therapeutic Recreation III,"* eds. Gary M. Robb and Gerald Hitzhusen. Columbia, Mo.: Department of Recreation and Park Administration, University of Missouri, 1976, pp. 17–26.

———, and Donna Price. "Individualizing Your Treatment Program: A Case Study Using LIMT," *Therapeutic Recreation Journal,* 9:4 (1975), pp. 127–139.

Farrell, Patricia, and Herberta M. Lundegren. *The Process of Recreation Programming.* New York: John Wiley and Sons, 1978.

Houts, Peter S., and Robert A. Scott. *Goal Planning in Mental Rehabilitation.* Hershey, Pa.: Hershey Medical Center, The Pennsylvania State University, 1972.

Krey, Russell, and Sharon Krey. *Activity Therapy: An Innovative Approach to Individual Program Planning.* Provo, Ut.: Dana Press, 1977.

Mager, Robert F. *Preparing Instruction Objectives* (2nd ed.). Belmont, Ca.: Fearon Publishers, 1977.

———,*Goal Analysis.* Belmont, Ca.: Fearon Publishers, 1972.

Mundy, Jean and Linda Odum. *Leisure Education: Theory and Practice.* New York: John Wiley and Sons, Inc., 1979.

Parker, Robert and others. "The Comprehensive Evaluation in Recreation Therapy Scale: A Tool for Patient Evaluation," *Therapeutic Recreation Journal,* 9:4 (1975), pp. 143–152.

Peterson, Carol A. "Application of Systems Analysis Procedures to Program Planning in Therapeutic Recreation Service," in *Therapeutic Recreation Service: An Applied Behavioral Science Approach,* ed. Elliott Avedon, Englewood Cliffs, N.J.: Prentice-Hall, Inc., 1974, pp. 128–155.

Plowman, P.D. *Behavioral Objectives.* Chicago: Science Research Associates, Inc., 1971.

Post, M. Sidney. "Therapeutic Activities: Objectives and Goals," *Therapeutic Recreation Journal,* 7:2 (1973), pp. 21–25.

Popovich, D. *A Prescriptive Behavioral Checklist for the Severely and Profoundly Retarded.* Baltimore: University Park Press, 1977.

Robitscher, Jonas, "Courts, State Hospitals and the Right to Treatment," *American Journal of Psychiatry,* 129:3 (1972), pp. 248–303.

Ruesch, Jurgen. *Therapeutic Communication.* New York: W. W. Norton and Company, Inc., 1961.

Saslow, Lynn D. "A Multidimensional Approach to Camper Assessment," *Therapeutic Recreation Journal,* 12:4 (1978), pp. 30–35.

Theobald, William F. *Evaluation of Recreation and Park Programs.* New York: John Wiley and Sons, 1979.

Touchstone, Williams A. "The Status of Client Evaluation Within Psychiatric Settings," *Therapeutic Recreation Journal,* 9:4 (1975), pp. 166–172.

Wickwise, George. "Activity Analysis for Rehabilitation," *The Archives of Physical Medicine and Rehabilitation* (September 1955), pp. 578–586.

Witt, Jo. E., and Peter A. Witt. "Planning and Evaluation of Recreation Activities in Therapeutic Settings," *Therapeutic Recreation Journal* 4:4 (1970), pp. 5–7, 35, 37.

chapter 9
the
therapeutic recreation
specialist

When considering a career in any field, you owe it to yourself to take a good look at the various possibilities and to evaluate them as best you can in the light of your abilities, needs, and desires. This is as true in therapeutic recreation as it is in any other professional career. For this reason I would like to give you a general idea of some of the things that are likely to be expected of you as a therapeutic recreation specialist.

The young man or woman who selects therapeutic recreation as a career has an opportunity to become a member of what may be one of the most important professional groups in our modern society. Therapeutic recreation is concerned with providing recreation service to persons with physical, emotional social, and intellectual problems. It is a challenging task that offers an opportunity for initiative and imagination.

At this point in your life, all of you have had varying degrees of interest in various human service helping professions. Undoubtedly for many of you this is your first awareness of therapeutic recreation. On the other hand, some of you perhaps have a concern because you were favorably influenced by a person already in the profession or by your teacher. Others of you may be interested because of the great enjoyment you have derived from being a participant in a student organization that volunteers time and service in a nursing home or a developmental learning center. Still others of you are perhaps undecided as to whether or not this is the type of career that you want to pursue.

Regardless of how your interest has been stimulated, there are many things that you should know about a therapeutic recreation specialist before you make a definite decision to accept it as a professional career. This chapter will discuss some of the roles assumed by therapeutic recreation specialists, regardless of agency or institution setting, as well as some of the responsibilities of these roles in relation to various agencies, special population members, service teams, other practitioners, and the like. Some of the positive personal qualities that are usually necessary to make a good therapeutic recreation specialist will also be considered.

leadership roles

It is not an easy matter to identify the roles engaged in by a therapeutic recreation specialist because of the varying conditions that exist from one community to another and from one agency or institution to another. As noted in Chapter 3, many types of agencies offer recreation service to special population members and they employ therapeutic recreation specialists who have various responsibilities.

The therapeutic recreation specialist, as a symbol or as a person, means different things to different individuals and groups, and also means different things to the same individuals or groups at different times. To some, he may be an activity leader; to others, a resource, a symbol of authority, a member of the group, a skilled performer, a counselor, or a teacher. Each individual and group views the therapeutic recreation specialist, whether he be employed within an institution or offering recreation service in the community, in light of particular needs and interests.

As therapeutic recreation has progressed through the years, more roles have been assumed by the specialist and the number of agencies and the like offering recreation service has increased. In the beginning the specialist was primarily a leader who offered direct recreation service of an activity nature within agencies or institutions providing service to the mentally ill or mentally retarded. Activity skill and ability to provide a wide variety of enjoyable activities were the primary requisites. Today, the specialist is an important figure among community recreation leaders and and equally important member of the treatment team within many different types of agencies and institutions; his role has broadened.

The developing concept of the place of therapeutic recreation in the social scene has created a variety of roles for the specialist. In general, the roles performed by a therapeutic recreation specialist can arbitrarily be placed in eight identifiable categories. It should be mentioned that the various roles suggested here have been subscribed to by a large number of therapeutic recreation specialists and are closely associated with the range of therapeutic recreation service that was discussed in Chapter 3. The eight roles are as follows[1]:

- Administrator
- Supervisor
- Community coordinator
- Consultant
- Educator
- Counselor
- Researcher
- Leader (master, technician, assistant)

These roles are not mutually exclusive. In some agencies or institutions, the specialist whose primary role is that of a leader may very well advise client/participants on their leisure needs (counselor), identify activity problems (researcher), teach skills (educator), plan new activities (administrator), and evaluate assistants (supervisor): Nesbitt describes the diversified role of the specialist in this way:

> In a short period of time a therapeutic recreation specialist will set up a day room for the evening . . . arrange for a large group of patients to participate in a community recreation program . . . set up a special party for a small group of patients not yet ready to go into the community or act on their own . . . and sit down for one-to-one counseling with a patient having problems socializing with other people. . .[2]

In other agencies, conditions such as the type of agency, population served, administrative structure, financial limitations, and staff ratio may restrict the flexibility with which the specialist assumes various roles.

The therapeutic recreation specialist, therefore, performs a variety of roles in attempting to achieve the goals and objectives that have been developed, whether they have been developed in relation to a community program or an institutional program. However, conditions may justify variations in the roles.

Although the roles that the specialist may peform have been identified, nothing has been said about the functions associated with these roles. The effectiveness of each role is measured in the final analysis by the extent to which the functions associated with each role are carried out. Let us now briefly characterize these functions.

administrator

The administrator of a therapeutic recreation department or service has responsibility for achieving the objectives of the agency or institution through planning, organizing, assembling resources, and directing and controlling the efforts of therapeutic recreation personnel toward specific goals. To some degree, the series of steps described in the therapeutic recreation process can be used in the total development of the therapeutic recreation department.

The good therapeutic recreation administrator is one who enables the personnel to achieve objectives with a minimum expenditure of resources and effort. Further, therapeutic recreation administrators are often individuals who possess outstanding abilities and skills in therapeutic recreation.

A good administrator, by virtue of education and experience, will have a store of valuable knowledge, an inner confidence, and a demonstrated usefulness on which he can rely. It is obvious that he or she will have the maturity and personal integrity that one expects of anyone in a responsible position. He will know something about the science as well as the art of administration. Likewise, he will appreciate the importance of business methods and techniques. He will be able to reach out and make use of the findings of research in therapeutic recreation, be aware of standards as set by official bodies, and be familiar with the sources of funds that might be available to improve provision of recreation service. Further, while he will respect and be a part of the informal organization in which people work together, he will never fail to recognize his position of responsibility and that of others in the formal organization.

He will be sensitive not only to the needs of special population members, but also to the needs of his staff. Sometimes he will need the courage to act in the face of opposition to better serve the needs of special populations.

He will be a hard worker, unafraid of irregular hours. Successful planning, coordinating, and budgeting to meet the needs of special populations, recruitment, and in-service training will occupy an important part of his time. He will be available to speak in public, and will feel an obligation to do so. He will fight for big things—adequate budget appropriations, research and training grants, and staff morale.

One final word about administrative behavior. The administrator is really a catalyst, dealing with people, assimilating and evaluating their ideas, determining action, and seeing that action takes place to meet the needs of special populations.

Obviously the administrator in a large agency or institution cannot perform all of these functions. Many of them will be carried on by an assistant.

In other agencies and institutions the functions will be performed with the cooperation of the administrator's staff. Such an arrangement is dependent on the size of the service, the number of specialists available, and the plan of allocation of duties based on a functional analysis and distribution of the tasks involved.

supervisor

The supervisor of a therapeutic recreation department or service shares, in many respects, the administration of the department with the administrator. A supervisor may be responsible for administrative, educational, or personnel function, or for all three. The supervisor may be responsible for a specific segment of the program or, if there is more than one supervisor, for various units or program areas.

In municipal recreation departments in larger communities, the term *supervisor* may apply to a person who is responsible for organizing, planning, promoting, and directing programs for special population members. In other municipal settings, the supervisor might outline a specific activity for the mentally retarded to be included in the regular playground program, determine the needed materials, estimate their cost, arrange for their purchase after approval, prepare bulletins and other suitable instructions for playground staff, arrange for instruction of staff at staff meetings, and possibly help conduct the activity.

community coordinator

Broad social and economic changes, technological advances, and changes in patterns of medical, health, and social care have all contributed to the increased need for therapeutic recreation specialists to function within communities. In some communities the coordinator might work independently, assessing and evaluating provision of recreation services for special populations in various agencies, or following through on the referral of an individual from an institution to a public recreation agency. At other times, the coordinator may work closely with a variety of professional workers in a team to promote healthful living.

The scope of the specialist's functions within a community can be as broad as the needs of people. To a large extent, the community coordinator functions as a consumer advocate, a role which is of increasing importance in the community as a result of PL 94-142 and Section 504 of the Rehabilitation Act of 1973. The student who is interested in working with individuals, groups, and families in the community setting outside of the agency or institution, in joining with other community professional workers in improving the community, and in drawing on all aspects of professional preparation to serve individuals, groups, and families will find this role both satisfying and enriching.

consultant

An important role in many health and correctional agencies is that of the therapeutic recreation consultant. With the expansion of knowledge in the health and correctional fields, no one therapeutic recreation specialist can know or be expected to know all there is to know in the various clinical or correctional fields. The function of the therapeutic recreation consultant is to provide assistance through consultation service to therapeutic recreation specialists and allied groups.

I have written elsewhere that consultation:

> ... has two basic elements: problem solving and facilitating change. The consultation process is set in motion as the result of a purposeful decision by an individual or group to bring about improvements in program or system. A consultant is engaged to assist in bringing resources to bear upon the situation.
>
> Consultation is generally understood to be a relationship between two or more individuals for the purpose of exchanging information, cooperating, or collaborating to help solve an existing or potential problem or improve skills and broaden knowledge. One of the individuals in this helping process is the therapeutic recreation specialist—the consultant. The other individual (or individuals)—who may represent a community recreation agency or a voluntary service group or an instituion—is known as the consultee. The consultant is the help-giver, and the consultee is the help-seeker. The consultant and the consultee come together to help the client group, agency, or service group in need.[3]

In the role of a therapeutic recreation consultant, the specialist represents not only himself or herself but the entire profession of therapeutic recreation. The consultant should be confident of his skills and knowledge, but aware of his limitations. He should also be aware of the important contributions from other fields and treat others with courtesy, respect, trust, and tact. He should not represent himself as infallible and omniscient; he should be neither overly critical nor unduly conciliatory.

It would seem reasonable to expect the specialist as a consultant to promote and expand the concept of therapeutic recreation as well as to encourage others to use recreation in connection with their services. The specialist should, when opportunities are available, advise the nurse, occupational therapist, municipal recreator, and others on how they can use recreation more effectively in their program of services.

educator

The role of the educator is primarily restricted to educational programs leading to associate, baccalaureate, or graduate degrees. However, all of the roles discussed here have "educator" aspects—e.g., teaching skills in a specific activity within an institution, consulting, directing an in-service training program on disabling conditions for public recreators. In general, the educator plans, teaches, supervises, and evaluates the learning experience of students; advises students; develops special areas of instruction; conducts research; participates in and contributes to the profession of therapeutic recreation; and carries out other educationally related functions.

It should be mentioned that at present there is a critical shortage of qualified educators—that is, those who have adequate educational preparation and practical experience in the field. It is hoped that some of you will consider the possibility of preparing for this important role. However, it is my personal opinion that the ability to teach includes the competence to plan, organize, direct, coordinate, stimulate, and evaluate programs that can only be obtained through a number of years of fulltime experience with special populations in the field.

counselor

Leisure counseling as a new service performed by therapeutic recreation specialists has been highlighted in Chapter 5. However, it is important to restate that this service is a specialized service which aims to provide guidance and support to persons who encounter problems relative to leisure functioning or who are facing new life situations that require a shift in their traditional leisure functioning. Thus, the specialist who acts as a counselor must have a proficiency in applying principles and techniques of counseling as well as an understanding about the concept and importance of leisure and recreation's contribution to all aspects of the growth and development of special population members. The student is urged to review those leisure counseling references found in Chapter 5 as well as those found in the Suggested References following this chapter.

researcher

Of increasing importance today is the role of the specialist in research. Every professional therapeutic recreation specialist has some responsibility for doing studies in therapeutic recreation. A profession depends on the research that its members carry out for the development of the scientific knowledge on which the profession rests.

Unfortunately, many therapeutic recreators look upon research as the prerogative of intellectuals. It is often thought of as the highly technical pursuit of abstract answers to complicated issues. This is far from the truth. Research is merely the human or rational approach to the solution of problems. Actually, the research attitude should be natural for the therapeutic recreator because of the multidisciplinary interaction required in providing services to special populations. Therapeutic recreators have learned to expect change. They see concepts formulated, tested, and reformulated. They deal daily with unpredictable behavior. Their skill of observation and their ability to analyze behavior have been developed to a far greater degree of expertise than many beginning researchers. In reality, their daily work is the never-ending search for the right answers. This is research; it merely needs to be formalized and communicated so that it can be recognized, appreciated, and used.

The extent of this role depends on a variety of factors. Some specialists will confine their efforts to carrying out simple studies in relation to their own work or to pointing out problems that need to be solved within the services they offer. Generally speaking, the roles that the therapeutic recreation specialist may assume in research are problem identifier, data collector, evaluator, expediter, teacher, or research director. Every specialist needs to develop some skills in conducting and evaluating research if he and the profession are to improve.

Therapeutic recreation specialists not only perform activities of a research nature in their daily functioning, but also are often involved in the research studies of related disciplines. Observations, anecdotal records, and the accumulation of case histories may offer important scientific rewards when carefully reflected upon and compared with like experiences by other people.

leader

As noted, therapeutic recreation has developed to such complexity that its functions are performed by a variety of workers who assume various roles at any one time. The greatest single factor in determining the success of provision of recreation service is the role of the specialist, who provides direct activity service and leadership to special population members. While this role was highlighted in an earlier chapter, its importance requires additional consideration.

In the final analysis, the effectiveness of therapeutic recreation is determined by the extent to which the specialist within the community, agency, or institutional setting performs this leadership role successfully. The nature of the role demands that the specialist not only attune himself to the member's specific problem but that he direct himself to the whole person. Likewise, well-phrased objectives; finely developed facilities; comprehensive, well-balanced programs; competent supervision; and an efficient system of administrative details can be fully utilized only if success is achieved in this role.

Learning results in modification of behavior. The role of the leader is to guide and direct behavior in such a way that participants will have worthwhile activity experiences that contribute satisfactorily to their optimum growth and development. This means that the leader must call upon all of his intelligence, resourcefulness, and ingenuity to provide the most desirable learning situation for his participants. This is most important because behavior change will take place most readily when existing conditions favorably influence the learning situation. It will be up to the leader to create those conditions.

The role of the leader is not limited to providing activities. Other desirable functions include planning, organizing, and evaluating activities; interacting with other members of the treatment team; attending diagnostic and disposition staffing meetings; and guiding the work of others in the provision of service.

Because of the demand for various services within various settings, a variety of workers with different roles and preparatory backgrounds are found performing leadership roles. Some are aides or assistant personnel trained on the job, and others are technicians or professional personnel prepared by junior colleges or colleges. Their specific functions within this leadership role vary from setting to setting. At present, however, those trained as assistants or aides assist in conducting and evaluating activities, teaching skills, maintaining supplies and equipment, or performing routine nonleadership duties that in turn free other more highly trained specialists to offer more specialized activities.

There is a growing number of agencies and institutions utilizing or employing specialists who, by education and experience, have developed a high level of knowledge and skills in special activity areas and leadership. The master leader is the expert practitioner responsible for improving the quality of service by working with specific individuals and by guiding the work of others giving direct service. The master leader has great potential as (1) a role model, (2) a participant-observer, (3) an informal teacher, (4) an investigator, (5) an innovator, and (6) an evaluator-assessor. As more aides, assistants, and technicians enter the profession, a greater movement will undoubtedly be seen in the use of the master leader role.

It has not been my purpose in this short discussion to inform you about the technical competencies that you should acquire to be a successful therapeutic recreation specialist because that will be the function of various other courses that you will take if you continue your studies in therapeutic recreation service. On the contrary, my primary purpose has been to impress upon you the magnitude of various responsibilities that you might assume in contributing to the physical, emotional, social, and intellectual growth and development of the special population members with whom you will be associated.

personal and professional relationships

In therapeutic recreation, because of the nature of the work, you will have one of the greatest opportunities to render a specialized social service. To do this requires that you maintain good human relationships with special population members and professionals alike.

The setting of any agency includes customs, roles, cultural values, and norms. These vary somewhat from community to community, but many characteristics are similar in agencies or institutions throughout the country.

The person outside a hospital, for example, sees the hospital as a different world—that is, as a place where life and death are in a delicate balance under the control of those who work there. Actually the personnel of the hospital, or for that matter the personnel of any agency or institution, are part of a highly structured bureaucratic organization, each person having his defined role and status, which are often indicated by special insignias or uniforms. Lines of authority are well defined, and they become apparent fairly quickly to the new employee. The differences between the therapeutic recreation intern and the recent graduate therapeutic recreation specialist are made obvious through behavior patterns and verbal communication. This hierarchy of the agency is justified as being necessary for quick, precise, and responsible action.

The rules and regulations within a setting, then, govern much of the activity of its personnel. The functions of various professional groups are often rigidly delimited, a situation that sometimes contributes to the difficulty encountered by specialists in assuming their primary responsibility. However, if the physical, emotional, social, and intellectual needs of special populations are to be met, it is essential to maintain sound professional relationships.

This section, therefore, is concerned with helping you realize some of the essentials of establishing and maintaining healthy professional relationships.

with special populations

Although I have discussed the relationship with special population members in various settings in the previous chapter, it seems to me to be important to review those factors again. No two persons are exactly alike, and regardless of the setting in which you work, you will find that you need to be prepared to understand, appreciate, and adjust yourself to persons who differ in racial characteristics, cultural background, and personality. It is important that each person be considered as a human being with problems and interests, not as just another case. It will be necessary to familiarize yourself with the likes and the dislikes of the person and to accustom yourself to differing viewpoints.

What special population members think of you is important. One who is ill or a first offender is particularly susceptible to suggestions; you may have much to do with influencing for the better the thoughts, attitudes, and actions of those with whom you come in contact. Study each person and learn what he is like. This is the first principle to apply if you are to give real help. Studying him means learning something about his home environment, social background, education, occupation, likes, dislikes, and interests. It is important that you be friendly and pleasant. Such a policy often facilitates speedy rapport in the approach to the person.

The impact of illness or incarceration on the special population member may be expressed through hostility toward and criticism of the specialist. If the person who is sick or incarcerated is the breadwinner, there is a natural concern about loss of ability to maintain financial responsibility for the family. There may be additional concern over the cost of illness. The head of the household may not be in a position to make decisions about family matters, and someone else will have to take over. Household routine is disrupted, and other family members must take on new responsibilities. When one of the children is sick or put in a juvenile training school, parents are usually very anxious. They may feel guilty in some way for the child's illness or the fact that the child got in trouble with the law. It is important, therefore, that the specialist understand some of the reasons behind the critical verbal expression of the individual and family members, and accept the hostility and criticism without showing anger and hostility in return.

In summary, a knowledge of human nature in general is a great advantage in working with special populations since they represent all types of people and may be fearful, dubious, or critical. It is important to learn to recognize and to deal with each, and to do this requires experience.

The other point to be considered here is the relationship with the family. In most settings the specialist will have very little contact with the family, although in leisure counseling, homebound programs, and public recreation programs for special members, the specialist may be thrown into close and constant contact with the individual's family and friends. Families and friends, under strain, are likely to be critical. They probably will make impossible suggestions and ask endless questions, but you can avoid much friction if instead of resenting the interference, you deal with them kindly, though firmly, thus inspiring in them the same confidence you wish the special population member to have in you.

with colleagues

In your relationships with members of your own profession, you will associate with two general groups: those to whom you are responsible and your co-specialists. Loyalty is all important. This includes a willingness to make some sacrifices for the good of all and to cooperate with your colleagues. To make this possible, good nature, an even good temperament, tolerance, cheerfulness, unselfishness, and understanding must be cultivated, and such traits as envy, jealousy, rivalry, and distrust must be weeded out.

In your association with those to whom you are responsible and who are directing you in your work, you can manifest your interest by attempting to understand and follow their directions, by accepting and profiting from their direction, and by accepting and profiting from their evaluation of you and your performance. Equally important are your willingness and your ability to adjust yourself quickly to the routines of the organization where you work. If you accept, without fault-finding, its policies and practices as well as the facilities that it offers, you are bound to fit well into the situation. Until you have earned your right to make suggestions by demonstrating your competence and developing an understanding of the underlying problems and their appropriate solutions, your evaluation should be reserved.

Knowing the total scheme of an organization and where you fit therein will lessen the danger of establishing and maintaining poor cooperative relationships. If you know your role in an organization, you will be less likely to take your problems or recommendations to the wrong group or person.

In your relations with your colleagues, remember that each person has obligations and responsibilities as well as privileges and rights. If you keep this in mind, you will have little difficulty in establishing a spirit of goodwill and in gaining the favorable opinion of your associates. However, if you are not careful of the rights of others, you will find yourself always forwarding your own vested interests to the exclusion of those of others.

with other professionals

Therapeutic recreation specialists work with a variety of professional personnel, whether in an agency or an institutional setting or in a community setting.

Characteristics that help to develop or maintain good relationships are a sense of fairness, a spirit of acceptance, a sense of humor, an insight into and an understanding of human nature, self-control, a respect for the views and individuality of the people with whom one is working, and an awareness of self and, therefore, of others. Characteristics that destroy or hinder the establishment of good relationships are a hot temper, oversensitiveness, touchiness, and resentment.

One must keep in mind that effective service is brought about through working with others. While the special population member always comes first, regardless of setting, in many instances you cannot accomplish your service without the assistance of others. A close working relationship with others brings more effective service, preventing duplications and gaps.

One way in which you might develop closer working relationships with members of other professions is by actually knowing them through attending meetings at which the various professions are represented. Inviting members of other professions to certain of your meetings will also help.

with the community

The decade of the 1960s has seen the emerging prevalence of concerened citizens demanding that they have not only the opportunity to be heard but also to participate in the decision-making process regarding the various social institutions of society that affect their lives. Special population members are a part of these concerned citizens. You, as a member of the community and as a member of a social welfare-conscious profession have the responsibility to improve leisure service for special population members. In addition, you have a responsibility to work in conjunction with special population consumers. In this regard, the therapeutic recreator as a consumer advocate has two basic responsibilities to the special population consumer according to Edginton and Compton:

> The therapeutic recreator has two basic responsibilities to the special populations consumer. First, he must accurately reflect their needs and desires with respect to the quality and quantity of recreation, leisure and cultural services. Second, he must provide the special populations consumer with the widest array of information about, and education opportunities in, recreation, leisure and cultural activities, so the individual can practice the art of "consumerism." By giving the individual the opportunity to make decisions from available information, and past or observed experiences, the outcome is a more enlightened and satisfied consumer.

They continue:

> It stands to reason that if our special populations are given more opportunities to engage in the decision-making process, they will eventually assume more dynamic roles in not only consumerism but advocacy. The end result is a special populations consumer who becomes self-actualizing. One who is determining his quality of life rather than passively participating in recreation, leisure and cultural pursuits which are planned for him. In addition, the quality, quantity and relevancy of recreation, leisure and cultural services will be vastly improved as the special populations consumer becomes a part of the planning process.[4]

To accomplish the responsibilities stated above and assist the special population member to become "self-actualizing" means that you must take part in the planning, the thinking, and the action in your community.

with oneself

To this point we have discussed the various roles that may be assumed by a therapeutic recreation specialist and his relationships with others. Here, we will attempt to summarize those personal qualities expected in the specialist. I look back upon my experiences and can't help but remember therapists who were therapeutic recreation specialists only because of the job and not because of a concern for people. Likewise, some instructors become too concerned with techniques as opposed to the human characteristics that are necessary to be a therapeutic recreation specialist.

The therapeutic recreation specialist should be personally concerned for the welfare of all people and should appreciate differences of nationality, race, creed, and other personality characteristics as sources of strength, not as barriers. The specialist must understand the interests and needs of people and have a genuine respect for human dignity as well as a sympathetic attitude toward the opinions and personalities of others. The specialist shows a maturity of judgment, has a sense of humor, has a desire to serve, and is able to work with many kinds of people, helping them discover and develop their own capacities. In other words, the specialist is a therapeutic agent. The specialist feels a deep responsibility to the job, to the community, and to himself. It goes without saying that the specialist has good physical, emotional, and social health.

occupational opportunities

Despite the fact that there has been an increase in the employment of therapeutic recreation specialists during the last decade and that this trend will undoubtedly continue, comparatively little, if any, information is available relative to the types of positions available and where specialists are employed. Some educators and practitioners will consider this section very elementary; however, my experience indicates that students are extremely concerned about these matters. For that matter, even specialists who have had a number of years of experience are still concerned.

The changes that have taken place in recent years and are now taking place in therapeutic recreation occupational opportunities have been noted elsewhere. However, in brief, they are due to economic influences, social and political developments, scientific advances, changing concepts such as those relating to occupational and team relationships, and other influences within the various health and correctional professions and within therapeutic recreation itself.

scope of therapeutic recreation occupations

In Chapter 3 we noted the agencies that provide service to special populations and that are the major employers of therapeutic recreation specialists. Within these employing agencies are many diverse job opportunities, enabling you to satisfy your interests and use your abilities as you progress in experience and continuing education.

The following list gives a general idea of the scope of therapeutic recreation positions:

Some Positions Usually Restricted to Therapeutic Recreation Specialists

- Director of therapeutic recreation service or recreation
- Assistant director of therapeutic recreation service or recreation
- Supervisor of therapeutic recreation service or recreation in a health or correctional facility
- Supervisor of therapeutic recreation service or recreation in a public recreation agency
- Therapeutic recreation specialist or recreation leader
- Therapeutic recreation technician or recreation technician
- Therapeutic recreation assistant or recreation assistant
- Therapeutic recreation aide or recreation aide
- Therapeutic recreation specialist in private practice
- Consultant in therapeutic recreation service or recreation in or to a public or private agency or to a professional organization—e.g., state board of health, department of correction, or other government units—or a community organization—e.g., community health council
- Camp director (supervisor or counselor) providing service in a residential or day camp for special populations
- Rehabilitation therapist[5]
- Patient activity therapist.[5]
- Activity therapist[5]
- Adjunctive therapist[5]
- Director or head of a specialty program in therapeutic recreation in a university or college
- Coordinator or supervisor of field work for any of the educational programs in therapeutic recreation service

Some Positions in Which Therapeutic Recreation Specialists Are Sometimes Employed[6]

- Administrator of an acute or chronic disease facility
- Administrator of mental health-mental retardation regions or districts
- Administrator of a nursing home, home for the aged, county home, orphanage, or convalescent home for children or adults
- Administrator of a special center—i.e., alcoholic or drug treatment or rehabilitation facility
- Administrator of a special school or training center for the mentally retarded, blind, deaf, etc.
- Chairman of a department or division of recreation in a university or college
- Coordinator or director of an activity therapy service or rehabilitation service in a health care facility
- Correctional counselor or officer
- Director of research program
- Director of volunteer service
- Feature writer on therapeutic recreation subjects
- Group therapist
- Hospital administrator or assistant
- Librarian in an institution
- Mental health supervisor or worker
- Patient care or homecare coordinator
- Probation or parole officer
- Social or welfare worker
- Specialist in child guidance
- Superintendent of a public park and recreation agency

job titles

Unlike many other professions and occupations, a job title in a therapeutic recreation department or service is not always necessarily descriptive of the specific roles or functions performed by the person holding that title. Almost all federal agencies and state agencies that employ therapeutic recreation specialists have adopted standardized job titles and descriptions used with their respective jurisdictions. However, not all private or public local agencies that are associated with national and state agencies and that provide similar services conform to the job titles. Job descriptions also vary according to the pattern of duties imposed upon the indvidual professional worker as a result of local conditions. Furthermore, while general functions may be similar, specific functions may differ markedly depending upon the agency, its size, the type of special population members being served, and its care and treatment philosophy.

The meanings of the many titles are especially confusing when it is found that specialists holding various titles may have practically the same general functions. The titles most commonly used today to designate a person just entering the therapeutic recreation profession with a baccalaureate degree and usually responsible for direct services to the disabled person or social offender are *Recreation Leader, Therapeutic Recreation Specialist, Activity Therapist,* or *Rehabilitation Therapist.* Theoretically, it might be assumed that the person holding the title of Therapeutic Recreation Specialist would be better trained and prepared than the person holding the title Activity Therapist. However, such is not necessarily the case. Depending upon the agency, the terms could very well be used interchangeably.

It is not uncommon in nursing homes or small agencies where only one therapeutic recreation specialist or activity therapist is employed for that person to hold the title of *Director.* The reason for having the title Director is that the person is responsible for all phases of the program — administering the program (including budgeting, ordering of supplies and equipment, etc.), arranging for residents to participate in an off-home program, and supervising volunteers, as well as planning, organizing, and directing activities within the home. In addition, most positions, if not all, concerned with offering services of an activity nature in nursing homes use the title *Activity Therapist.*

In larger agencies there are likely to be numerous titles given to various therapeutic recreation specialists. For example, the person in complete charge of the therapeutic recreation department or service might hold the title Director. However, what is more commonly found in federal and state agencies is the use of a Roman numeral after the title to indicate the level of responsiblity. The title *Therapeutic Recreation Specialist V, Activity Therapist V,* or *Rehabilitation Therapist V* may very well correspond with Director, and numeral IV with Supervisor, and III with a specialist who has had one year of experience, and so on down the scale to the beginning specialist with no experience. All of these individuals in one way or another direct their efforts toward helping special population members.

employment opportunities

While we have identified to some degree where therapeutic recreation specialists work in Chapter 3, it is well to list those agencies and institutions through which the specialist secures employment:

- Alcoholic rehabilitation centers
- Armed forces hospitals
- Boards of health: state, county, or local
- Community mental health-mental retardation centers
- Community volunteer coordination centers
- Correctional institutions: federal, state, county, or local; for juveniles or adults, men or women
- Day care centers
- Departments of mental health, mental retardation, and correction
- Developmental centers
- Educational institutions—i.e., colleges and universities
- Extended care facilities
- Halfway houses, hotels, and group homes
- Health project agencies
- Homes for the aged
- Hospitals: public, nonprofit, and proprietary; general and special
- Intermediate care facilities
- Manpower programs
- Narcotic treatment centers
- National and state therapeutic recreation or recreation associations
- Neuropsychiatric facilities
- Nursing homes
- Private voluntary health agencies
- Public recreation agencies at state, county, and local levels of government
- Public school systems
- Recreation services of the American Red Cross
- Rehabilitation centers
- Residential and day camps or specialized camps
- Settlement houses
- Special recreation centers for the disabled
- Special schools and training centers for the mentally retarded, blind, deaf, etc.
- Voluntary health and welfare organizations
- Youth-serving agencies and organizations

selection of a position

Socioeconomic factors such as salaries, fringe benefits, hours of work, opportunities for advancement, and retirement plans are often critical in vocational choice. However, they are not the only factors to be considered. Another reason for career choice springs from altruistic or humanitarian motives, based on a desire to give a social service to mankind. Still another reason for a certain choice is to gain ability and training. This is an important reason for the specialist who is concerned about long-range vocational planning. One type of work may be used as a steppingstone to another or as a basis for further education. A graduate of an associate degree program may look for a position where he can combine work with attendance at a four-year college or university. Some institutions allow time off to attend school, and others may provide tuition. A combination of several of these reasons may be found in one person.

obtaining career information

It is not enough to know your aptitudes, abilities, and interests. These need to be related to conditions in therapeutic service, occupational trends, and requirements. Develop an appreciation of occupational trends, and survey the scope of opportunities in the profession as a whole. Learn the requirements of each type of therapeutic recreation position that interests you as a possible choice. If any specialization within the field reveals definite personnel shortages, you may want to train for it if you are potentially suitable and like it sufficiently. It is not easy to obtain this information. However, your college adviser, if he has a therapeutic recreation background, should be able to assist. Analyze your personal and professional qualifications and interests, determine how they can be used to best advantage, and finally compare the opportunities from which you will make your final selection.

There are several ways to get acquainted with the many available areas within therapeutic recreation service, the following being some of the most important:

1. Read books, pamphlets, and brochures on what others have to say about different areas of therapeutic recreation service.
2. Talk with those in particular areas of specialization to learn what they like about each, the pleasant and unpleasant sides of work.
3. Relate all experiences in the basic curriculum to occupational planning.
4. Make use of every opportunity to observe and learn about the work.

5. Make personal investigations of the work and even volunteer your service.

6. Secure available information from headquarters of professional therapeutic recreation groups—national and state.

7. Review employment standards and job descriptions.

You yourself should make the final decision about which area you will enter. Study the whole situation. Get all the counseling and help you can obtain. It should be in an area where you can be of real service and one that offers opportunities for professional and personal development and advancement. It should offer you personal satisfaction and a sense of fulfillment. Understand clearly that you cannot, immediately after graduation, go into too advanced a position because you probably lack sufficient academic and professional preparation and you certainly do not have enough experience. Some have, and have never been happy; nor could they progress or make valuable contributions.

The key to making an occupational choice appears to be in the way you appraise yourself and the work you want to do. Much depends on your future goals—goals for practice, goals for continuing education, and goals for your future life in general.

locating a position

The way you go about finding a position depends to some extent on your field of interest in therapeutic recreation. In general, the channels are the professional organization of recreation (National Recreation and Park Association), the placement office in the educational institution from which you are being or were graduated, announcements of civil service examinations, advertisements in professional periodicals, relatives, friends, acquaintances, and direct contacts with employers.

Therapeutic recreation specialists are selected by the following three main methods: (1) by the agency empowered to select its own workers; (2) by Civil Service commissions or boards; and (3) by central personnel agencies responsible to local administrators. Furthermore, the procedures used in the selection process to reveal the qualifications of the applicant may consist of a written test, a practical performance test, and/or a personal interview. The relative weight given to each of these varies with the nature of the position and the employer.

Because private agencies and institutions employ proportionately fewer specialists than public agencies, they select their own specialists directly. They usually require a personal interview and may require a written test. Public agencies, on the other hand, require a written test and may require a personal interview. Most appointments made to federal, state, county and city agencies or institutions are made from Civil Service lists. The general procedure is for the Civil Service to certify three eligibles for each vacancy, and the appointing authorities make the appointment from the list. The person best qualified of the three, in the opinion of the authority, receives the appointment. Specialists qualifying for a position but who do not receive an appointment are placed on an eligible list, which is used in case of subsequent vacancies.

All appointments are made on a temporary basis. A probation period of at least six months appears to be standard procedure, regardless of the type of agency or institution. At intervals during the probation period, the specialist is evaluated as to his ability to do the job. No permanent appointment is made until the director or supervisor certifies in writing that the specialist is capable of carrying out his duties in a responsible manner.

applying for a position

The two most common methods of applying for a position are the written application, which may be either a letter or a formal application form, and the personal interview. The second often results from the first.

A letter of application is important because the prospective employer uses it to judge your scholarship and ability, much of your personality, and possibly how you keep records. If it is well written, it may open the way for further consideration. This is often prevented if it is poorly written. Make sure that you have followed the principles of correct letter writing; further, see that your letter is clear, complete, concise, and courteous and that it conveys your exact meaning, with correct spelling, punctuation, and paragraphing. The letter should be no more than one or, at most, two typewritten pages. If your record of personal and professional education and experience has preceded your letter, you need not attach such.

You cannot be too careful in completing application forms because frequently inexactness and carelessness in this respect have been the chief causes of failure to secure a desirable position. Many candidates for positions leave significant gaps in their history and experience. Gaps should always be explained, at least by some brief reference. There is no point in concealing any relevant fact from a prospective employer.

A personal interview, when seeking employment, is very important, not only because it gives the employer a chance to review your qualifications, but also because it gives you an opportunity to visit the agency or institution, to meet some of the people with whom you may be working, and to learn about the philosophy, policies, and practices of the employer or association. Likewise, it gives the employer an opportunity to find out about you and your philosophy.

In preparation for the interview, find out all you can about the position in view and the organization. A definite appointment may be obtained by letter or by telephone. You will want to appear for the interview on time and in good physical condition. If it has been arranged for you to tour the agency or institution and talk to potential co-workers, plan sufficient time to do so.

It is best to let the interviewer introduce the subject of salary. The amount of the salary depends on the nature of the position, the responsibilities of the position, your capacity and skill in doing the work, and the personnel policies of the agency or institution. Salaries are usually commensurate with the training and qualifications required to secure and retain competent personnel. Any statement relating to specific salary scales has only limited or temporary value because of the changing costs of consumer goods and the widely different pay scales for all levels of workers both in different sections of the country and in different size agencies and institutions. It is sufficient to say that salaries in private settings are usually open and negotiable, while in public settings there are salary schedules or ranges for each position that have been set by the personnel commission or board.

After the interview, write the interviewer a short letter expressing again your appreciation of his courtesy, and if further interviews seem advisable, arrange for them. If you are appointed to the desired position, your letter of acceptance is important because it gives you the opportunity of defining your interpretation of what already has been decided concerning salary, functions, and the exact date of beginning your service. It is equally important to write a follow-up even though you are not accepted for the position.

SUGGESTED REFERENCES

Bannon, Joseph J. *Leisure Resources: Its Comprehensive Planning.* Englewood Cliffs, N.J.: Prentice-Hall, Inc., 1976

Bernsten, L. and R. H. Dana. *Interviewing and the Health Professions.* New York: Appleton-Century-Crofts, 1970.

Blake, R. R. and J. S. Mouton. *Consultation.* Reading, Ma.: Addison Wesley, 1976.

Edginton, Christopher R. and John G. Williams. *Productive Management of Leisure Service Organizations: A Behavioral Approach.* New York: John Wiley and Sons, 1978.

"Getting Your Ideas Across," *Hospital Supervision,* 5:19 (1972).

Goldstein, Judith E. (ed.) *Consultation: Enhancing Leisure Service Delivery to Handicapped Children and Youth.* Arlington, Va.: National Recreation and Park Association, May 1977.

Hillman, William A. "Therapeutic Recreation Specialist as Advocate," *Therapeutic Recreation Journal,* 6:2 (1972), p. 50.

"Keys to Effective Listening," *Hospital Supervision,* 5:20 (1972).

Kinney, W. B. and others, "Rules for Radical Recreation Workers," *Therapeutic Recreation Journal,* 11:3 (1977) pp. 105–111.

Lippitt, Gordon, and Ronald Lippitt. *The Consulting Process in Action.* La Jolla, Ca.: University Associates, Inc., 1978.

Mathieu, Robert P. *Hospital and Nursing Home Management: An Instructional and Administrative Manual.* Philadelphia: W. B. Saunders Company, 1971

Mayeroff, Milton. *On Caring.* New York: Harper and Row, Publishers, 1972.

McDowell, Jr., Chester F. "Leisure Counseling: Professional Consideration for Therapeutic Recreation," *Journal of Physical Education and Recreation.* 47:1 (1976), p. 27.

National Recreation and Park Association, "Position Statement—Advocacy," *Therapeutic Recreation Journal,* 11:1 (1977), pp. 3–5.

O'Morrow, Gerald S. (ed.) *Administration of Activity Therapy Service.* Springfield, Ill.: Charles C Thomas Publishers, 1966.

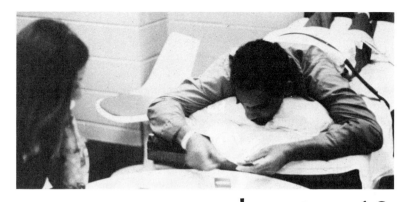

chapter 10
personal professional development in therapeutic recreation

There is no individual, in my opinion, who has a greater opportunity for contributing in the broadest sense to the wholesome growth and development of special population members than the therapeutic recreation specialist. By reason of this fact alone, there is no group of specialists who face a greater obligation to undertake their task with the most thorough preparation and the most profound realization of the responsibilities involved.

Before you can be a therapeutic recreation specialist, it is important for you to realize what is involved in the educational preparation of the specialist as well as to become acquainted with the organizations that concern themselves with therapeutic recreation. In this way you, as a potential future specialist, will not only develop a sound personal philosophy of therapeutic recreation and the therapeutic recreation process, but also become imbued with a spirit that will enable you to assume, eventually, your place as a leader in offering recreation service to special populations.

professional education

Among the events of one's life, selecting a vocation is one of the most crucial. The final choice of one's work is a powerful determiner of the people one meets, the kind of relationships one has with them, the types of experiences one has, where one lives, and so on. Most young men and women want to make this decision early in their college life. It would be helpful if they could have experience in several vocations before deciding. But this would mean that several of their best years would be spent in extraneous activities. There is no question that a student should find out early about the vocation he has selected.

Therapeutic recreation is one of the careers requiring a high school diploma and further academic work at the college or university level as basic preparation. Advancement beyond the apprentice stage or professional leader level position usually requires advanced study.

According to a recent survey conducted in 1979 by Anderson and Stewart, 137 institutions of 156 responding institutions of higher learning (junior and senior colleges and universities) offer an option or concentration in therapeutic recreation. At the time of the survey, nearly 8000 students at both the undergraduate and graduate level were enrolled in a therapeutic recreation option. In addition, the study also showed that 85 percent of the 137 institutions give attention to a broad range of special population types.[1]

therapeutic recreation curricula

Before discussing the general and professional education requirements necessary to becoming a therapeutic recreation specialist, it is well for us to consider how a curriculum in therapeutic recreation is developed.

It is not at all uncommon for students who are specializing in some subject to wonder why they "have to take all this other stuff." Engineering students, for example, always seem to have difficulty understanding why they have to take English. "You don't have to know English to be an engineer," they say.

Similarly students who are specializing in a particular area of a field frequently have difficulty in understanding why they have to know something about the field as a whole in addition to their specialized area of interest. Thus, the medical student who plans to be a nose, throat, and ear specialist is sometimes prone to be a little impatient with his genetics courses, psychiatric lectures, and the like.

The same kinds of protests are common in the fields of recreation and therapeutic recreation. "Why," students ask, "do we have to take all these other things when we're going to work only with the mentally ill?" "Or the mentally retarded?" "Or the physically disabled in the community?" "Or inmates?"

There are very good reasons for requiring certain courses. Research investigations and conferences involving leading educators and practitioners in this field have resulted in recommended course requirements. These professionals have attempted to answer the question: What academic preparation is needed to qualify as a therapeutic recreation specialist?

As early as 1953, the Standards and Training Committee of the Hospital Recreation Section of the American Recreation Society made recommendations. The National Recreation Association's Consulting Service on Recreation for the Ill and Handicapped in 1961 brought together leaders in the field to discuss and suggest curriculum models and competencies in therapeutic recreation.[2]

In the early 1970s some 40 therapeutic recreation practitioners and educators worked together to suggest practical and functional directions for teachers to take in preparing professional programs in therapeutic recreation.[3] Therapeutic recreation educators working independently and others with funding from the Bureau of Education for the Handicapped have studied the relative importance of specific therapeutic recreation courses as well as identifying tasks and competencies needed by therapeutic recreation professionals.[4,5,6,7,8,9] In 1976, in association with the NRPA Council on Accreditation, the NTRS Board of Directors approved competencies needed for professional practice.[10] These competencies will be discussed shortly.

Because of these types of conferences, investigations, and professional committee work, course requirements are becoming more standardized. But there are still variations from college to college, and the student is cautioned to investigate the course offerings as well as the academic, professional, and personal qualifications of the faculty members responsible for teaching the therapeutic recreation courses. Likewise, the student is cautioned about attempting to specialize at the undergraduate level. The undergraduate student should attempt to obtain as broad an education as possible in therapeutic recreation.

There are, however, common considerations in the development of any professional curriculum. McGlothlin has said that professional education must help the student to achieve five sets of attributes:

1. Competence to practice his profession, with sufficient knowledge and skill to satisfy its requirements.
2. Social understanding, with sufficient breadth to place his practice in the context of the society which supports it, and to develop capacity for leadership in public affairs.

3. Personality characteristics which make possible effective practice.

4. Zest for continued study which will steadily increase knowledge and skill needed by practice.

5. Competence in conducting or interpreting research so that he can add to human knowledge either through discovery or application of new facts.[11]

Generally speaking, a combination of general liberal education and occupational preparation should lay the foundation for practice, for growth, and for future education. Therapeutic recreation education is the process that transforms an individual from a high school graduate to a therapeutic recreation student to a competent practitioner. During this time the student must learn the necessary skills and the values and expectations of the professional role.

In brief, the major areas of learning experience in therapeutic recreation are derived from (1) the concept that recreation is essentially an area of living and as such should be available to all people; (2) the major health and social problems of society; (3) the health and social problems of all people regardless of age, race, creed, and socioeconomic status; (4) all phases of health and social work—promotion, maintenance, improvement of illness, and rehabilitation; and (5) consideration of normal health and social conditions and deviations from these. Learning experiences include practicing in situations where health and social problems are dealt with—in hospitals and institutions, nursing homes, comprehensive health agencies, correctional institutions, special schools and training centers, homes for the aged, rehabilitation centers, and public recreation agencies at all levels of government.

General Education

The importance of general education cannot be minimized. Anyone desiring to enter a professional field must necessarily have a basic preparation. This requirement is characteristic of all professions and is, likewise, found among community and junior colleges and institutions of higher learning. Its purpose is to enrich the personal life of the individual and help him to meet his responsibility to society. It also serves another purpose—that of acquiring skills necessary for serving sociey. The student of therapeutic recreation needs a good understanding of his or her own motivation, of society, of human nature in general, and of human needs and their social expression and skill in interpersonal relations in particular. Also needed is training in the intellectual skills of analysis and interpretation and the ability to use the written and spoken language effectively as a method of communication. Knowledge of other disciplines such as history, biology and the physical sciences, political science, government and economics, psychology, social psychology, sociology, and statistics is necessary if you are to utilize the discipline of therapeutic recreation to its fullest. The independence of each discipline does not preclude the necessity for relating or tying together various disciplines if we are to solve the increasing number of health and social problems arising from special populations.

The specific general education requirements will vary with each institution and you will probably be permitted to select courses within some or all of the areas of general education listed below:

1. *Communication arts:* English, speech.
2. *Philosophy and the arts:* art, literature, foreign language, philosophy, music, drama.
3. *Science and mathematics:* chemistry, geography, geology, astronomy, biology, botany, zoology, physics, mathematics.
4. *Social and behavioral sciences:* anthropology, economics, history, political science, psychology, sociology, health, criminology.
5. *Physical education activity courses.*

If you are permitted to choose areas, or courses within areas, in satisfying the general education requirements of your institution, give careful consideration to the selection of courses representing disciplines that are related to therapeutic recreation. For example, the therapeutic recreation student who has an idea that he would like to work eventually with social offenders would do well to select introductory courses in psychology, sociology, social psychology, and criminology. Whatever the requirements and selection of courses in general education, this should be viewed as an opportunity to obtain the broad background in the humanities and the social and behavioral sciences necessary to the growth of a well-rounded professional person.

Professional Education

In addition to the general education common to all, there is a further area of preparation upon which the effectiveness of therapeutic recreation leadership depends: the area of education designed to train the therapeutic recreation specialist. Built upon the foundation of general education, this area is that part of the prospective therapeutic recreation specialist's education that enables him to become competent in the specific knowledge, understanding, and skills peculiar to recreation and therapeutic recreation, and that makes him a true specialist.

Many students frequently do not realize until later that the beginning general courses required aid them in developing greater understanding of their major area of study. Many general education courses and major prerequisites provide a firm foundation of knowledge for studying required courses in the major subject area and lead quite logically into more technical professional courses. These will be preceded by a foundation or orientation course in the major, an introduction to recreation or therapeutic recreation, which may include materials such as are offered in this book, so that the students may realize almost immediately what is in store for them as professionals. While persons in charge of professional curricula in recreation or therapeutic recreation do not agree on professional course names, they do agree that the education must not be narrow or too highly specialized at the junior or senior college level; rather it must prepare students to be flexible so as to meet new and constantly changing social conditions. They agree also that the professional program must prepare students to solve problems, think effectively, communicate effectively, make relevant judgments, and discriminate among values. In short, the professional program must be functional. When all is said and done, the fact that students have been exposed to courses by certain names has little significance. The worth of any curriculum will depend largely upon the integrity of the institution and its faculty.

Since therapeutic recreation is accomplished by one human being dealing with another human being or group of human beings, the professional educational curriculum today should supply well-rounded training in the biological, social, and clinical sciences, each of which is closely bound to the principles and the practice of therapeutic recreation and to the applied therapeutic activities.

The primary function of therapeutic recreation service is to provide widespread service to meet the various physical, emotional, social, and intellectual needs of special population members as they exist within various social and economic backgrounds. Thus, the successful therapeutic recreation specialist must not only be competent in the appreciation, knowledge, and skills basic to all leaders in recreation, but also possess competencies in his own specialization. The professional competencies in therapeutic recreation which have been accepted and approved by the NRPA Council on Accreditation relative to undergraduate preparation are as follows:

- Knowledge of illness and disability with implications for recreation programming, i.e., physically handicapped, mentally ill, emotionally disturbed, developmentally disabled, penally incarcerated, and aging.
- Knowledge of specific service delivery systems related to treatment and rehabilitation, i.e. medical models, leisure education models.
- Knowledge of administrative policies and procedures associated with treatment and rehabilitation settings.

- Knowledge of specific facilitation and counseling techniques predominantly used with special populations.
- Knowledge of specific needs of special populations, and activity modification techniques needed to adapt activities to individual needs.
- Understanding of procedures used in formulating individual and group assessment, prescription, and evaluation plans with special populations.
- Understanding of principles used for recording and reporting client information in treatment and rehabilitation settings.
- Understanding of administrative principles related to community recreation programs for special populations.
- Knowledge of facility design and equipment modification related to accessibility and mainstreaming concepts.
- Knowledge of institution to community service continuum designs.
- Knowledge of both normal and abnormal growth and development as traditionally taught in related fields, including: special education; psychology; sociology; anatomy/physiology/kinesiology.
- Ability to apply the unique practices and principles of therapeutic recreation in authorized practicum experiences commensurate with the approved NTRS guidelines for field placement.[12]

In sum, the process of therapeutic recreation education is demanding. Over a period of four years you will acquire not only massive amounts of information and a great variety of skills but also a sense of confidence in your ability to help others and a frame of mind oriented toward action.

professional organizations

What are professional organizations? Why do we have them? What do they do? Should I be concerned about them now? Later?

Any or all of these questions you have undoubtedly asked yourself, or will ask yourself at some time early in your professional career. They are questions frequently asked by persons in the profession, and ones deserving thoughtful consideration. This section provides some helpful information about professional organizations.

meaning of professional organizations

The full meaning of a profession cannot be grasped without understanding its relationship to a specific discipline. Simply defined, a *discipline* includes an arrangement, from simple to complex, of all the facts and understandings related to a specialized body of knowledge. For example, the discipline of zoology includes the study of general physiology, vertebrate physiology, embryology, invertebrate zoology, endocrinology, heredity and evolution, genetics, cytology, and neurology.

Development of a discipline is not enough. Without an organized effort to educate people in the discipline, to discover new knowledge in the discipline, and to educate leaders in the application of the discipline, it would soon fall by the wayside in the fast pace of our modern society. This is one reason why professions have sprung up around specific disciplines. For example, theology has the ministry as its profession, jurisprudence has the law, and the teaching of various disciplines is supported by education. One of the major purposes and justifications for any profession is to serve society and not the ends of a particular interest group. Therefore, it becomes the responsibility of a given profession to establish standards for education in the discipline, to recruit qualified candidates, to push back the frontiers of knowledge in the discipline through study and research, to develop a code of ethics by which members of the profession operate, and to establish and promote organizations that enable members to share interests and new knowledge in the discipline.

Many writers have listed criteria of professionalization. One such listing, prepared by Horton, is as follows:

1. A profession must satisfy an indispensable social need and be based upon a well-established and socially accepted scientific principle.

2. It must demand adequate preprofessional and cultural training.

3. It must demand the possession of a body of specialized and systematized knowledge.

4. It must give evidence of needed skills which the public does not possess; that is, skills which are partly native and partly acquired.

5. It must have developed a scientific technique which is the result of tested experience.

6. It must require the exercise of discretion and judgment as to time and manner of the performance of duty. This is in contrast to the kind of work which is subject to immediate direction and supervision.

7. It must be a type of beneficial work, the result of which is not subject to standardization in terms of unit performance or time element.

8. It must have a group consciousness designed to extend scientific knowledge in technical language.

9. It must have sufficient self-impelling power to retain its members

throughout life. It must not be used as a mere stepping stone to other occupations.

10. It must recognize its obligations to society by insisting that its members live up to an established code of ethics.[13]

In addition to the above, the author would like to offer the following additional criteria as a basis for determining professional activities in therapeutic recreation service:

1. A profession has the responsibility for determining its own goals and responsibilities for meeting society's needs for service. In deciding its own goals, consideration must be given to the profession's role and function in relation to the other correctional and health professions.

2. It needs to decide its own specific functions and responsibilities as a unique profession and as a member of the interdisciplinary group composed of the correctional and health professions.

3. It needs to include in its code of ethics what the particular professional group ought to know in order to have an understanding of the ethical principles that govern professional practice. Another important point to stress is the ethical obligation of the professional specialist to give service to the public above all—above personal considerations such as remuneration, although, of course, "the laborer is worthy of his hire."

The potential specialist may now ask: How well does therapeutic recreation measure up to these various criteria? While the growth toward professional status has been uneven at times and even questioned, there has been a movement over the years toward greater professionalization. In the last decade or so, therapeutic recreation has been recognized and accepted as meeting the recreation needs of special populations by health and correctional professionals and other interested citizens, programs for the preparation of therapeutic recreation specialists have been developed, professional standards of practice conducive to high-quality service have been developed, a voluntary registration program has been initiated, and research toward the identification and elaboration of knowledge in therapeutic recreation has been conducted, all of which point to a growth of professionalization. Park describes this growing effort toward professionalism in these terms:

As a profession, we have begun to take pride in ourselves as a professional body; we believe that we have a unique and valuable service to perform; and we are beginning to assert ourselves on behalf of the people we serve. This is

an important step toward assuming full responsibility as a member of a professional team that provides services to the ill, disabled, or handicapped.[14]
...Today we can affirm that therapeutic recreation does have a unique service to perform. We are beginning to identify a body of knowledge necessary to provide that service. Through the work and efforts of many individuals over the years, a strong professional organization, so necessary to the development of our field has emerged.[15]

To this point we can say that professional organizations are associations formed voluntarily by persons working in a profession, primarily for the purpose of organizing the resources of the members for effective service to others; second, to advance the quality and standards of the profession and its members; and third, to advance the welfare of the members.

Obviously, the continuing improvement of the profession and its members does not "just happen." Recognizing that concerted, purposeful, planned action is needed, members voluntarily form professional organizations in order to serve more effectively than they could as individuals or small groups. It is a characteristic of the time-honored professions that they accept responsibility for the quality of their service, standards of professional practice, and behavior of members.

Professional organizations do not carry legal authority since they are voluntary organizations. However, they often work closely with state and federal governments and other professional organizations on matters pertaining to their profession's interest.

function of professional organizations

There are many ways in which the purpose of a professional organization is achieved. Most of these ways can be included within the following three types: (1) meetings, such as conventions or conferences, usually held annually; workshops on special problems, symposiums, and demonstrations; (2) working committees or groups, consisting of standing, special, and joint committees; and (3) publications and audio-visual aids. If you analyze any one of these three functions directed toward the purpose of a professional organization, you will quickly recognize that they contribute in some way to the improvement of the quality of the profession either directly or indirectly by contributing to the professional growth of its members.

structure of professional organizations

There is no one best structural pattern for professional organizations. Each organization attempts to design that structure that permits it to work effectively toward it objectives. There are, however, some structural elements that most organizations have in common. First, most professions have a national organization, and within this national structure smaller geographical districts or regions, each made up of several states, are formed to permit better communication and more opportunity for face-to-face meetings. Another common pattern is the state organization, which makes it easier to communicate and work on problems and topics of local interest. Many state associations have subdivisions, wherein professionals can meet together on topics and problems of special interest to them.

A second common element of professional organizations is that their elected officers and board of directors are responsible for planning and effecting the activities of the organization. When there are national, district, state, and section organizations, each has its own set of officers, board members, and program of activities. In addition, many organizations employ executive secretaries, consultants, and other specialists to help with the administrative work in the operation of the organization.

A third common element of professional organizations is found in many national, district, and state organizations. This element is a provision to permit persons with special interests within the profession to work together on their respective common problems and topics. Thus, we have a subdivision of the main organization devoted to some special interest.

Within the NRPA, there is provision for accomplishing this purpose. Persons particularly interested in therapeutic recreation work on their problems and interests related to that area within the structure of the National Therapeutic Recreation Society. The NTRS plans that portion of the NRPA annual conference that has to do with therapeutic recreation as well as recommends sessions and speakers that have an appeal for all delegates. Likewise, they may sponsor institutes or workshops, or co-sponsor or work cooperatively with other organizations in such matters. The NTRS also plans for and organizes committees that work throughout the year on problems pertaining to therapeutic recreation. In addition, NTRS employs an executive secretary and has representation on the NRPA Board of Trustees and NRPA Regional Councils.

This same divisional structure is followed in some states, and even in state sections or districts. In Georgia, for example, there are five special interest sections—educators, therapeutic, board and commissioners, municipal/county, and outdoor. The purpose? To make possible, indeed to facilitate, the working together of persons with similar interests within a geographical area.

In summary, then, we may say that the purpose of the structure of a professional organization is to facilitate effective working toward the organization's purposes or objectives. Each professional organization has its own structure, but there are elements common to most of them. These are organizations on the geographical basis, to facilitate functioning on national, district, state, and local levels; elected officers and an executive group to plan and carry out policies and programs, usually with the assistance of a paid staff; and provision for and structure within the geographical organization that permits persons of similar interests to work together.

Professional organizations are supported from dues paid by professional members of the association. Many organizations seek other sources of income in order to keep the dues as low as possible. Other sources of income may include federal and philanthropic grants, convention fees, exhibitors' charges at conventions, and advertising in programs, journals, and the like. A professional organization's services to a member are partially dependent upon the financial status and reserve of the organization.

therapeutic recreation organizations

There are a number of organizations functioning within the United States and Canada that promote the concept of recreation. However, there is only one overall professional organization concerned solely with the park, recreation, and leisure field—the National Recreation and Park Association. This Association is an

> ... independent, nonprofit, public interest organization representing citizens and professional leadership in the recreation and park movement in the United States and Canada. It provides comprehensive community service to all facets of the park, recreation, and leisure field. Its members are dedicated to human conservation through service, education, and research.[16]

As there are seven special interest branches in the NRPA, we will limit this brief overview to the branch, as I have indicated before, directly concerned with therapeutic recreation—namely, the National Therapeutic Recreation Society. We will also consider, in passing, those organizations allied with therapeutic recreation service.

It is not expected that you will long remember all of the organizations and facts presented. The dates when they were founded and their original names are of interest, but are not something to be memorized. As a member of the profession you should have at least a general acquaintance with them. We will name them by their "initial names" since many of your professional colleagues will refer to them in that way, and then give the full name.

NTRS—national therapeutic recreation society

The NTRS was established in 1967 as the result of a merger between a special interest section of a professional organization (Hospital Recreation Section, American Recreation Society) and a professional organization solely concerned with therapeutic recreation (National Association of Recreational Therapists). According to its Charter and By-Laws, the NTRS indicates its purposes as follows:

The purpose of this Society shall include and conform to the purposes of the National Recreation and Park Association, Inc. These shall include, but not be limited to: gathering and disseminating facts and information with reference to therapeutic recreation; furthering the rehabilitation of participants through recreation; engendering a spirit of cooperation between all professions and agencies related to our common cause; and developing standards for personnel, programs and facilities that will result in improved services for the participant.[17]

This society is organized and carries out its functions as described earlier under "Structure of Professional Organizations." However, to give some idea of its vastness, the 1977–1978 approved boards and committees are presented below:

- Priority projects (Presidential Commission on Assessment of Critical Issues): Curriculum Accreditation, Credentialing/Licensing, Implementation of PL 94-142, NTRS Branch Governance, and Program/Personnel Standards (relative to physical medicine/rehabilitation, drug abuse centers, pediatric play therapy, general medical hospitals, community program for mentally retarded and developmental disorders, skilled nursing homes and intermediate care facilities, mental retardation facilities, alcohol rehabilitation facilities, and PSRO).
- Standing committees: Executive, Budget, Nominations, Charter and By-Laws, Elections, Awards, and Congress Program.
- Special committees: Third-Party Payment, Legislation, Community Recreation Guidelines, International Liaison, Correctional Recreation, Resource Development, Camping, Ten-Year History, Aging, Logo, and 14th World Rehabilitation Congress.
- Publications: *Therapeutic Recreation Journal* and *Therapeutic Recreation Newsletter.*
- NTRS Representatives to NRPA Committees: Council on Accreditation, Registration, Personnel Advisory, Continuing Education and Training, Internship/Field Work, National Issues, Leisure Counseling Task Force, and APRS/NTRS Liaison.
- Approved Boards: Voluntary Registration Board, Continuing Professional Development Program, 750-Hour Training Program, and State and Regional Advisory Council.[18]

AAHPER — American alliance for health, physical education, recreation, and dance

Founded in 1885 as the American Association for the Advancement of Physical Education, the organization's name was changed in 1903 to the American Physical Education Association. In 1937 it became the American

Association for Health and Physical Education, a department of the National Education Association, and in 1938 *Recreation* was added to the title. In 1974, the title *American Alliance for Health, Physical Education, and Recreation* was adopted as a result of a reorganization. In March 1979 *Dance* was added to the title.

This association is organized and carries out its functions by means of divisions, as described earlier. At present, there are seven divisions, one of which is the American Association for Leisure and Recreation Service (AALRS). The purposes of the divisions are to promote programs on education for leisure throughout the community school system and into the college and universities, as well as community recreation programs and recreation for senior citizens. Its membership consists primarily of college and university educators and those recreation specialists employed by the community school system who offer recreation service through such a system.

The Recreational Therapy Section of AAPHER was established in 1952. With the formation of the NTRS in 1967, this specific special interest section dissolved and was replaced by a Council on Leisure for Special Populations, one of several councils and committees that at that time made up the Recreation Division (now AALRS).

NCRA—national correctional recreation association

The NCRA was established in 1966 during the annual meeting of the Amateur Athletic Union National Committee for Sports in Correctional Institutions at Indiana State Prison for Adults in Michigan City. Its objectives are to create and maintain professional standards and to foster national interest in correctional recreation as well as to promote, through recreation, the reorientation of offenders to society. The association sponsors and encourages postal prison meets wherein offenders participate in various physical and social activities through use of the mails.[19]

recreation subdivision, American association on mental deficiency

This subdivision of the AAMD was organized in 1966 to give recreation professionals a voice in the association business, to allow for regular representation in the sessions at annual and regional meetings, and to promote professional recreation services in dealing with the mentally retarded.

Probably the most significant work done by the AAMD Recreation Subdivision has been related to standards.[20] Enlisting the participation of the National Therapeutic Recreation Society and the American Alliance for Health, Physical Education, and Recreation, it was assured that adequate input was given in regard to recreation services in both the "Standards for

Residential Facilities for the Mentally Retarded" and "Standards for Community Agencies: Serving Persons with Mental Retardation and Other Development Disabilities" developed and published by the Accreditation Council for Facilities for the Mentally Retarded, Joint Commission on Accreditation of Hospitals.[21]

ACA—American camping association

The American Camping Association was established in 1910 for the purpose of promoting the well-being of adults and children through camping as well as for extending the educational and recreational benefits obtained from living in the out-of-doors. The association serves as a spokesman for camp leaders throughout the nation. Its inclusion here is the result of its concern and contribution in meeting the needs of special members through camping.

There are other national professional and voluntary organizations which are concerned with recreation services provided either directly or indirectly to special population members. A partial listing of these organizations is found in Appendix E.

In the preceding paragraphs we have looked at professional organizations and their functions and the organizations in our profession. It is now time to discuss whether you should participate or not. The decision is yours alone to make, now or in the future. Your professional future is not dependent upon your belonging to and taking an active part in professional organizations. It is dependent upon your profession. You need to plan to work thoughtfully and intelligently if these kinds of growth are to occur. They do not "just happen."

There are many means of growing up professionally. However, an understanding of the purposes, programs, and opportunities offered by professional organizations makes it apparent that active participation in selected ones can further professional growth in many ways. It is impossible to find some of the kinds of opportunities for growth elsewhere.

The quality and strength of a profession are not solely dependent upon the quality and strength of its professional organizations. More important is the effectiveness of organizations in achieving their primary purpose—the advancement and improvement of the profession. Through contributions of ideas, leadership, and just plain work, we can help make the profession even better. One person may not seem important, but the profession is made up of many "one persons" working together. The quality and strength of the organization are dependent upon the quality and support of its members.

You may be now asking yourself: How can I participate? The answer to this question depends partly on whether you are now studying or working in the field. There is great variation in plans among states and among colleges and universities. Your instructor can help you find answers.

Many colleges and universities have their own major clubs or student associations, called by various names. The programs they conduct to promote the professional growth of their student members are planned and conducted by student officers with the guidance of faculty advisors. A second way you might participate is to join the NRPA and belong to the NTRS. Many state associations offer student memberships, some carrying all of the responsibilities and privileges of regular membership at a reduced dues rate. Receiving the publications and attending local and state meetings are usual privileges.

Becoming a student member, now, of the national and state association as well as your own school professional organization may provide you with another way of growing professionally. It should give you an even better understanding and perspective of your profession. It will start a habit that will help you to continue your professional growth and give you a way of making your contribution to the profession you have chosen as your life work. Further, by becoming acquainted with the leaders and extending your acquaintanceship to include others of your age who come to national, district, and state meetings, you increase your chances of being asked to serve in ever more important ways.

personal philosophy

Before bringing this chapter to a close it is well for us to spend some time considering the development of a personal philosophy about therapeutic recreation.

The philosophy that motivates an excellent therapeutic recreation specialist has evolved from wisdom and experience. The specialists who exert the greatest influence are those who have an objective, can think with logic and reason, can make practical application of factual information, and have a sincere and profound interest in the betterment of mankind. All of these processes are fundamental to the philosophy of the specialist.

An individual may have one or several philosophies, such as a philosophy of life, a philosophy of recreation, and a philosophy of therapeutic recreation. Each one of these philosophies will of necessity have some bearing on each of the others.

A philosophy is interpreted here as the fundamental beliefs that stimulate and guide the specialist in his thoughts and actions in offering provisions of therapeutic recreation. These beliefs are based on facts and accepted theories and come as a result of extensive reading, contemplation, reasoning, study, and experience in the professional field of therapeutic recreation. A philosophy cannot be acquired over a short period of time; it must grow and develop with the years. It is not easily changed, but it is always subject to change. A philosophy based on sound principles is the core around which the entire concept of therapeutic recreation is built.

A philosophy is needed because the specialist with a sound philosophy of therapeutic recreation, therapeutic recreation process, and therapeutic recreation service has a goal, a purpose; he knows the direction in which he is going. He knows what he is trying to do and why. He understands the meanings, the values, and the significance of what he is doing. He utilizes only those activities and those services that lead to the fulfillment of stated goals, and in a way that is in accordance with meeting the needs of special population members.

The philosophy of the specialist is developed from his experience as a specialist and as a member of a professional group. As a specialist he has an opportunity to test his beliefs, to prove the practicability of many of his theories, and to learn from working with other specialists who have had more experience than he has. As a member of a professional organization he may read the professional literature and attend conventions, workshops, and other meetings where the reporting of what is being done in therapeutic recreation by therapeutic recreation specialists in various parts of the country may challenge or strengthen his philosophy.

In summary, it is highly important that the philosophy of the specialist be sound and that he be actively and consistently aware of it as a directing force—in other words, that he express it vividly and attempt to live it always.

SUGGESTED REFERENCES

American Psychological Association. *Ethical Standards of Psychologists.* Washington, D.C.: the Association, 1953.

Blankenship, Ralph L., ed. *Colleagues in Organization: The Social Construction of Professional Work.* New York: John Wiley and Sons, 1977.

Ferguson, C.M. "Professions, Professionals and Motivations," *Journal of the American Diabetic Association,* 53 (September 1968), pp. 197–201.

Hall, R.N, "Professionalization and Bureaucratization," *American Sociological Review,* 33 (February 1968), pp. 99–104.

Hartsoe, Charles E. "Recreation—A Profession in Transition," Unpublished paper, University of Illinois, October 3, 1967.

Hendrix, John. *Invitation to Dialogue: The Professional World.* Nashville, Tenn.: Broadman Press, 1970.

Hillman, William A. "Development of Personnel Standards in Therapeutic Recreation," *Therapeutic Recreation Journal,* 2:4 (1968), pp. 20–22.

Marston, J. "Hallmarks of a Profession," *Public Relations Journal,* 24 (July 1968), pp. 8–10.

Martin, Fred W. "Therapeutic Recreation Service: A Philosophic Overview," *Leisurability,* 1:1 (1974), p. 22.

Meyer, Lee E. "An Analysis of views of Recreation Professionals Towards Therapeutic Recreation and Its Professionalization." Unpublished doctoral dissertation, University of North Carolina, Chapel Hill, 1978.

Park, David C. "The Effects of Future Shock on Our Profession," in *Expanding Horizons in Therapeutic Recreation III,* eds. Gary Robb and Gerald Hitzhusen. Columbia, Mo.: Department of Recreation and Park Administration, University of Missouri, 1976, pp. 7–16.

Park, David C., "Role of a National Organization for Therapeutic Recreation," *Therapeutic Recreation Journal,* 3:4 (1969), pp. 7–10.

Tague, Jean R. "The Challenge and the Commitment," *Therapeutic Recreation Journal,* 9:1 (1975), pp. 4–6.

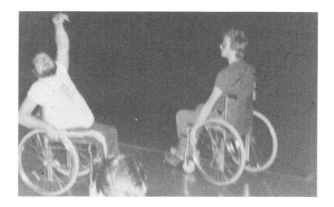

chapter 11
the future of
therapeutic recreation

Therapeutic recreation is not a static process. Its patterns of services and programs will continue to change with the thinking and the practices of future years. No simple blueprint of future development can be readily sketched at this time, yet it is well to ponder expectations for therapeutic recreation in the future.

Therapeutic recreation cannot grow apart from other human service fields. As Park has stated: ". . .we (therapeutic recreators) must. . .never lose sight of the fact that one of the most intrinsic values of our profession is to allow people to be people and we should take pride in that fact."[1] I would therefore expect therapeutic recreation service to be a meaningful service of the eighties and into the nineties. I foresee therapeutic recreation service as becoming more of an integral part of clinical services and of becoming more involved in community health, welfare, and social service. Its imprint, hopefully, will be on every action and reaction connected in any way with special population members.

In this era of great political, social, and economic change, we are conditioned to hearing and reading of ideologies, social theories, economic trends, progressive education, communal planning, governmental domination, and the like. Perhaps we have lost sight of what may well be the most significant change of all, the fact that "people have become more important." This simple phrase concisely describes the reason for our concern with the whole process of therapeutic recreation, from philosophy to practice. One can hardly advocate or carry on therapeutic recreation activity unless one is convinced of the importance of human life, of the dignity of man, of the right to full oportunity for all individuals.

The future of therapeutic recreation is seen briefly from four points of view: (1) continuing development and refinement of the therapeutic recreation process itself; (2) contribution toward the growth and development of the profession of therapeutic recreation through its use; (3) influences upon the personal and professional growth and the development of users of the therapeutic recreation process; and (4) improvement of the physical, emotional, social, and intellectual status of recipients of the process.

As therapeutic recreation specialists continue to use the therapeutic recreation process in a deliberate way, its components and component elements are likely to be refined. Following are goals of the continuing development of the therapeutic recreation process: improved design of therapeutic recreation plans; more astute specifications of expected special population behaviors; improved relationship with leisure service agencies in the community; more effective recording of observations about the member; more sensible, purposeful, and effective therapeutic recreation actions; more emphasis on evaluation as well as on the development of tools of evaluation; more, or more accurate, activity analysis; better judgment concerning what to communicate to whom, when to communicate, and how.

Numerous recreators have developed and are developing tools and techniques that can be incorporated into the therapeutic recreation process. Continuing development, testing, and refinement of these tools in a variety of health and social care settings and with the therapeutic recreation specialist and other recreators and health and social team members are in order, as is narrowing the lag that exists from the discovery of new knowledge to the application in new methods to their incorporation into therapeutic recreation practice.

The contribution toward growth and development of the profession of therapeutic recreation through the use of the therapeutic recreation process is easily evidenced. Since the heart of therapeutic recreation practice is to a large degree the solution of special population members' problems through recreative experiences, any theories or scientific materials developed to explain, direct, or influence therapeutic recreation practice will contribute to the quality of service rendered the member and hence advance the profession and sanction its place as designated by society.

When considering the influence of the therapeutic recreation process upon the therapist's personal and professional growth and development as a person and as a practitioner, a few topics need to be considered.

The therapeutic process lends itself to the therapist's own quest for self-improvement. Continuous evaluation of one's intellectual, interpersonal, and technical skills and one's perceptual, communicative, and decision-making abilities will reveal strengths and limitations. Interest in enhancing one's strengths and minimizing one's limitations gives direction for study and the selection of programs, workshops, and professional associations and interactions. Increasing one's accuracy in problem solving and in predicting the impact of recreative experiences upon special population behavior is an important factor in achieving success in therapeutic recreation practice. The continuing focus on self-improvement results in the better use of self and improved contribution to special populations. In summary, the therapeutic recreation process could and should be viewed as an effective method to prevent and minimize obsolescence.

For the special population member, the more knowledgeable, confident, creative, and person-centered the specialist is, the more likely it is that the member will benefit. The special population member further benefits by being an active participant in the identification and resolution of his problem. It enhances his personhood, his need to remain a thinking, feeling person whether he is in the community or in the health care setting. The specialist, too, will be stimulated to continue self-development, as he reaps the feeling of accomplishment from doing his best.

The therapeutic recreation process contributes to the specialist's feeling of camaraderie with other members of the health or social team as well as with other public and private recreation service agency personnel. The specialist places value on his contributions and enhances his success and that of the other team members by sharing his perceptions and goals for the special population member. The specialist is, in turn, enhanced by being open and receptive to suggestions of other therapeutic recreation specialists and health and social team members.

Inherent in each point of view relating to the future of the therapeutic recreation process is the research process. Presently, the need for research is generally recognized by all therapeutic recreators, and it is predictable that the quantity and quality of therapeutic recreation research will improve as we move into the eighties. The need for increased research in therapeutic recreation service and practice is documented in the preliminary reports of the *Presidential Commission on Assessment of Critical Issues.*[2] The reports appear to indicate the need for a body of facts to guide and/or assess the providing of better service by therapeutic recreators to consumers. A clear knowledge of the differences in the benefits to the special population member from therapeutic recreation interventions and establishing means to assess the results of varied interventions are based upon sound research.

Research plays an important role in the development and refinement of the therapeutic recreation process and in the development of therapeutic recreation service. Sharing the results of research can benefit both the therapeutic recreator and special population member directly. The therapeutic recreation process not only opens the way for research into a multitude of problems but each component with each of its elements is itself a fruitful area for research. Research studies might be undertaken in those areas related to:

- Determining special activity needs and the therapeutic recreation plan
- Decisions inherent in the therapeutic recreation process
- Professional role responsibilities and practices of therapeutic recreation
- Settings in which the therapeutic recreation process is used
- Utilization of the process by therapeutic recreators with varying backrounds in education and experience
- Roles of the special population member, his family, and others in implementing the therapeutic recreation plan
- Varying patterns of problem resolution according to age, sex, geographic location, socioeconomic level, and education and cultural background
- Defining the special population member's role in the development of the therapeutic recreation plan
- Rationale used by therapeutic recreators in selecting a specific therapeutic recreation activity to resolve a problem
- Determining variations of and common solutions made by therapeutic recreators in different settings when confronted with a given member problem, a designated number of staff, and selected equipment and supplies
- Developing further tools to evaluate impact of therapeutic recreation plan.

It goes without saying that it is imperative that therapeutic recreators use research findings and incorporate them into their use of the therapeutic recreation process. Likewise, they should also incorporate human behavior research findings into their therapeutic recreation practice.

The quality of the therapeutic recreation process in the practice of therapeutic recreation will be determined by accountability. Accountability suggests responsibility, an obligation to answer to someone. Inherent within this obligation is the suggestion that the therapeutic recreator is expected to have certain basic knowledge; he is obliged to make decisions, and to use judgment based on that knowledge. Within this context he is responsible for taking appropriate actions, whether dependent or independent.

Implementing independent actions by the therapeutic recreator requires adherence to the therapeutic recreation process, regardless of setting, to determine the scope of his responsibility and to insure qualitative fulfillment of actions necessary to help the special population member. As dependent actions are necessary, the therapeutic recreator visualizes responsibilities along several avenues; he continually keeps in mind his responsibilities to the member, yet simultaneously is aware of his accountability to himself, to other therapeutic recreators and health and community members, and to his employer. Hence, this mosaic of accountability and responsibility takes on many dimensions.

The primary focus for the therapeutic recreator is the special population member and his problem. Helping the member to cope with his problem, the therapeutic recreator is directly accountable to him. Likewise, every therapeutic recreator is accountable to himself. He knows best his intentions and he can best explain to what extent he is accountable. Usually, if the therapeutic recreator is comfortably sure in his own mind that he has measured up to his own demands, then his accountability to others can be coped with successfully.

Another facet of accountability and responsibility is the willingness to share experiences through the professional publication of practical experiences inlcuding research. The therapeutic recreator will accumulate qualitative and quantitative physiologic and behavioral data about a member. The critical analysis of these data will render valuable information to serve as guidelines for the therapeutic recreator's future action. In addition to benefits to himself, the therapeutic recreator has a professional responsibility to share these data with his colleagues, not only to enlighten them but to stimulate their thinking and to propose ideas to a forum for reaction, refinement, and development by other therapeutic recreators of the therapeutic recreation profession. This sharing fosters the growth and development of the profession.

To conclude this text on therapeutic recreation as a helping profession, I would like to repeat this often-quoted story: A chicken and a pig were walking down the street. As they walked they came to a bill-board displaying a breakfast of ham and eggs. The chicken said to the pig: "Look at the wonderful contribution I have made to mankind." The pig listened, then said: "Yes, that fine, but my contribution involves a total commitment."

appendix A
medical terminology

Every profession has its jargon. Thus, the therapeutic recreation specialist working with special populations must be aware not only of the jargon used in his own profession, but also of the jargon used by other professional disciplines that offer services to special populations. The therapeutic recreation specialist who works in a general medical hospital or medical rehabilitation setting must become familiar with medical jargon. Its purpose, according to JeHarned, is to "describe the human body, its functions, its normal state, its abnormal states, the diseases and injuries which affect it, and the various means, agents and procedures employed to prevent, minimize or cure the effects of disease and injury."*

Medical jargon is very precise. There can be no chance for misunderstanding. The misinterpretation or omission of a single word may completely alter a meaning. Likewise, in the process of analyzing medical words by breaking them down into meaningful parts, great care must be taken to spell accurately. Misspelling a word may easily change its meaning. Lastly, care is needed for the acquisition of good pronunciation of

* Je Harned, *Medical Terminology Made Easy* (Chicago: Physician's Record Company, 1956). p. 7.

medical words. Do not slur. If anything, be on the side of *overenunciation*. Mispronunciation and misspelling go together and cause confusion that may result in a change of meaning.

Acquiring a medical vocabulary becomes a matter of memorizing a number of Greek and Latin words, and then combining them systematically to make thousands of other precise terms.

The first step into medical terminology is to make one's acquaintance with the base word, which is called the *root* or *stem;* the modifying or amplifying term is called the *prefix* when it is attached before the root and the *suffix* when attached to the end of the root. For example, *endo* (meaning *within*) when attached to *cardium* (heart) means *within the heart* or *heart lining,* and *ophthalmo* (eye) plus scope becomes *ophthalmoscope, an instrument for studying the eye.* Combining *itis,* a suffix meaning *inflammation,* with various roots results in such words as *tonsilitis, peritonitis,* and *osteitis.*

Some of the more commonly used prefixes, suffixes, and roots are considered below.

Prefix	Meaning	Example
a-	without or not	*apnea,* without breathing, *atrophy,* organ that has never grown or has wasted away
ab-	from, away from	*abnormal,* away from normal
acro-	extremity	*acromegaly,* large extremity
ad-	to, at	*adrenal,* adjoining the kidney
adeno-	gland	*adenitis,* inflammation of a gland
ambi-	both	*ambidextrous,* able to use both hands equally well
ante-	before	*antemortem,* before death
anti-	against	*antiseptic,* an agent used against infection
apo-	from	*apoplexy,* a stroke from
arthro-	joint	*arthritis,* inflammation of a joint
bi-	two	*bilateral,* affecting two sides
blast-	germ	*blastomycosis,* a condition caused by fungus
brady-	slow	*bradycardia,* a slow heartbeat
circum-	around	*circumocular,* around the eye
con-	with, together	*congenital,* with birth
contra-	against	*contraindicative,* indicating against
cyano-	blue	*cyanosis,* blueness of the skin
cyst-	bladder	*cystitis,* inflammation of the bladder
cyto-	cell	*cytoid,* resembling a cell
dia-	through	*diarrhea,* a flowing through
dis-	apart from	*disarticulation,* taking a joint apart

Prefix	Meaning	Example
dys-	difficult, bad	*dysmenorrhea*, difficult menstruation
ecto-	outside of	*ectonuclear*, outside nucleus of cell
en-	in	*encapsulated*, in a capsule
endo-	within	*endocardium*, within the heart or heart lining
entero-	intestine	*enteritis*, inflammation of the intestine
epi-	upon, outside	*epidermis*, outer layer of true skin
erythro-	red	*erythrocyte*, red blood cell
eso-	inward	*esotropia*, a turning inward of the eye (cross-eyed)
ex-	out from	*exhale*, to breathe out
ex-, ec-	out of, away from	*exostosis*, bony growth from surface of bone
gyn-	woman	*gynecology*, the study of diseases peculiar to women
hem-hemo-	blood	*hemoglobin*, coloring matter of red blood cells
histo-	weblike	*histology*, the study of tissues
homeo-	similar	*homeostasis*, stability of normal body states
hydro-	water	*hydrotherapy*, treatment by the use of water
hyper-	above, excessive	*hyperacidity*, excessive acidity
hypo-	deficiency, less or beneath	*hypodermic*, beneath the skin
in-	not	*incurable*, not curable
inter-	between	*intercellular*, between cells
intra-	within	*intracellular*, within cells
intro-	into	*introflexion*, a bending into or a leading into
iso-	equal	*isotonic*, of equal tension
leuko-	white	*leukocyte*, a white blood cell
macro-	great	*macrogyria*, a congenital defect characterized by unusually great cerebral convolutions
mal-	bad	*malnutrition*, poor nutrition
media-	middle of	*median*, situated in the middle
micro-	small	*microscope*, an instrument for viewing small things
myo-	muscle	*myositis*, inflammation of muscle
necro-	death	*necrosis*, death of a cell

Prefix	Meaning	Example
neo-	new	*neoplasm*, new growth or tumor
nephr-	kidney	*nephritis*, inflammation of kidney
ortho-	straight	*orthopedist*, one who straightens deformities of children
osteo-	bone	*osteomyelitis*, inflammation of bone
para-	beside	*paravertebral*, beside the spine
peri-	around	*pericardium*, the membrane around the heart
phleb-	vein	*phlebitis*, inflammation of a vein
polio-	gray	*poliomyelitis*, inflammation of gray matter of spinal cord
poly-	many	*polycythemia*, excess in number of red blood cells
post-	after	*postmortem*, after death
pro-	before	*prophylaxis*, measures taken to prevent disease
pseudo-	false	*pseudocyesis*, false pregnancy
pyo-	pus	*pyorrhea*, a flow of pus
retro-	backward	*retroflexion*, a bending backward
scolio-	curved	*scoliosis*, curvature of the spine
steno-	contracted	*stenocardia*, narrowing of the coronary arteries of the heart
sub-	less (deficient)	*subnormal*, less than normal
super-	above	*superciliary*, above area of the eyebrow
syn-	together with	*syndrome*, a constant complex of symptoms
thermo-	heat	*thermometer*, an instrument for measuring temperature
toxi-	poison	*toxicology*, the study of poisons
vaso-	vessel	*vasospasm*, spasm of the blood vessels
xantho-	yellow	*xanthochromia*, yellow coloration of the cerebrospinal fluid

Suffix	Meaning	Example
-ac	related to	*cardiac*, relating to the heart or the cardia of the stomach
-ago	disease	*lumbago*, lumbar disease
-algia	pain	*neuralgia*, nerve pain
-cele	swelling, protrusion	*meningocele*, a hernial protrusion of the meninges

Suffix	Meaning	Example
-centesis	perforating or tapping	thoracentesis, aspiring fluid from the thorax
-cide	a killer	bactericide, an agent that kills bacteria
-cleisis	a closure	enterocleisis, a closure of the intestine
-cyst	sac of fluid	dacrocyst, tear duct
-cyte	cell	leukocyte, a white blood cell
-ectasis	dilate	bronchiectasis, dilatation of the bronchi
-ectomy	to excise, to cut out	tonsillectomy, removal of a tonsil
-emesis	vomiting	hematemesis, vomiting blood
-emia	blood	anemia, deficiency of red blood cells
-esthesia	sensation	anesthesia, absence of sensation
-genesis	generation of	pathogenesis, generation of disease
-gram	a writing	electrocardiogram, a record of the heart's action made by an electrocardiograph
-graphy	writing	encephalography, examination of the brain
-id	condition	flaccid, the condition of being soft
-ism	condition	mutism, the condition of being mute
-ist	agent	allergist, one skilled in the treatment of allergies
-itis	inflammation	appendicitis, inflammation of the vermiform appendix
-lith	stone	nephrolith, stone in the kidney
-logy	study of	pathology, study of disease
-malacia	softening	osteomalacia, softening of bone
-mania	madness	dipsomania, pathological drinker of alcoholic beverages
-meter	measure	thermometer, an instrument for measuring temperature
-oid	like, resembling	mucoid, like mucus
-oma	tumor	osteoma, a tumor of bone
-opia	vision	diplopia, double vision
-osis	condition	tuberculosis, the condition of infection by bacillus tuberculosis
-otomy	to cut into	gastrotomy, to cut into the stomach
-pathy	disease	neuropathy, any nervous disease
-plasia	formation	hyperplasia, overgrowth of tissue
-plegia	paralysis	hemiplegia, paralysis of one half (side) of the body
-pnea	breathing	dyspnea, difficult breathing

Suffix	Meaning	Example
-ptosis	a falling	*gastroptosis,* a falling of the stomach
-(r)rhage	a bursting forth	*hemorrhage,* flow of blood
-(r)rhea	a flow	*diarrhea,* abnormal flow from bowel
-sclerosis	hardening	*arteriosclerosis,* hardening of the arteries
-scope	to look within	*esophagoscope,* an instrument used to view the esophagus
-spasm	contraction	*laryngospasm,* contraction of the vocal cords
-stasis	position	*hemostasis,* arrest of circulation
-tasis	stretching	*myotasis,* stretching of a muscle
-therapy	treatment	*radiotherapy,* treatment by use of radium
-trophy	nourish	*atrophy,* wasting
-uria	relating to urine	*anuria,* absence of urine

Root	Meaning	Example
aden	gland	*adenoblast,* a gland cell
aorte	aorta	*aortostenosis,* narrowing of the aorta
bios	life	*biochemics,* the chemistry of life
cardia	heart	*pericardium,* the membranous sac enclosing the heart
carpus	wrist	*metacarpal,* pertaining to that part of the hand between the wrist and the fingers
core	pupil	*coreometer,* instrument for measuring the pupil of the eye
coxa	hip	*coxalgia,* pain in the hip
cutis	skin	*subcutaneous,* under the skin
cystis	bladder	*cystoma,* tumor of the bladder
derma	skin	*dermatologist,* a physician specializing in the diagnosis and treatment of persons suffering from skin disorders
desmo	ligament	*desmotomy,* division of ligaments
encephalos	encephalon (brain)	*encephalitis,* inflammation of the brain
gaster	stomach	*gastroscope,* an instrument for the inspection of the interior of the stomach
gnosis	knowledge	*prognosis,* a forecast
keras	cornea	*keratocentesis,* puncture of the cornea
kinesis	movement	*kinetocyte,* a wandering cell
larynx	larynx (throat)	*laryngitis,* inflammation of the larynx
lepesis	seizure	*epilepsy,* convulsive seizures

Suffix	Meaning	Example
meninx	meninges	*meningitis*, inflammation of the membranes of the brain and spinal cord
mnesis	memory	*amnesia*, loss of memory
myelos	marrow	*myelathrophy*, wasting of the spinal cord
ophthalmos	eye	*ophthalmia*, inflammation of eye
oto	ear	*otitis*, inflammation of the ear
pathos	disease	*psychopath*, one ill in the mind
phagein	swallowing	dysphagia, difficulty in swallowing
phasis	speech	*aphasis*, inability to articulate words or sentences
phobos	fear	*claustrophobia*, fear of confined spaces
pituita	pituitary	*pituitrin*, a preparation made from the posterior lobe of the pituitary gland
pneumon	lung	*pneumonia*, inflammation of the lung
pod	foot	*podiatrist*, one who treats the foot (a chiropodist)
psyche	mind	*psychosis*, any morbid mental state
ren	kidney	*adrenal*, adjacent to the kidney
sphygmos	pulse	*sphygmomanometer*, an instrument for measuring pulse pressure—i.e., blood pressure
tracheia	windpipe	*tracheotomy*, surgical incision in the windpipe

other helpful information

Measurements

Oral temperature range	36.4°–37.2° C. (97.6°–99° F.)
"Average" pulse rate	70 beats/min.
Pulse rate range at rest	60–90 beats/min.
Pulse rate for everyday activities	Women, 72–80 beats/min; Men, slightly lower
Respiratory rate range	14–20 respirations/min.
Average blood pressure (B.F.)	120 mm. Hg
	80 mm. Hg

Definitions

- *Pathology* refers to the disease process itself; it is generally classified as either *organic* or *functional.*

- *Organic pathology* refers to diseases that can be identified physically—a tumor, for example.
- *Functional pathology* refers to diseases that have no apparent physical basis; emotional disturbances frequently come under this heading.
- *Medical diagnosis* is the physician's opinion as to the nature of the disease.
- *Prognosis* means the medical opinion as to the final outcome of the disease process.
- A *symptom* is evidence that there is a disease process or disturbance in body function.
- *Subjective symptoms* are those symptoms that can be perceived only by the patient.
- *Objective symptoms* are those that can be observed and described by others.
- A *sign* is an objective symptom that is detected through special examination—an abnormal heart beat detected by a stethoscope, for example.
- *Temperature*—Degree of heat of a living body.
- *Pulse*—Alternate expansion and recoil of an artery.
- *Pulse deficit*—Difference between radial pulse and apical pulse.
- *Pulse pressure*—Difference between systolic and diastolic blood pressures.
- *Respiration*—Act of breathing; inspiration and expiration.
- *Blood pressure*—Pressure exerted by blood on wall of vessel, written as systolic pressure/second diastolic pressure or systolic pressure/first diastolic pressure/second diastolic pressure.
- *Systole*—Contraction of heart (producing maximum blood pressure).
- *Diastole*—Relaxation of heart (producing minimum blood pressure).

SUGGESTED REFERENCES

American Psychiatric Association. *A Psychiatric Glossary* (2nd ed.). Washington, D.C.: the Association, 1964.

Anthony, Charles P. *Textbook of Anatomy and Physiology* (8 ed.). St. Louis: The C. V. Mosby Company, 1971.

Dorland's Pocket Medical Dictionary (21st ed.). Philadelphia: W. B. Saunders Company, 1968.

Gunn, Scout Lee. *Basic Terminology for Therapeutic Recreation and Other Action Therapies.* Champaign, Ill.: Stipes Publishing Company, 1975.

Kamenetz, Herman L. *Physiatric Directory.* Springfield, Ill.: Charles C Thomas, Publisher, 1965.

Sessoms, H. Douglas. *Glossary of Recreation and Park Terms.* Management Aids Bulletin No. 95. Arlington, Va.: National Recreation and Park Association, 1972.

Smith, Genevieve Love, and Phyllis E. Davis. *Medical Terminology: A Programed Text* (2nd ed). New York: John Wiley & Sons, Inc., 1963.

Taber's Cyclopedic Medical Dictionary (12th ed). Philadelphia: F. A. Davis Company, 1973.

appendix B
drug therapy

Drugs occupy a prominent place in the care and treatment of individuals. Their use as a therapeutic agent has been known throughout the ages. The science of pharmacology is a highly developed medical field. The number of different drugs manufactured commercially for distribution has increased enormously in recent years. As each new drug is added, its composition, physiological action, uses, and dosage are recorded in the *Materia Medica, Pharmacopea,* and *Physicians Desk Reference* (drug reference publications). Furthermore, any one drug can have as many as four names: its trademark, its official name, its chemical name, and its generic name.

Today, there is considerable controversy surrounding the writing of prescriptions—generic vs. brand name drugs. What's the difference, you may ask, between brand name (trade) and generic name drugs anyway? Cost is one factor since brand name prescriptions cost more and are the sole property of the original manufacturer for seventeen years before passing into the public domain. Another factor, as you will shortly read, is public vocabulary and memory.

When a newly developed drug is prepared for clinical testing, it's given an official name or so-called generic name. Once the drug has passed its tests and is ready for the medical marketplace the company assigns it a new trade or proprietary name. This is what is called a brand name. Usually brand names are catchy, easy to pronounce and easy to remember. Generic names are often tongue twisters. For example, Valium is a household word, but few people would recognize its generic name, Diazepam. How about Tylenol vs. Acetaminophen or Darvon vs. Propoxyphene? You can see why doctors and others would opt for the easy-to-spell-pronounce-and-remember brand name version.

Drugs are put up as tablets, capsules, powders, or fluids. They are given usually by mouth, occasionally by rectum. Drugs may be inhaled or rubbed into the skin (inunction). They may be injected (parenteral) into the skin (intradermal), under the skin (subcutaneous), or into the muscle (intramuscular). Lastly, drugs may be introduced into a vein (intravenous therapy) or into the peritoneum (intraperitoneal therapy). The method of administration is partially determined by the age of the individual, his orientation, his degree of consciousness, and his disease. The role of administering the drug affects the optimal dosage of the drug. And the effect (or action) of the drug on the body may be *systemic* (affecting the whole body) or *local* (affecting a specific area).

The quickest and most profound results are obtained by hypodermic injection and are given (1) when an immediate effect from the drug is desired, (2) when for any reason it is inadvisable or impossible to administer the drug by mouth, and (3) when the chemical nature of the drug is such that it is rendered ineffective by the action of the digestive juices. The slowest results are obtained from inunction.

As a result of the fact that a large number of drugs are utilized in the care and treatment of hospitalized and nonhospitalized individuals, this discussion of drug therapy will be limited to those drugs more frequently used in the care and treatment of individuals with emotional problems. However, the student should be aware that many of these same drugs are used in general medical practice, surgery, and the like.

In the years since the advent of psychopharmacological therapy, there have been sweeping changes in the care and treatment of those with emotional problems. All professional disciplines, including therapeutic recreation, have been directly affected by these changes. The coming of drug therapy has profoundly altered the routines of therapeutic recreation specialists, expanding their role and offering them an opportunity to make greater contributions to patient progress. The specialist's task has become more challenging—and more rewarding—than ever before. Closer and more frequent contacts with patients allow the specialist to become a more active member of the psychotherapeutic team and, at the same time, demand that greater imagination and foresight be exercised in developing a therapeutic program that will enable patients to obtain full benefits from drug therapy.

Drugs used in the care and treatment of individuals with emotional problems may be divided into three types: (1) sedatives (those used to induce sleep and to relieve anxiety), (2) antipsychotic tranquilizers (those primarily used in the management of psychotic behavior rather than neurotic behavior) and lithium (an alternative or supplement to major tranquilizers in the control of the manic stage of manic-depressive psychosis), and (3) antidepressants (used in the treatment of depressions). The student should be aware that the term *tranquilizer* has been misused as the result of its proliferation in the treatment of emotional problems. The term, in the main, is restricted to use in reference to the "antipsychotic" drugs.

Listed below are some of the more commonly used drugs—sedatives, antipsychotic tranquilizers, and antidepressants as well as amphetamines and stimulant amines (by trade name and chemical name). Also included are their uses and side effects.

Drug	Use	Side Effect
Artane	Treat Parkinsonism; prevent or control side effects of Thorazine or Stelazine.	Dryness of mouth; blurring of vision; dizziness; mild nausea.
Benzedrine, Dexedrine (amphetamine)	Relieve mild depression; control appetite and narcolepsy.	Dryness of mouth; anxiety; euphoria; tremors; insomnia; psychological dependence potential.
Cogentin	Counteract Thorazine and Stelazine, which induce extrapyramidal reactions; relieve rigidity, tremors associated with Parkinsonism; treat Parkinsonism.	Dryness of mouth; elevated temperature; delirium; may cause glaucoma; absence of sweating.
Compazine (prochlorperazine)	Control anxiety, tension, agitation, and confusion.	Transitory extrapyramidal reactions; drowsiness; dizziness; skin reactions; jitteriness; insomnia.
Crystodigin	Treat some heart conditions.	Lack of appetite; nausea; vomiting; restlessness; pulse rate below 60.
Digitoxin	Treat some heart conditions.	Vomiting; diarrhea; pulse rate below 60.

Drug	Use	Side Effect
Dilantin	Control convulsions.	Initially nausea, weight loss, nervousness; sleeplessness; skin rashes; fever.
Elavil (amitriptyline)	Manage depression, anxiety, tension, and fear; insomnia; psychomotor retardation; feelings of guilt; Anorexia.	Drowsiness and dizziness; nausea; headaches; temporary confusion; dryness of mouth; difficulty in passing urine (especially in older men).
Haldol (haloperidol)	Treat psychoses, especially those withdrawn and inactive (older aged psychotics whose medication affects blood pressure).	Dryness of mouth; blurred vision; drowsiness; nasal congestion; side effects more rigid than either Thorazine or Mellaril.
Miltown, Equanil (meprobamate)	Anticonvulsant; muscle relaxant; value in anxiety and tension states, phobias, psychosomatic disorders.	Continued use creates physical dependence; abrupt withdrawal can cause convulsions; dermal hypersensitivity reactions; large doses may result in suicidal respiratory and vaso motor collapse.
Librium (chlordiazepoxide)	Relief of anxiety and tension.	Drowsiness; excitement; skin rashes; nausea; constipation.
Marplan (isocarboxazid)	Treat depression.	Dizziness; headaches; overactivity; jitteriness; blurred vision; skin rashes.
Mellaril (thioridazine)	Control anxiety, agitation, and confusion.	Same as Thorazine but occur less frequently.
Mysoline	Control convulsions.	Initially nausea, vomiting dizziness, and fatigue
Norpramine (Pertofrane	Antidepressant; shortens duration of suicidal risk; psychotic depression; involutional depression;	Dryness of mouth; constipation; dizziness; agitation and stimulation; nausea; drowsiness; blurred

Drug	Use	Side Effect
	reaction depression; psychoneurotic depression.	vision; tremors.
Parnate (tranylcypromine)	Treat depression.	Individual should not eat cheese; headaches.
Phenobarbital	Control convulsions; sedation.	Can become habit-forming; skin rashes; headaches; dizziness.
Prolixin, permitil (fluphenazine)	Relieve anxiety and tension	Parkinsonism; skin rashes
Sparine (promazine)	Same as Mellaril.	Drowsiness; pseudo-Parkinsonism; dryness of mouth; skin reactions.
Stalazine (trifluoperazine)	Control anxiety, tension, agitation, and confusion; treat psychosis and neurosis; mainly those who are withdrawn, inactive, and apathetic.	Drowsiness; dizziness; mild skin reaction; dryness of mouth; insomnia; amenorrhea; fatigue; extrapyramidal reactions on high dosages as well as muscular weakness, anorexia, rash, lactation, and blurred vision.
Taractan (chlorprothixene)	Relieve anxiety in psychosis and neurosis.	Drowsiness; dizziness; insomnia.
Thorazine (chlorpromazine)	Control anxiety, agitation, and confusion; treat psychosis and neurosis.	Excessive drowsiness; momentary fainting or dizziness; dryness of mouth; nasal congestion; photosensitivity, sunburn, skin rash; extrapyramidal reaction.
Tofranil (imipramine)	Treat depression.	Dryness of mouth; sweating; dizziness; increase in appetite; agitation.
Valium (diazepam)	Control anxiety reaction (moderate to severe); relieve muscle spasm; treat alcoholism (impending acute DTs and hallucinations); when somatic complaints are symptomatic of emotional factors.	Fatigue, drowsiness, and ataxia; mild nausea; dizziness; blurred vision; headaches; slurred speech; tremors; skin rash

You will note from the above listing that such drugs as compazine, stalazine, and thorazine produce a neurologic side effect called Parkinsonism. This side effect occurs most commonly from use of the more potent and effective tranquilizers. It is a sign that the drug is working. The functional changes occur in the basal ganglia and related portions of the brain (extrapyramidal system).

The manifestations of Parkinsonism are as follows:

1. Rigidity
   a. Immobile face—lack of eye blinking for periods of time
   b. Rigidly maintained posture
   c. Lack of smiling
2. Tremor
   a. Localized or generalized
   b. During waking hours
3. Salivation—resulting from
   a. Infrequency of swallowing
   b. Overproduction of saliva by stimulated salivary glands
4. Abnormal gait
   a. Type varies from patient to patient
   b. Loss of associated swinging of arms
   c. Shuffling (most frequent type)
   d. Trotting
   e. Retropulsion (involuntary backward movement while trying to move forward)
5. Akathisia (literally "inability to sit down")
   a. Restlessness
   b. Driven motor activity
   c. Inability to maintain relaxed posture
   d. Rigidity
   e. Continuous motion

Dystonia is a side effect most commonly seen in children and young adults either early in treatment or immediately following the injection of a phenothiazine (antipsychotic tranquilizer) or as a result of an accidental ingestion of a single large dose. For the beginning specialist, a dystonic reaction is quite frightening and may be mistaken for a convulsion. It comes on suddenly, produces marked discomfort, and seems to be life threatening. However, the reaction is usually well tolerated by the individual. The manifestations are:

1. Generalized
    a. Oculogyric effect (eyes "fixed" in upward position due to muscle spasm)
    b. Carpopedal spasm (wrist and foot)
    c. Opisthotonos (tetanic spasm in which head and heels are bent backward and body bowed forward)
    d. Trismus (motor disturbance of trigeminal nerve: spasm of masticatory muscles with difficulty in opening the mouth)
2. Oculogyric crises
3. Torticollis ("wry neck"—from stiffness of stermocleidomastoid muscle)
4. Trismus

other helpful information

abbreviations commonly used in medication orders

a.a.	of each (equal parts)
a.c.	before meals
add.	add to
ad lib.	as much as desired
a.m.	morning
Aq.	water
b.i.d.	twice a day
c.	with
caps.	capsules
dil.	dilute
fl.	fluid
h.	hour
h.s.	hour of sleep (bedtime)
mist.	mixture
non rep.	not to be repeated
O.D.	right eye
O.S.	left eye
Ol.	oil
os.	mouth
p.c.	after meals
per.	by
P.O.	by mouth

p.r.n.	when required
q.	every
q.d.	every day
q.h.	every hour
q.2.h.	every two hours
q.3.h.	every three hours
q.4.h.	every four hours
q.i.h.	four times a day
q.o.d.	every other day
s.	without
Sol.	solution
Stat.	immediately
tab.	tablet
t.i.d.	three times a day
tr. or tinct.	tincture
ung.	ointment

abbreviations associated with administering medications (metric system)

linear measure:

decimeter	dm.
centimeters	cm.
millimeters	mm.
dekameter	Dm.
hectometer	Hm.
kilometer	Km.

Volume:

liter	L
deciliters	dl.
centiliters	cl.
milliliters	ml.
dekaliter	Dl.
hectoliter	Hl.
kiloliter	Kl.

Weight:

gram	Gm.
decigram	dg.
centigrams	cg.
milligrams	mg.
dekagram	Dg.
hectogram	Hg.
kilogram	Kg.
microgram	mcg. or μg.

SUGGESTED REFERENCES

Klein, D. F., and J. M. Davis. *Diagnosis and Drug Treatment of Psychiatric Disorders.* Baltimore, Md.: Williams and Wilkins Company, 1969.

Kline, Nathan S. and Leslie Baer. "Psychotropic Drugs in the Rehabilitation of Mental Patients," in *Rehabilitation Medicine and Psychiatry,* ed. Jack Meislin. Springfield, Ill.: Charles C Thomas Publishers, 1976, pp. 317–346.

Nursing 79, *Nurse's Guide to Drugs.* Hicksville, N.Y.: The Skillbook Company, 1979.

Shader, R. I., and A. DiMascio. *Psychotropic Drug Side Effects.* Baltimore, Md.: Williams and Wilkins Company, 1970.

Solomon, Philip. *Psychiatric Drugs.* New York: Grune and Stratton, Inc., 1966.

appendix C
progress note
terminology guide

Regardless of the setting, therapeutic recreation specialists are usually required not only to file reports and keep necessary administrative and statistical records as indicated earlier, but to provide a report of the special population members' progress in program services. Although there exist wide variations with relation to progress note writing and the value attached to the note, great effort should be made to write a progress note that contains significant information.

Generally speaking, progress notes are written into the record at stated intervals or when necessary, dated and signed by the therapeutic recreator, kept current, and made available to those granted the privilege of review. The initial progress note should include the member's identifying information, initial therapeutic recreation evaluation, and therapeutic recreation objectives and plan of implementation. Subsequent progress notes may include any or all of the following information: member's progress or lack of progress, problems or symptoms which may be affecting progress, changes in plan, devices or adaptive equipment used and the member's proficiency in using them, and evaluations. At the time the member is terminated or discharged, there should be a final evaluation related to the initial one made.

Experience in health settings indicates that some therapeutic recreators incorporate too much irrelevant material and have little command of behavior terminology. Likewise, their comments tend to be confined to physical manifestations; abnormalities and pathological signs are consistently recorded, whereas favorable signs and normal behavior are neglected. A technical vocabulary is essential, but the use of medical terms can be greatly overdone. Abbreviations and hospital slang are to be avoided. Symbols are convenient and proper in certain cases, but they are likely to be used too frequently and indiscriminately. A progress note, to be effective, should be a concise, written account objectively based upon how the member is progressing or responding to provided services.

To assist the student in the development of behavior terminology, a progress note terminology guide is provided below. It is not all inclusive, and it is certainly not a substitute for a dictionary. Hopefully, it will help you as a student to begin to develop precise and exact communication skills that are necessary for progress note writing in a therapeutic recreation program development course.

Appearance
Unkempt
Neat and clean
Takes pride in appearance

Behavior

In Relation to Therapeutic Recreation Activities
Shows interest in activities
Sits, unless directed into activities
Initiates activities
Remembers rules and directions
Shows initial ability to comprehend directions
Moves slowly or sluggishly
Rigid
Hyperactive
Responds inadequately to a situation
Participates easily in activities
Maintains attention span
Conflicts with or defies authority
Reacts to competition
Becomes involved (enjoys the activity, desires to win, etc.)
Reacts to winning or losing

In Relation to Other Patients and/or Personnel
Tries to be friendly with others
Attempts to manipulate others
Is withdrawn
Seeks attention
Forms specific friendships
Forms relationships with the rest of the group

In Relation to Emotional Behavior and Its Appropriateness
Is impatient
Loses temper frequently
Is easily upset
Laughs or smiles at funny comments or events
Giggles or smiles to himself for no apparent reason
Irritable or grouchy
Depressed
Tearful
Shy or aloof
Suspicious
Immature
Hostile
Aggressive
Helpless
Dependent
Overconscientious
Selfish
Autistic
Anxious
Hostile

In Relation to Individual Behavior Characteristics
Hallucinatory
Delusional
Memory and retention
Orientation
Intellectual functioning
Quality of judgment
Affect
Sexual identification
Physical complaints
Quality of associations
Ambivalence
Characteristics of self-image
Frequently tries doors and exits

Conversation
Hypertalkative
Initiates conversation
Quiet, but responds to verbal approach
Refuses to speak
Is able to express himself adequately and appropriately
Talks of death
Exhibits pattern to subject matter
Mentions future plans

Intensity Scaling of Terms Used to Describe Personality*

Verbal Hostility
venomous
abusive
threatening
derisive
derogatory
scornful
sarcastic
argumentative
overcritical
nagging
outspoken
frank
tactful
soft-spoken
complimentary
praising
flattering
mealy-mouthed
apple-polishing
eulogistic

Physical Hostility
murderous
assaultive
destructive
combative
hot-blooded

even-tempered
peaceable
harmless
inhibited
placating
cringing

Hostile Attitudes
malicious
embittered
quarrelsome
surly
provocative
resentful
irritable
grouchy
petulant
grudging
civil
inoffensive
unresentful
agreeable
gentle
gracious
conciliatory
ingratiating
oily
fawning

Anxiety
terrified
panicky
agitated
tremulous
apprehensive
tense
fretful
uneasy
composed
calm
nonchalant
unconcerned
cool
bland
stolid
imperturbable
phlegmatic

Mood
euphoric
elated
frivolous
buoyant
gay
jovial
light-hearted
cheerful

* Source: Arnold H. Buss, "The Scaling of Terms Used to Describe Personality," *Journal of Consulting Psychology*, 21:5 (1957), 361–369.

placid
sober
serious
solemn
mirthless
grave
gloomy
brooding
dejected
disconsolate
despondent
hopeless

Guilt
self-condemning
self-reproachful
remorseful
ashamed
chagrined
regretful
concerned
indifferent
unfeeling
unreformed
cynical
unrepentant
hardened
shameless
conscienceless
unscrupulous
incorrigible

Self-esteem
self-exalting
pompous
conceited
boastful
vain
cocky
confident
self-respecting
modest
unassuming
humble

self-doubting
self-effacing
self-deprecatory
forlorn
self-abasing

Ideation
delusional
ruminative
day-dreaming
fanciful
musing
contemplative
thoughtful
matter-of-fact
literal
unreflective
unimaginative
stolid
vacuous

Impulsiveness
incontinent
reckless
rash
impetuous
excitable
hasty
abrupt
restless
mobile
spontaneous
self-possessed
cool-headed
deliberate
controlled
restrained
staid
overcautious
retarded
sluggish

Flexibility
spineless

yielding
changeable
amenable
adaptable
conventional
persistent
habit-bound
stubborn
persevering
unbending
mulish

Emotional Warmth
overindulgent
doting
affectionate
sentimental
tender
sympathetic
kindly
considerate
cool
unresponsive
detached
unfeeling
hardened
rejecting
frigid

Sociability
intrusive
meddlesome
gregarious
convivial
intimate
comradely
companionable
agreeable
accessible
hesitant
reserved
bashful
reticent
retiring

shrinking
seclusive
withdrawn
solitary
isolated

Dominance
dictatorial
autocratic
high-handed
masterful
forceful
assertive
decisive

cooperative
assenting
conforming
compliant
acquiescent
imitative
deferent
timid
meek
servile

Ambition
grandiose
pretentious

aspiring
enterprising
persistent
eager
self-satisfied
complacent
lackadaisical
indifferent
listless
indolent
apathetic
lethargic

SUGGESTED REFERENCES

Fabun, Don. *Communication* (rev. ed.). Beverly Hills, Calif.: The Glencoe
Press, 1968.

appendix D
voluntary registration program standards of the national therapeutic recreation society

(A Branch of the National Recreation and Park Association)

1. *Therapeutic Recreation Assistant*
   a. Two years of successful full-time paid experience in the therapeutic recreation field.
   b. Two-hundred clock hours in-service training in the therapeutic recreation field.
   c. A combination of *a* and *b* may be substituted.

2. *Therapeutic Recreation Technician I*
   a. Successful completion of the NTRS 750-Hour Training Program for therapeutic recreation personnel.

3. *Therapeutic Recreation Technician II*
   a. Associate of Arts degree from an accredited college or university with an emphasis in therapeutic recreation.
   b. Certification or other proof of satisfactory completion of two academic years of study in recreation with an emphasis or option

in therapeutic recreation *and* current employment in therapeutic recreation.

c. Certification or other proof of satisfactory completion of two academic years of study in a skills area (art, arts and crafts, dance, drama, music, physical education) *and* two years of full-time paid experience in therapeutic recreation.

4. *Therapeutic Recreation Leader*

a. (Provisional and nonrenewable) Baccalaureate degree from an accredited college or university with a major in recreation.

b. Baccalaureate degree from an accredited college or university with a major in therapeutic recreation *or* a major in recreation and an emphasis or option in therapeutic recreation.

c. Baccalaureate degree from an accredited college or university with a major in recreation *and* one year of full-time paid experience in therapeutic recreation.

5. *Therapeutic Recreation Specialist*

a. Master's degree from an accredited college or university with a major in therapeutic recreation *or* a major in recreation and an emphasis or option in therapeutic recreation.

b. Master's degree from an accredited college or university with a major in recreation and one year of full-time paid experience in therapeutic recreation.

c. Baccalaureate degree from an accredited college or university with a major in therapeutic recreation *or* a major in recreation and an emphasis or option in therapeutic recreation *and* three years of full-time paid experience in therapeutic recreation.

d. Baccalaureate degree from an accredited college or university with a major in recreation *and* four years in full-time paid experience in therapeutic recreation.

6. *Master Therapeutic Recreation Specialist*

a. Master's degree from an accredited college or university with a major in therapeutic recreation or a major in recreation *and* an emphasis or option in therapeutic recreation *plus* two years of full-time paid experience in therapeutic recreation.

b. Master's degree from an accredited college or university with a major in recreation *and* three years of full-time paid experience in therapeutic recreation.

c. Baccalaureate degree from an accredited college or university with a major in therapeutic recreation or a major in recreation *and* an emphasis or option in therapeutic recreation *and* six graduate credits in therapeutic recreation *plus* five years in full-time paid experience in therapeutic recreation.

d. Baccalaureate degree from an accredited college or university with a major in recreation *and* twelve graduate credits in therapeutic recreation *plus* six years of full-time paid experience in therapeutic recreation.

Note: There are equivalency registration standards for registration at the Therapeutic Recreation Technician II, Therapeutic Recreation Leader and Therapeutic Recreation Specialist levels. Individuals interested in registration at any of these three levels under equivalency standards should write the National Therapeutic Recreation Society for this information. The entire equivalency registration program is scheduled for termination on October 1, 1980.

appendix E
therapeutic recreation resources

national professional and voluntary organizations and agencies serving special populations*

Academy of Dentistry for the Handicapped, 1240 East Main Street, Springfield, Ohio 45503

Administration on Aging, 330 C Street, S.W., Washington, D.C. 20201

Allergy Foundation of America, 801 2nd Avenue, New York, New York 10017

American Alliance for Health, Physical Education, and Recreation, Unit on Programs for the Handicapped, 1201 16th Street, N.W., Washington, D.C. 20036

American Art Therapy Association, 6010 Broad Branch Road, N.W., Washington, D.C. 20015

American Association for Rehabilitation Therapy, Box 4093, North Little Rock, Arkansas 72216

* For complete listing see Nancy Yakes and Denise Akey, eds., *Encyclopedia of Associations,* Vol. 1, 13th ed. (Detroit, Mi: Gale Research Company, 1979).

American Association of Retired Persons, 420 Lexington Avenue, New York, New York 10017

American Association on Mental Deficiency, 5201 Connecticut Avenue, N.W., Washington, D.C. 20015

American Camping Association, Bradford Woods, Martinsville, Indiana 46151

American Cancer Society, Inc., 219 East 42nd Street, New York, New York 10017

American Coalition of Citizens with Disabilities, 1346 Connecticut Avenue, N.W., Room 817, Washington, D.C. 20036.

American Correctional Association, 4321 Hartwick Road, College Park, Maryland 20740

American Corrective Therapy Association, 4015 Broadway, No. 21, Houston, Texas 77017

American Council on Alcohol Problems, Inc., 119 Constitution Avenue, N.W., Washington, D.C. 20001

American Diabetes Association, 18 East 48th Street, New York, New York 10017

American Federation of the Physically Handicapped, Inc., 1376 National Press Building, Washington, D.C. 20004

American Foundation for the Blind, 15 West 16th Street, New York, New York 10011

American Heart Association, 44 East 23rd Street, New York, New York 10010

American Hospital Association, 840 North Shore Drive, Chicago, Illinois 60611

American Lung Association, 1740 Broadway, New York, New York 10019

American National Red Cross, 17th and D Streets, N.W., Washington, D.C. 20006

American Nurses Association, 10 Columbus Circle, New York, New York 10019

American Nursing Home Association, 1346 Connecticut Avenue, N.W., Washington, D.C. 20006

American Occupational Therapy Association, 600 Executive Boulevard, Suite 200, Rockville, Maryland 20852

American Orthotics and Prosthetics Association, 1440 N Street, N.W., Washington, D.C. 20005

American Park and Recreation Society, 1601 North Kent Street, Arlington, Virginia 22209

American Physical Therapy Association, 1156 15th Street, N.W., Washington, D.C. 20005

American Psychiatric Association, 1700 18th Street, N.W., Washington, D.C. 20000

American Speech and Hearing Association, 9030 Old Georgetown Road, Washington, D.C. 20014

Arthritis and Rheumatism Foundation, 10 Columbus Circle, New York, New York 10019

Association for Children with Learning Disabilities, 4156 Library Road, Pittsburgh, Pennsylvania 15234

Association for the Aid of Crippled Children, 345 East 46th Street, New York New York 10017

Bureau of Education for the Handicapped, U.S. Office of Education, 400 Maryland Avenue, S.W., Washington, D.C. 20202

Children's Bureau, Office of Child Development, 300 Independence Avenue, S.W., Washington, D.C. 20201

Council for Exceptional Children, 1411 South Jefferson Davis Highway, Suite 900, Jefferson Plaza, Arlington, Virginia 22202

Epilepsy Foundation of America, 733 15th Street, N.W., Washington, D.C. 20005

International Council for Exceptional Children, 1201 16th Street, N.W., Washington, D.C. 20036

International Society for Rehabilitation of the Disabled, 219 East 44th Street, New York, New York 10017

Joseph P. Kennedy, Jr., Foundation, 1411 K Street, N.W., Washington, D.C. 20005

Muscular Dystrophy Association of America, 1790 Broadway, New York, New York 10019

National Amputation Foundation, 12–45 150th Street, Whitstone, New York 11357

National Association for Mental Health, 1800 North Kent Street, Arlington, Virginia 22209

National Association for Music Therapy, P.O. Box 610, Lawrence, Kansas 66044

National Association for Retarded Citizens, 2709 Avenue E East, Arlington, Texas 76011

National Association of Activity Therapy and Rehabilitation Program Directors, Box 111, Independence, Iowa 50644

National Association of the Deaf, 814 Thayer Avenue, Silver Spring, Maryland 20910

National Association of the Physically Handicapped, 76 Elm Street, London, Ohio 43140

National Congress of Organizations for the Physically Handicapped, 1627 Deborah Avenue, Rockford, Illinois 61103

National Correctional Recreation Association, Box 7, Moberly, Missouri 65270

National Council on Rehabilitation, 1790 Broadway, New York, New York 10019

National Council on the Aging, 375 Park Avenue South, New York, New York 10010

National Cystic Fibrosis Research Foundation, 521 5th Avenue, New York, New York 10017

National Easter Seal Society for Crippled Children and Adults, 2023 West Ogden Avenue, Chicago, Illinois 60612

National Epilepsy League, 203 North Wabash Avenue, Chicago, Illinois 60601

The National Foundation, 800 2nd Avenue, New York, New York 10017

National Foundation for Neuromuscular Diseases, 250 West 57th Street, New York, New York 10019

National Hemophilia Foundation, 25 West 39th Street, New York, New York 10018

National Institute for Advanced Study in Teaching Disadvantaged Youth, Room 112, 1126 16th Street, N.W., Washington, D.C. 20036

National Institutes of Health, 9000 Rockville Pike, Bethesda, Maryland 20010

National Kidney Disease Foundation, 342 Madison Avenue, New York, New York 10017

National Multiple Sclerosis Society, 257 Park Avenue South, New York, New York 10010

National Paraplegia Foundation, 333 North Michigan Avenue, Chicago, Illinois 60601

National Recreation and Park Association, 1601 North Kent Street, Arlington, Virginia 22209

National Rehabilitation Association, 1522 K Street, N.W., Washington, D.C. 20005

National Society for the Prevention of Blindness, 79 Madison Avenue, New York, New York 10016

National Therapeutic Recreation Society, 1601 North Kent Street, Arlington, Virginia 22209

Pope Foundation, 197 South West Avenue, Kankakee, Illinois 60901

President's Committee on Mental Retardation, U.S. Department of Health, Education, and Welfare, Washington, D.C. 20201

Rehabilitation Service Administration, 330 C Street, S.W., Washington, D.C. 20201

Special Olympics, Inc. 1701 K Street, N.W., Washington, D.C. 20006

United Cerebral Palsy Association, 66 East 34th Street, New York, New York 10036

Also see Committee for the Handicapped, People to People Program, *Directory of Organizations Interested in the Handicapped* (Washington, D.C.: the Committee, Suite 610, LaSalle Building, Connecticut Ave. and L Street, N.W., 20036, 1974).

recreation and competitive sport organizations
serving special populations

American Athletic Association for the Deaf, 3916 Lantern Drive, Silver Spring, Maryland 20902

American Blind Bowling Association, 5338 Queensbridge Road, Madison, Wisconsin 53714

American Junior Bowling Association, Route 2, Box 750, Lutz, Florida 33549

Blind Outdoor Leisure Development, 533 East Main Street, Aspen, Colorado 81611

Indoor Sports Club, 1145 Highland Street, Napoleon, Ohio 43545

National Amputation Foundation (Golf), 12–45 150th Street, Whitestone, New York 11357

National Amputee Skiing Association, 3738 Walnut Avenue, Carmichael, California 95608

National Foundation for Happy Horsemanship for the Handicapped, Box 462, Malvern, Pennsylvania 19355

National Handicapped Sports and Recreation Association, 4105 East Florida Avenue, Denver, Colorado 80222

National Inconvenienced Sportsmen's Association, 3738 Walnut Avenue, Carmel, California 96508

National Track and Field Committee for the Visually Impaired, 4244 Heather Road, Long Beach, California 90808

National Wheelchair Athletic Association, 40–24 62nd Street, Woodside, New York 11377

National Wheelchair Basketball Association, 101 Seaton Building, University of Kentucky, Lexington, Kentucky 40506

National Wheelchair Bowling Association, 2635 Northeast 19th Street., Pompano Beach, Florida 33062

National Wheelchair Softball Association, P. O. Box 737, Sioux Falls, South Dakota 57101

Special Olympics, Inc., 1701 K. Street, N.W., Suite 205, Washington, D.C. 20006

U.S. Deaf Skiers Association, 159 Davis Avenue, Hackensack, New Jersey 07601

periodicals

The following list of periodicals was assembled to give the instructor and the student an idea of the extensive body of literature that concerns itself with rehabilitation. This list does not pretend to be exhaustive. Further, a majority of these periodicals have published articles on recreation and therapeutic recreation in the rehabilitation process.

Aging
American Archives of Rehabilitation Therapy
American Corrective Therapy Journal
American Journal of Art Therapy
American Journal of Corrections
American Journal of Mental Deficiency
American Journal of Nursing
American Journal of Occupational Therapy
American Journal of Orthopsychiatry
American Journal of Psychiatry
American Journal of Psychology
American Journal of Public Health
American Journal of Sociology
Camping Magazine
Challenge: Recreation and Fitness for the Mentally Retarded
Children Today
Community Mental Health Journal
Exceptional Children
Federal Probation
Geriatrics
Hospital and Community Psychiatry
Hospitals
International Rehabilitation Review
Journal of Applied Rehabilitation Counseling
Journal of Counseling Psychology
Journal of Criminal Law, Criminology and Police Science
Journal of Gerontology
Journal of Health and Social Behavior
Journal of Health, Physical Education, and Recreation
Journal of Learning Disabilities
Journal of Leisure Research
Journal of Rehabilitation
Leisurability
Leisure Today
Mental Hygiene

Mental Retardation Abstracts
Mental Retardation News
MR/Mental Retardation
New Outlook for the Blind
Nursing Outlook
Parks and Recreation
Performance
Physical Therapy
Prison Journal
Programs for the Handicapped
Psychological Abstracts
Rehabilitation Literature
Rehabilitation Record
Social Work
Therapeutic Recreation Journal
Today's Child
Today's Health

footnotes

chapter one — footnotes

[1] Charles B. Wilkinson, "The Quality of Fitness," *Parks and Recreation,* 1:2 (1966), p. 149.

[2] William C. Menninger, "Recreation and Mental Health," *Recreation* (November 1948), p. 17.

[3] Virginia Frye and Martha Peters, *Therapeutic Recreation: Its Theory, Philosophy, and Practice* (Harrisburg, Pa.: The Stackpole Co., (1972), pp. 48–127

[4] President's Committee on the Employment of the Handicapped and National Recreation and Park Association, *Recreation and Handicapped People,* Proceedings of National Forum on Meeting the Recreation and Park Needs of Handicapped People, August 15–16, 1974 (Washington, D.C.: U.S. Government Printing Office, n.d.).

[5] "Trustee Margalis Urges Expansion of Leisure Services for Disabled," *Dateline: NRPA,* 2:4 (June-July 1979), p. 10.

chapter two—footnotes

1. National Center for Health Statistics, *Chronic Conditions Causing Activity Limitations,* Public Health Service, U.S. Department of Health, Education, and Welfare, Series 10, No. 51 (Washington, D.C.: U.S. Government Printing Office, 1969).
2. Lawrence D. Haber, *Social Security Survey of the Disabled: 1966,* U.S. Department of Health, Education, and Welfare Reports No. 2, 3, and 6 (Washington, D.C.: U.S. Government Printing Office, 1968-69).
3. President's Committee on Employment of the Handicapped, *One In Eleven Handicapped Adults In America* (Washington, D.C.: U.S. Government Printing Office, 1975), pp. 1-3.
4. "The Broad Picture," *The Coalition,* 1:2 (Fall 1977), p. 1.
5. Myra MacPherson, "America's New Militants," *The Atlanta Journal and Constitution,* May 15, 1977, Sec. D, p. 20.
6. Terri Schultz, "The Handicapped, A Minority Demanding Its Rights," *The New York Times,* February 13, 1977, Sec. E, p. 8.
7. MacPherson, "America's New Militants," Sec. D., p. 20.
8. U.S. Bureau of the Census, *Statistical Abstracts of the United States* (Washington, D.C.: U.S. Government Printing Office, 1976), p. 86.
9. "Mentally Ill Americans," *Parade* (October 30, 1977), p. 13.
10. "Elderly Needs Outlined," *The Athens Banner-Herald/Daily News* (Georgia), May 6, 1979, Sec. C, p. 4.
11. U.S. Department of Labor, "Employment Problems of Disabled Persons," *Monthly Labor Review* (March 1977), p. 3.
12. Regional Rehabilitation Research Institute on Attitudinal Legal and Leisure Barriers, *The Invisible Battle: Attitudes Toward Disability* (Washington, D.C.: the Institute, George Washington University, Barrier Awareness Project, n.d.), p. 5.
13. President's Commission on Law Enforcement and Administration of Justice, *The Challenge of Crime in a Free Society* (Washington, D.C.: U.S. Government Printing Office, 1967), p. 160.
14. "U.S. Prison Population Hits All-Time High," *Corrections,* 2 (March 1976), 9-20.
15. Cited in "Crime Study Says Juvenile System Is Found Ineffective," *The Athens Banner-Herald* (Georgia), July 9, 1978, p. 7, col. 1.
16. Association of State Correctional Administrators, *Uniform Correctional Policies and Procedures* (Columbia, S.C.: the Association, 1972).
17. E. H. Muth, "Prison Recreation in 1990," *Parks and Recreation,* 9:9 (1974), pp. 27-29.
18. U.S. Bureau of the Census, "Characteristics of the Low-Income Populations: 1973," *Current Populations Reports* (Washington, D.C.: U.S. Government Printing Office, 1975), pp. 159-162.

[19] National Advisory Commission on Rural Poverty, *The People Left Behind* (Washington, D.C.: U.S. Government Printing Office, 1967).

[20] President's Committee on Mental Retardation, *Mental Retardation: Century of Decision* (Washington, D.C.: U.S. Government Printing Office, March 1976), p. 80.

[21] Clara G. Schiffer and Eleanor P. Hunt, *Illness Among Children* (Washington, D.C.: U.S. Government Printing Office, n.d.).

[22] President's Committee on Mental Retardation, *MR70: The Decisive Decade* (Washington, D.C.: U.S. Government Printing Office, 1970), p. 6.

[23] Office of Mental Retardation Coordination, *Mental Retardation Activities* (Washington, D.C.: U.S. Government Printing Office, 1972), p. 23

[24] President's Committee on Employment of the Handicapped, *One In Eleven*, p. 8.

[25] President's Committee on Employment of the Handicapped, *A Long, Long Way* (Washington, D.C.: U.S. Government Printing Office, 1972), p. 9.

[26] MacPherson, "America's New Militants," p. 20.

[27] U.S. Department of Labor, "Employment Problems," p. 3.

[28] "Handicapped No Longer Act Like It," *The New York Times,* October 2, 1977, Sec. F, p. 6.

[29] Lee Meyerson, "Physical Disability as a Social-Psychological Problem" *Journal of Social Issues,* 4:4 (1948), pp. 2–10.

[30] Mariann Soulek, "A Look At Stigmas and the Roles of Recreators and Physical Educators," *Journal of Physical Education and Recreation,* 46:5 (1975), p. 28.

[31] Beatrice A. Wright, *Physical Disability: A Psychological Approach* (New York: Harper and Row, Publ., 1960).

[32] Edward J. Hamilton "An Examination of the Effects of Selected Integrated Leisure Activities on Able-Bodied Persons' Attitudes Toward the Physically Disabled" (Master's thesis, University of Maryland, College Park, 1978), p. 28.

[33] David Mechanic, *Medical Sociology,* 2nd ed. (New York: The Free Press, 1978), pp. 31–32.

[34] Howard S. Hoyman, "An Ecologic View of Health and Health Education," in *Science and Theory of Health,* eds. Herbert L. Jones, Margaret B. Schutt, and Ann L. Shelton (Dubuque, Io.: Wm. C. Brown Company Publishers, 1966), pp. 8–10.

[35] Hoyman, "An Ecologic View of Health and Health Education," pp. 8–10.

[36] René Dubos, *Mirage of Health: Utopias, Progress, and Biological Change* (New York: Harper and Row, Publishers, 1959), p. 25.

[37] Judith G. Rabkin and Elmer L. Struening, "Life Events, Stress, and Illness," *Science,* 194 (December 3, 1976), pp. 1013–1020.

[38] Barbara Baumann, "Diversities in Conceptions of Health and Physical Fitness," in *Social Interaction and Patient Care,* eds. James K. Skipper, Jr., and Robert C. Leonard (Philadelphia: J. B. Lippincott company, 1965), pp. 206–210.

[39] David Mechanic, "Stress, Illness, and Illness Behavior," *Journal of Human Stress,* 2 (June 1976), pp. 2–6.

[40] Richard A. McGee, "Preface," in *Correctional Institutions,* eds. Robert M. Carter, Daniel Glaser, and Leslie T. Wilkins (Philadelphia: J. B. Lippincott Company, 1972), p. x.

[41] Thorstein Sellin, "Correction in Historical Perspective," in *Correctional Institutions,* pp. 8–16

[42] American Correctional Association, *Manual of Correctional Standards* (Washington, D.C.: the Association, 1966), pp. 6–10.

[43] Ronald G. Caldwell, *Criminology,* 2nd ed. (New York: The Ronald Press Company, 1965), p. 435.

[44] "Texas Prison," ABC-TV 20/20 Productions, New York, July 5, 1979.

[45] Tom Tided, " 'Chain Gangs' Labor on Unshackled," *The Athens Banner-Herald/Daily News,* June 17, 1979, Sec. 1, p. 1.

[46] Cited in "Crime Study Says Juvenile System Is Found Ineffective," p. 7, col. 1.

[47] Jerome M. Rosow, "The Role of Jobs in a New National Strategy Against Crime," *Federal Probation,* (June 1971), pp. 14–18.

[48] President's Task Force on Prisoner Rehabilitation, *The Criminal Of-fender—What Should Be Done* (Washington, D.C.: U.S. Government Printing Office, 1970).

[49] President's Committee, *Mental Retardation: Century of Decision,* p. 7.

[50] President's Committee on Mental Retardation, *Mental Retardation: The Known and the Unknown* (Washington, D.C.: U.S. Government Printing Office, 1976), p. 66.

[51] *Ibid.*

[52] *Ibid,* p. 9.

[53] Richard Conley, *The Economics of Mental Retardation* (Baltimore: Johns Hopkins Press, 1973), p. 27.

[54] President's Committee, *Mental Retardation: The Known and the Unknown,* p. 10.

[55] See J. W. Conroy and K. E. Deer, "Survey and Analysis of the Habilitation and Rehabilitation Status of the Mentally Retarded with Associated Handicapping Conditions." cited in *Mental Retardation: The Known and the Unknown,* pp. 14–15

[56] American Association on Mental Deficiency, *A Manual on Terminology and Classification in Mental Retardation,* 2nd ed., prepared by R. F. Heber, monograph supplement to the *American Journal of Mental Deficiency* (1961).

[57] *Ibid.*

[58] Herbert Grossman, ed., *Manual on Terminology and Classification in Mental Retardation* (Washington, D.C.: American Association of Mental Deficiency, 1973), p. 5.

[59] President's Task Force on the Physically Handicapped, *A National Effort for the Physically Handicapped* (Washington, D.C.: U.S. Government Printing Office, 1970), p. 1.

[60] Laura J. Rief, "Cardias and Normals: The Social Construction of a Disability" (Doctoral dissertation, University of California, San Francisco, 1975).

[61] National Center for Health Statistics, *Use of Special Aids* (Washington, D.C.: U.S. Government Printing Office, 1972), pp. 1–21.

[62] "Trends for the Handicapped," *Trends*, 3rd. qtr. (Arlington, Va.: National Recreation and Park Association, 1974).

[63] *Facts on the Major and Crippling Diseases in the United States Today*, The National Health Education Committee (1971).

[64] Paula Dranov, "A New Drug That Relieves the Pain of Arthritis," *Family Weekly* (January 21, 1979), p. 23.

[65] National Institute of Health, *Neurological and Sensory Disabilities: Estimated Numbers and Cost* (Washington, D.C.: U.S. Government Printing Office, 1973).

[66] Keith Coulbourn, "MCG Helps Epileptics Out of the Closet," *MCG Today*, 8:1 (Spring 1979), pp. 3–9.

[67] Lawrence Galton, "The Miracle of Microsurgery," *Parade* (November 5, 1978), p. 6.

[68] *Consequences—Spinal Cord Injury* (Film). Sponsored by Regional Spinal Cord Injury Center, University of Washington, Seattle (Aspen, Co.: Crystal Productions, 1979).

[69] American Heart Association, *Cardiovascular Diseases in the United States—Facts and Figures* (New York: the Association, n.d.).

[70] Harold S. Diekl and William Dalrymple, *Healthful Living*, 9th ed. (New York: McGraw-Hill Book Company, 1973), p. 282.

[71] American Cancer Society, *Cancer Facts and Figures* (New York: the Society, n.d.), p. 6.

[72] Paula Dranov, "Better Ways to Control Diabetes," *Family Weekly* (April 29, 1979), pp. 23–25.

[73] F. E. Graham and Bonnalie N. Abbot, *Allergies* (No. Pomfret, Vt.: David and Charles, Inc., 1970), p. 17.

[74] American Foundation for the Blind, *Facts About Blindness* (New York: the Foundation, n.d.), p. 5.

[75] *Ibid.*, p. 7.

[76] President's Committee, *A Long, Long Way*, p. 15.

[77] U.S. Office of Education, *Better Education for the Handicapped*, Annual Report (Washington, D.C.: U.S. Government Printing Office, 1970), p. 25.

[78] National Association for Mental Health, *Facts About Mental Illness* (New York: the Association, n.d.).

[79] National Center for Health Statistics, *Health Resource Statistics: Health Manpower and Health Facilities, 1974,* Public Health Service, U.S. Department of Health, Education, and Welfare (Washington, D.C.: U.S. Government Printing Office, 1974).

[80] President's Committee, *A Long, Long Way,* p. 11.

[81] "Mentally Ill Americans," *Parade* (October 20, 1977), p. 13.

[82] National Institute on Alcohol Abuse and Alcoholism, *Facts About Alcohol and Alcoholism* (Washington, D.C.: U.S. Government Printing Office, 1974), p. 15.

[83] "Alcoholism: Age of Enlightenment?," *Medical World News,* 13 (March 17, 1972), p. 6.

[84] "Drinking Generation," *Parade* (November 12, 1978), p. 19.

[85] Indiana State Annual, *Burns,* 22-1052/b.

[86] National Institute, "Facts About Alcohol and Alcoholism," pp. 16-17.

[87] For additional terminology, see *Glossary of Terms in the Drug Culture,* Bureau of Narcotics and Dangerous Drugs, U.S. Department of Justice (Washington, D.C.: U.S. Government Printing Office, 1972).

[88] "Drug Abuse In Billions, 15,000 Lives," *The Indianapolis News,* May 30, 1975, p. 1.

[89] Bureau of Narcotics and Dangerous Drugs, *Drugs Abuse and Law Enforcement Statistics* (Washington, D.C.: U.S. Government Printing Office, 1970).

[90] "The Aged: Rising Challenge To A Nation," *The Chicago Tribune,* September 24, 1978, Sec. 1, pp. 22-23.

[91] *Ibid.*

[92] "The Graying of America," *Newsweek* (February 28, 1977), pp. 50-64.

[93] "The Aged: Rising Challenge To A Nation," p. 21.

chapter three—footnotes

[1] Federal Programs Advisory Service, *Handicapped Requirement Handbook* (Washington, D.C.: the Service, 1978), Appendix III: c:i.

[2] John Conrad, *Crime and Its Correction: An Introductory Survey of Attitudes and Practices* (Berkeley: University of California Press, 1965).

[3] President's Commission on Law Enforcement and Administration of Justice, *The Challenge of Crime in a Free Society* (Washington, D.C.: U.S. Government Printing Office, 1967).

[4] A partial listing of voluntary organizations and their addresses is found in Appendix E.

[5] A partial listing of professional health and correctional organizations and their addresses is found in Appendix E.

⁶ Adapted from the American Correctional Association, *Manual of Correctional Standards,* 3rd. ed. (College Park, Md.: the Association, 1966); the President's Committee on Law Enforcement and Administration of Justice, *Task Force Report: Corrections* (Washington D.C.: U.S. Government Printing Office, 1967); and Elmer H. Johnson, *Crime, Correction, and Society,* (Homewood, II.: The Dorsey Press, 1978), pp. 553–559.

⁷ National Center for Health Statistics, *Health Resource Statistics, 1975,* Public Health Service, U.S. Department of Health, Education, and Welfare (Washington, D.C.: U.S. Government Printing Office, 1976), p. 3.

⁸ Maryland Y. Pennell and David B. Hoover, *Health Manpower Source Book 21,* Public Health Service Publication No. 263 (Washington, D.C.: U.S. Government Printing Office, 1970) p. 35.

⁹ "Toward a Comprehensive Health Policy for the 1970's," *A White Paper* (Washington, D.C.: U.S. Government Printing Office, 1971), pp. 38–43.

¹⁰ Peter J. Verhoven, "Needed: 18,000 Therapeutic Recreation Service Personnel by 1980," *Therapeutic Recreation Journal,* 3:1 (1969), pp. 4–7.

¹¹ National Center for Health Statistics, *Health Resources Statistics: Health Manpower and Health Facilities, 1975,* Public Health Service, U.S. Department of Health, Education, and Welfare (Washington, D.C.: U.S. Government Printing Office, 1976), p. 11.

¹² Job titles and descriptions are adapted from National Center for Health Statistics, *Health Resources Statistics, 1975.*

¹³ Job descriptions are adapted from Caldwell, *Criminology,* pp. 572–579, 678–680, 682, and American Correctional Association, *Manual of Correctional Standards,* pp. 99–104, 119–123, 155–159, 314–315.

¹⁴ U.S. Bureau of the Census, *Statistical Abstract of the United States: 1970* (Washington, D.C.: U.S. Government Printing Office, 1971), p. 149.

¹⁵ *Delinquent Children: A Survey,* Children's Bureau Statistical Series No. 86 (Washington, D.C.: U.S. Government Printing Office, 1967), p. 7.

¹⁶ National Center for Health Statistics, *Health Resources Statistics, 1975,* p. 329.

¹⁷ Adapted from National Center for Health Statistics, *Health Resources Statistics, 1975,* pp. 377–380, 389–499.

¹⁸ Malcolm T. MacEachern, *Hospital Organization and Management,* 3rd ed. (Chicago: Physicians Record Company, 1957), pp. 34–35.

¹⁹ Caldwell, *Criminology,* p. 493.

²⁰ Thorsten Sellin, "Penal Institutions," *Encyclopedia of the Social Sciences* 1934 (1935), pp. 12, 57–64.

²¹ Johnson, Crime, Correction, and Society, p. 370.

²² Larry L. Neal, "Manpower Needs in the Correctional Field," *Therapeutic Recreation Journal,* 6:3 (1972), p. 125.

²³ Caldwell, *Criminology,* pp. 568–572.

²⁴ Johnson, *Crime, Correction, and Society,* p. 331.

[25] Adapted from American Correctional Association, *Manual of Correctional Standards,* and President's Commission, *Task Force Report: Corrections* (1967).

[26] U.S. Bureau of Health Manpower Education, *Certification in Allied Health Professions: 1971 Conference Proceedings* (Washington, D.C.: U.S. Government Printing Office, 1972), p. 8.

[27] National Center for Health Statistics, *Health Resources Statistics, 1975,* p. 529.

[28] National Center for Health Statistics, *State Licensing of Health Occupations* (Washington, D.C.: U.S. Government Printing Office, 1967).

[29] Requirements for voluntary registration with the National Therapeutic Recreation Society are found in Appendix D.

chapter four—footnotes

[1] Henry E. Sigerist, *A History of Medicine, Volume I* (New York: Oxford University Press, 1951), pp. 154–155.

[2] Quoted in Elliott M. Avedon, "The Public and Therapeutic Recreation," *Recreation in Treatment Centers,* 2 (1963), p. 42.

[3] Virginia Frye, "Historical Sketch of Recreation in the Medical Setting," *Recreation in Treatment Centers,* 1 (1962), p. 40.

[4] Felix Marti-Ibanez, ed., *The Epic of Medicine* (New York: Clarkson N. Potter, Inc., 1962), pp. 51–52.

[5] Elliott M. Avedon, *Therapeutic Recreation Service: An Applied Behavioral Science Approach* (Englewood Cliffs, N.J.: Prentice-Hall, Inc., 1974), p. 8

[6] Richard Kraus, *Therapeutic Recreation Service: Principles and Practices,* 2nd ed. (Philadelphia: W. B. Saunders Company, 1978), p. 16.

[7] Avedon, *Therapeutic Recreation Service,* p. 8.

[8] Exod. 21: 23–24.

[9] Marti-Ibanez, *The Epic of Medicine,* p. 34.

[10] George Rosen, *A History of Public Health* (New York: MD Publications, Inc., 1958), p. 47.

[11] Sigerist, *A History of Medicine,* p. 431.

[12] Marti-Ibanez, *The Epic of Medicine,* p. 64.

[13] Kenneth M. Walker, *The Story of Medicine* (New York: Oxford University Press, 1955), p. 60.

[14] Nathaniel W. Faxon, "A History of Hospitals," in *The Hospital in Modern Society,* eds. Arthur C. Bachmeyer and Gerhard Hartman (New York: The Commonwealth Fund, 1943), p. 5.

[15] Charles M. Frank, *The Historical Development of Nursing* (Philadelphia: W. B. Saunders Company, 1953), pp. 47–53, 71, 68–69.

[16] Avedon, "The Public and Therapeutic Recreation," p. 43.

[17] Marti-Ibanez, *The Epic of Medicine,* p. 130.

[18] Avedon, *Therapeutic Recreation Service,* p. 9.

[19] Marti-Ibanez, *The Epic of Medicine,* p. 130.

[20] Gladys Sellew and M. E. Ebel, *A History of Nursing,* 3rd ed. (St. Louis: C. V. Mosby Co., 19-5), p. 132.

[21] Sigerist, A History of Medicine, p. 223.

[22] Donald A. Read and Walter H. Greene, *Health and Modern Man* (New York: The Macmillan Company, 1973), p. 484.

[23] James O. Hepner and Donna M. Hepner, *The Health Strategy Game* (St. Louis: The C. V. Mosby Company, 1973), p. 9.

[24] Hyman Pleasure, "The Mental Hospitals," in *Rehabilitation Medicine and Psychiatry,* ed. Jack Meislin (Springfield, Il.: Charles C. Thomas Publishers, 1976), p. 234.

[25] B. R. Gearheart, *Administration of Special Education* (Springfield, Il.: Charles C. Thomas Publishers, 1967), pp. 3-14.

[26] The National Council on the Aging, *Senior Centers: Report of Senior Group Programs in America* (Washington, D.C.: the Council, 1975), p. 3.

[27] Thomas G. Morton, *History of Pennsylvania Hospitals, 1751-1895* (New York: Arno Press, 1973), p. 149.

[28] Frye, "Historical Sketch of Recreation," p. 41.

[29] J. Sanbourne Bockovern, "Moral Treatment in American Psychiatry," *Journal of Nervous and Mental Diseases* (August 1956), pp. 167-194.

[30] Gregory Zilboorg, *A History of Medical Psychology* (New York: W. W. Norton, 1941), p. 149.

[31] Norma Dain, *Concept of Insanity in the United States 1789-1865* (New Brunswick, N.J.: Rutgers University Press, 1964), pp. 117-119.

[32] Quoted in Williams R. Dunton, Jr., *Occupational Therapy* (Philadelphia: W. B. Saunders Company, 1915), p. 14

[33] Quoted in William R. Dunton, Jr., "History of Occupational Therapy," in *Occupational Therapy,* 2nd ed., eds. William R. Dunton, Jr. and Sidney Light (Springfield, Il.: Charles C. Thomas Publishers, 1957), p. 8.

[34] *Ibid.*

[35] Florence Nightingale, *Notes on Nursing: What It is and What It Is Not* (New York: D. Appleton and Co., 1873), pp. 95-104.

[36] Sellew and Ebel, *A History of Nursing,* p. 247.

[37] D. Zietz, *Child Welfare* (New York: John Wiley and Sons, Inc., 1959), p. 125.

[38] H. Lende, *What of the Blind* (Chicago: American Foundation for the Blind, 1938), p. 17.

[39] Sellin, "Penal Institutions," 12, pp. 57-64.

[40] An interesting history of the roots of correctional practice is to be found in Johnson, *Crime, Corrections, and Society,* pp. 351-383.

[41] Richard A. McGee, "Preface," in *Correctional Institutions,* eds. Robert M. Carter, Daniel Glaser, and Leslie T. Wilkins (Philadelphia: J. B. Lippincott Company, 1972), p. xiv.

[42] Lillian Summers, "The American Red Cross Program in Recreation in Military Hospitals: A Retrospective View," *Recreation in Treatment Centers,* I (1962), p. 18.

[43] *Ibid.*

[44] R. F. L. Ridgway, "Recreation for Mental Cases," *American Journal of Psychiatry.* 78:7 (1921), pp. 87–95.

[45] William Menninger and Isabelle McCall, cited in Lee E. Meyer, "Recreation and the Mentally Ill," in *Recreation and Special Populations,* 2nd ed., eds. Thomas A. Stein and H. Douglas Sessoms (Boston: Holbrook Press, Inc., 1973), p. 147.

[46] Bertha E. Schlotter and Margaret Svendsen, *An Experiment in Recreation with the Mentally Retarded,* rev. ed. (New York: National Mental Health, 1951).

[47] Frye and Peters, *Therapeutic Recreation,* p. 23.

[48] *Ibid.,* p. 25.

[49] C. C. Bream, Jr., "Rehabilitative Recreation in the Veterans Adminstration," *Recreation in Treatment Centers,* I (1962), p. 36.

[50] Lee E. Meyer, "Recreation and the Mentally Ill," in *Recreation and Special Populations,* p. 152.

[51] *Proceedings of the Annual Congress of the American Prison Association* (Washington, D.C.: the Association, 1912).

[52] American Correctional Association, *Manual of Correctional Standards* (Washington, D.C.: the Association, 1959), pp. 603–604.

[53] Garrett Heyne, "Penal Institutions," *Annals of the American Academy of Political Science,* 313:0 (1957), pp. 71–75.

[54] Harold D. Myer and Charles K. Brightbill, *Recreation Administration: A Guide to Its Practice* (Englewood Cliffs, N.J.: Prentice-Hall, Inc., 1956).

[55] *Standard Minimum Rules for the Treatment of Prisoners and Related Recommendations* (New York: United Nations, Department of Economic and Social Affairs, 1958).

[56] Margaret J. Staples, "A Survey of Recreation in Prisons" (unpublished manuscript, Temple University, 1950), cited in Harry E. Barnes and Negley K. Teeters, *New Horizons in Criminology* (Englewood, N.J.: Prentice-Hall Inc., 1951), pp. 676–677.

[57] Digested from a Master's thesis by Richard Haley, University of Colorado, 1949, cited in Barnes and Teeters, *New Horizons in Criminology,* p. 686.

[58] American Correctional Standards, *Manual of Correctional Standards* (1966), pp. 519–540.

[59] President's Commission, *Task Force Report: Corrections,* pp. 209–210.

[60] "Recreation and Correctional Administration," *Therapeutic Recreation Journal,* 6:3 (1972), pp. 141–142.

[61] Marion Hormachea and Carrol Hormachea, "Recreation and the Youthful and Adult Offenders," in *Recreation and Special Populations,* p. 113.

[62] Arthur Williams, "Notes on History and Theory," in *Recreation: Pertinent Readings — Guideposts to the Future,* ed. Jay B. Nash (Dubuque, Iowa: Wm. C. Brown, Co., 1965), p. 19.

[63] Ira J. Hutchison, Jr., "Recreation and Racial Minorities," in *Recreation and Special Populations,* p. 330.

[64] The National Council on the Aging, *Senior Centers,* p. 2.

[65] *Ibid.,* p. 10.

[66] David C. Park, "Therapeutic Recreation: A Community Responsibility," in *Parks and Recreation* (July 1970), 25.

[67] George D. Butler, *Introduction to Community Recreation* (New York: McGraw-Hill Book Co., 1940), p. 223.

[68] James F. Murphy, "Recreation and the Economically Deprived," in *Recreation and Special Populations,* pp. 300–302.

[69] Richard Kraus, "Providing for Recreation and Aesthetic Enjoyment," in *Governing the City,* eds. Robert H. Connery and Demetrios Caraley (New York: Frederick A. Praeger, Publishers, 1969).

[70] Murphy, "Recreation and the Economically Deprived," p. 302.

[71] John A. Nesbitt, "To Make the Disadvantaged a Part of the American Dream: The Possible Dream," in *Recreation and Leisure Service for the Disadvantaged,* eds. John A. Nesbitt, Paul D. Brown, and James F. Murphy (Philadelphia: Lea and Febiger, 1970), pp. 528–529.

[72] American Recreation Society, *The Hospital Recreation Section: Its History, 1948–1964* (Washington, D.C.: the Society, 1965), p. 8.

[73] Martin W. Meyer, personal communication, March 24, 1975.

[74] Charlotte L. Cox, personal communication, April 15, 1974.

[75] For a well-documented historical account of the NTRS development see David Austin and Benjamin K. Hunnicutt, "The First Twelve Years," *Therapeutic Recreation Journal,* 12:3 (1978), pp. 4–14. For a discussion of some of the problematic areas in the initial article see Benjamin K. Hunnicutt, "A Rejoinder to the Twelve-Year History of the NTRS," in the same issue.

[76] Dorothy A. Mullen, *Recreation in Nursing Homes,* National Recreation and Park Association Management Aids Series No. 88 (Washington, D.C.: the Association, 1970).

[77] George T. Wilson, *Community Recreation Programming for Handicapped Children,* National Recreation and Park Association Management Aids Series No. 96 (Arlington, Va.: the Association, 1974).

78 "Trends for the Handicapped," *Trends,* Park Practice Program, 3rd. Qtr. (Arlington, Va.: National Recreation and Park Association, 1974).

79 "Leisure and Handicapped People," *Park and Recreation,* 12:11 (1977).

80 Gerald S. Fain and Gerald L. Hitzhusen, eds. *Therapeutic Recreation—State of the Art* (Arlington, Va.: National Recreation and Park Association, 1977).

81 Austin and Hunnicutt, "The First Twelve Years," p. 7.

82 Yvonne Washington, personal communication, August 13, 1979.

83 David C. Park, "Professionalism in the '79's," in *Expanding Horizons in Therapeutic Recreation II,* ed. Jerry D. Kelley (Champaign, Il.: Office of Recreation and Park Resources, University of Illinois, 1974), p. 67.

84 Judith Goldstein and Glen E. Van Andel, eds. *National Therapeutic Recreation Society Guidelines for Therapeutic Recreation Service and Residential Facilities* (Arlington, Va.: National Recreation and Park Association, 1978).

85 Jackie Vaughan and Robert Winslow, eds. *Guidelines for Community Recreation for Special Populations* (Arlington, Va.: National Recreation and Park Association, in publication).

86 Kraus, *Therapeutic Recreation Service,* pp. 65–69.

87 President's Committee, *Recreation and Handicapped People.*

88 *Leisure Activity Participation and Handicapped Populations: An Assessment of Research Needs* (Arlington, Va.: National Recreation and Park Association, April 1976).

89 John E. Silson, Elliott M. Cohen, and Beatrice H. Hill, *Recreation in Hospitals: Report of a Study of Organized Recreation Programs in Hospitals and the Personnel Conducting Them* (New York: National Recreation Association, 1959).

90 Ruth Marson, "National Survey of Community Recreation Services to the Mentally Retarded and Physically Handicapped," (Master's thesis, New York University, 1965).

91 *Therapeutic Recreation Curriculum Development Conference,* February 1961 (New York: Comeback, Inc., n.d.).

92 Beatrice H. Hill, *Starting a Recreation Program in a Civilian Hospital* (New York: National Recreation Association, 1952).

93 *Recreation for the Handicapped in the Community Setting* (New York: National Recreation Association, 1965).

94 American Association for Health, Physical Education, and Recreation, *Recreation for the Mentally Ill,* Conference Report (Washington, D.C.: the Association, 1958).

95 American Association for Health, Physical Education, and Recreation, *Guidelines for Professional Preparation for Personnel in Physical Education and Recreation for Handicapped* (Washington, D.C.: the Association, 1973).

[96] American Alliance for Health, Physical Education, and Recreation, *Physical Education and Recreation for Impaired, Disabled, and Handicapped Individuals — Past, Present, and Future* (Washington, D.C.: the Alliance, 1976.)

[97] Daniel Blain and Pat Vosburgh, *Recreational Trends in North American Mental Institutions* (Washington, D.C.: American Psychiatric Association, 1952).

[98] American Psychiatric Association, *Leisure and Mental Health: A Psychiatric Viewpoint* (Washington, D.C.: the Association, 1967).

[99] American Medical Association, *Proceedings of the Committee to Study the Relationship of Medicine with Allied Health Professions and Services*, Unpublished report (Chicago: the Association, 1960).

[100] Jerry D. Kelley, Gary M. Robb, Wood Park, and Kathleen J. Halberg, *Therapeutic Recreation Education: Developing a Competency-Based Entry-Level Curriculum* (Champaign, Il.: Office of Recreation and Park Resource and Department of Leisure Studies, University of Illinois, 1976).

[101] Jerry J. Jordan, William P. Dayton, and Kathryn H. Brill, *Theory and Design of Competency-Based Education in Therapeutic Recreation* (Philadelphia: Department of Recreation and Leisure Studies, Temple University, 1978).

[102] Jerry D. Kelley and others, *Therapeutic Recreation: Guidelines for A Competency-Based Entry-Level Curriculum* (Arlington, Va.: National Recreation and Park Association, 1978).

[103] American Recreation Society, *The Hospital Recreation Section: Its History*, p. 3.

[104] Kraus, *Therapeutic Recreation Service*, p. 75.

[105] Thomas A. Stein, "Therapeutic Recreation Education: 1969 Survey," *Therapeutic Recreation Journal*, 4:2 (1970), pp. 4–7.

[106] Thomas A. Stein, *Report on the State of Recreation and Park Education in Canada and the United States* (Arlington, Va.: National Recreation and Park Association, 1975).

[107] Virginia Frye, "A Philosophical Statement on Therapeutic Recreation Service," *Therapeutic Recreation Journal*, 3:4 (1969), pp. 11–14.

[108] Edith L. Ball, "The Meaning of Therapeutic Recreation," *Therapeutic Recreation Journal*, 4:1 (1970), pp. 17–18.

[109] Park, "Professionalism in the '70's," pp. 63–64.

chapter five — footnotes

[1] Lee E. Meyer, "An Analysis of Views of Recreation Professionals Toward Therapeutic Recreation and Its Professionalization" (Doctoral dissertation, University of North Carolina, Chapel Hill, 1978), p. 151.

[2] David E. Gray, "Recreation: An Interpretation," in *Summary of Research*

Findings (Long Beach, Ca.: California State University, December 12, 1971).

3 Menninger, "Recreation and Mental Health," p. 340.

4 Hospital Recreation Section, *Basic Concepts of Hospital Recreation* (Washington, D.C.: American Recreation Society, 1953), p. 2.

5 Howard A. Rusk, quoted in *Basic Concepts of Hospital Recreation,* p. 7.

6 Paul Haun, *Recreation: A Medical Viewpoint,* eds. Elliott M. Avedon and Francis B. Arje (New York: Teachers College Press, 1965), pp. 55–56.

7 Joseph B. Wolffe, "Recreation, Medicine and the Humanities," in *The Doctors and Recreation in the Hospital Setting* (Raleigh, N.C.: North Carolina Recreation Commission, 1962), p. 21.

8 Martin W. Meyer, "The Rationale of Recreation as Therapy," *Recreation in Treatment Centers I* (1962), p. 24.

9 Mullen, *Recreation in Nursing Homes,* p. 7.

10 Frye and Peters, *Therapeutic Recreation,* p. 40.

11 Edith E. Flynn, "Recreation—A Privilege or a Necessity," *Parks and Recreation* (September 1974), pp. 36, 57.

12 Scout Lee Gunn and Carol Ann Peterson, *Therapeutic Recreation Program Design: Principles and Procedures* (Englewood Cliffs, N.J.: Prentice-Hall, Inc., 1978), p. 8.

13 Meyer, "An Analysis of Views of Recreation Professionals," p. 154.

14 Peter A. Witt, "Therapeutic Recreation: An Outmodel Label," *Therapeutic Recreation Journal,* 11:2 (1977), pp. 39–41.

15 Quoted in Frye and Peters, *Therapeutic Recreation,* p. 41.

16 Frye and Peters, *Therapeutic Recreation,* p. 44.

17 Fred Humphrey, "Therapeutic Recreation and the 1970's: Challenge or Progress?" *Therapeutic Recreation Annual,* 7 (1970), p. 9.

18 Gerald S. O'Morrow, *Therapeutic Recreation: A Helping Profession* (Reston, Va.: Reston Publishing Company, Inc., 1976), p. 121.

19 National Center for Health Statistics, *Health Resources Statistics—1968,* Public Health Service, U.S. Department of Health, Education, and Welfare (Washington, D.C.: U.S. Government Printing Office, 1968), p. 185.

20 Avedon, *Therapeutic Recreation Service,* pp. 26–27.

21 Jay S. Shivers and Hollis F. Fait, *Therapeutic and Adapted Recreational Services* (Philadelphia: Lee and Febiger, 1975), p. 1.

22 Kraus, *Therapeutic Recreation Service,* p. 4.

23 Gunn and Peterson, *Therapeutic Recreation Program Design,* p. 12.

24 *Ibid.,* p. 10–27.

25 O'Morrow, *Therapeutic Recreation,* p. 122.

26 *Ibid.,* pp. 122–123.

27 *Ibid.,* p. 125.

28 *Ibid.,* p. 125

29 Meyer, "An Analysis of Views of Recreation Professionals," p. 150.

[30] Fred W. Martin, "Therapeutic Recreation Service: A Philosophic Overview," *Leisureability*, 1:1 (1974), p. 22.

[31] Ora R. Ackerman, "Medical Recreation," in *Administration of Activity Therapy Service*, ed. Gerald S. O'Morrow, (Springfield, Il.: Charles C. Thomas Publisher, 1966), p. 54.

[32] Goldstein and Van Andel, *National Therapeutic Recreation Society Guidelines*.

[33] Vaughan and Winslow, *Guidelines for Community Recreation*.

[34] Carroll Hormachea, "Philosophy of Recreation in Corrections," *Therapeutic Recreation Journal*, 6:3 (1972), p. 102.

[35] Leigh M. Roberts and John B. McAndrew, "The Role of Recreation Therapy in a Mental Hospital Setting as Seen by the Psychiatrist," *Recreation for the Ill and Handicapped*, 10 (1966), p. 24.

[36] "1976 Mini-Conference on Leisure Counseling," National Recreation and Park Association Congress, Boston, Massachusetts, October 20, 1976. Proceedings published under title *Perspectives in Leisure Counseling*, eds. David M. Compton and Judith E. Goldstein (Arlington, Va.: National Recreation and Park Association, 1977).

[37] For example, Arlin Epperson, Peter A. Witt, and Gerald Hitzhusen, eds. *Leisure Counseling: An Aspect of Leisure Education* (Springfield, Il.: Charles C. Thomas, Publishers, 1977).

[38] For example, Laurel Leff, "Leisure Consultants Are Part Dr. Freud and Part Dear Abby," *The Wall Street Journal*, September 12, 1978, p. 1, 23.

[39] "National Forum on Leisure Counseling," Wilson Lodge, Oglebay Park, Wheeling, West Virginia, March 16–18, 1979. (Sponsored by the Department of Recreation, University of Maryland under a grant from U.S. Bureau of Education for the Handicapped.)

[40] Andrea Farbman Morris, "A Delphi Determination of Levels of Consensus on Selected Definitions of Leisure Counseling" (Master's thesis, University of Maryland, 1978).

[41] For a more therapeutic orientation concerning leisure counseling see Gene Hayes, "Leisure Education and Recreation Counseling," in *Leisure Counseling: An Aspect of Leisure Education*, pp. 208–218.

[42] Chester F. McDowell, Jr., *Leisure Counseling: Selected Lifestyle Processes* (Eugene, Or.: Center for Leisure Studies, University of Oregon, 1976), pp. 9–28.

[43] For a discussion of other models see Gerald Fain, "Leisure Counseling," in *Therapeutic Recreation Management School: First Year Curriculum*, eds. Stephen C. Anderson, Gerald S. O'Morrow, and Morris W. Stewart (College Park, Md.: Department of Recreation, University of Maryland, 1979), pp. 71–86.

[44] Howard Rusk, "Therapeutic Recreation," *Hospital Management* (April 1960), pp. 35–36.

[45] Sidney H. Acuff, "Recreation Counseling as an Aspect of Programming

for the Short-Term Psychiatric Patient," *Recreation in Treatment Centers,* 5 (1966), pp. 5-7.

⁴⁶ Fred Humphrey, "Recreation Counseling for the Institutional Discharge," paper presented before the Forty-sixth National Recreation Congress, Miami Beach, Florida, October 7, 1964.

⁴⁷ *Specifications for Making Buildings and Facilities Accessible* are in the process of being revised and should be published shortly.

⁴⁸ Avedon, *Therapeutic Recreation Service,* p.67.

⁴⁹ Alexander R. Martin, "A Philosophy of Recreation," *Doctors and Recreation in the Hospital Setting,* pp. 5-13

chapter six—footnotes

¹ Abraham H. Maslow, *Motivation and Personality,* 2nd ed. (New York: Harper and Row, 1970), and Sidney M. Jourard, *Personal Adjustment,* 2nd ed. (New York: Macmillan 1963), p. 12.

² Erich Fromm, *The Art of Loving* (New York: Bantam Books, 1936), p. 8

³ E. S. Shneidman, "Classification of Suicidal Phenomena," *Bulletin of Suicidology* (July 1968), pp. 1-9.

⁴ Nathaniel Branden, *The Psychology of Self-Esteem* (Los Angeles: Nash Publishing Corporation, 1969), p. 220.

⁵ Claire Schmais, "Dance Therapy in Perspective," in *Dance Therapy, Focus on Dance VII* (Washington, D.C.: American Association for Health, Physical Education and Recreation, 1974), p. 11.

⁶ See Appendix E for addresses of various sport and activity associations for the handicapped.

⁷ See Holly K. Christian, "An Activity Analysis of Electronic Game Simulators," *Therapeutic Recreation Journal,* 12:2 (1978), pp. 21-25, for an interesting evaluation of these types of games.

⁸ *Prime Times* (Washington, D.C.: ACTION, April-May 1979).

⁹ Avedon, *Therapeutic Recreation Service,* pp. 173-214 and "The Structural Elements of Games," in *The Study of Games,* eds. Elliott M. Avedon and B. Sutton-Smith (New York: John Wiley and Sons, 1971), pp. 419-426.

¹⁰ Carol A. Peterson, "State of the Art: Activity Analysis," in *Leisure Activity Participation and Handicapped Populations: Assessment of Research Needs* (Arlington, Va.: National Recreation and Park Association, 1976), pp. 81-93, and Gunn and Peterson, *Therapeutic Recreation Program Design,* pp. 156-195.

¹¹ Doris Berryman and others, *Prescriptive Therapeutic Recreation Programming: A Computer Based System* (New York: Department of Leisure Studies, New York University, 1976).

¹² Description of other models and activity classifications (Caillois, McIntosh, Kenyon, Petrie, and Overs) can be found in the Suggested References at the end of the chapter.

[13] Gene Hayes, "Activity Analysis: Finger Painting for the Mentally Retarded," *Therapeutic Recreation Journal,* 5:3 (1971), pp. 133-138.

[14] Peterson, "State of the Art: Activity Analysis," p. 82.

[15] Gunn and Peterson, *Therapeutic Recreation Program Design,* p. 158.

[16] *Ibid.,* pp. 158-173.

[17] Avedon, *Therapeutic Recreation Service,* p. 176.

[18] *Ibid.,* pp. 174-176.

[19] P.A.C.E. *Training Manual for Therapeutic Activity Worker Trainee* (Harrisburg, Pa.: Pennsylvania Department of Public Welfare, 1973).

[20] Doris Berryman, "Activity Analysis," in *Therapeutic Recreation Management School: First Year Curriculum,* p. 62.

[21] Avedon, *Therapeutic Recreation Service,* pp. 80-103.

[22] Daniel N. Wiener, "Personality Characteristics of Selected Disability Groups," *Journal of Clinical Psychology,* 4 (1948), pp. 285-290.

[23] The student is referred to the "Activity Value References" at the end of this chapter.

[24] Adapted from the following sources: Gerald S. O'Morrow, "The Whys of Recreation Activities for Psychiatric Patients," in *Therapeutic Recreation State of the Art,* eds. Gerald S. Fain and Gerald L. Hitzhusen (Arlington, Va.: National Recreation and Park Association, 1977), pp. 33-41; Frye and Peters, *Therapeutic Recreation,* pp. 49-98; and Richard Kraus, *Recreation and Related Therapies in Psychiatric Rehabilitation: A Research Study* (New York: Herbert H. Lehman College, The City University of New York, 1972), pp. 23-24.

[25] Haun, *Recreation: A Medical Viewpoint,* p. 53.

[26] Aristotle, quoted in G. Zilboorg, "Historical Perspective," *Psychosomatic Medicine,* 6:3 (1944), p. 3.

[27] Avedon, *Therapeutic Recreation Service,* pp. 162-172.

[28] Christopher R. Edginton and John G. Williams, *Productive Management of Leisure Service Organization* (New York: John Wiley and Sons, 1978), p. 210.

[29] Howard G. Danford and Max Shirley, *Creative Leadership in Recreation,* 2nd ed. (Boston, Allyn and Bacon, Inc., 1970), p. 89.

[30] Avedon, *Therapeutic Recreation Service,* p. 157.

[31] *Ibid.,* pp. 157-158.

[32] Robert Tannenbaum and Warren H. Schmidt, "How to Choose a Leadership Pattern," cited in *Recreation and Special Populations,* pp. 35-36.

chapter seven—footnotes

[1] Gerald S. Fain, Lynn Champion, and Daniel G. Scully, "Employment Status Study of Therapeutic Recreation Personnel," (Unpublished study) Department of Movement, Health, and Leisure, Boston University, Massachusetts 1977, personal copy.

[2] Haun, *Recreation: A Medical Viewpoint,* p. 92.

[3] See pages 68-70 for potential professional disciplines which may be involved.

[4] Fred Humphrey, "Interpreting the Role of Therapeutic Recreation to Other Disciplines," *Therapeutic Recreation Journal,* 2:4 (1968), p. 33.

[5] *Ibid.*

[6] George Tourney, "A History of Therapeutic Fashions in Psychiatry, 1800-1966," *American Journal of Psychiatry,* 124 (1967), pp. 92-104.

[7] Caldwell, *Criminology,* pp. 419-632.

[8] Lucy D. Ozarin, "Moral Treatment and the Mental Hospital," *American Journal of Psychiatry,* 111 (1954), pp. 371-378.

[9] "Patient Participation and Freedom," Proceedings of the Seventh Mental Hospital Institute, *Mental Hospitals,* 7 (1956), pp. 37-49.

[10] Albert Deutsch, *The Mentally Ill in America: A History of Their Care and Treatment from Colonial Times,* 2nd ed. (New York: Columbia University Press, 1949), pp. 91-92.

[11] Ozarin, "Moral Treatment," pp. 371-378.

[12] Donald Pratt, "Making the Environmental Respond to Basic Emotional Needs: A Challenge to the Mental Health Movement," *Psychiatry,* 15 (1952), pp. 179-188.

[13] Alfred H. Stantion and Morris S. Schwartz, *The Mental Hospital: A Study of Institutional Participation in Psychiatric Illness and Treatment* (New York: Basic Books, 1954).

[14] Milton Greenblatt, Richard H. York, and Esther L. Brown, *From Custodial to Therapeutic Patient Care in Mental Hospitals* (New York: Russell Sage Foundation, 1955), p. 7.

[15] Kathleen J. Halberg, "Individualized Planning for the Aging Resident," in *Expanding Horizons in Therapeutic Recreation II,* ed. Jerry D. Kelley (Champaign, Il.: Office of Recreation and Park Resources, University of Illinois, 1973), pp. 107-112.

[16] Larry E. Decker, "Recreation in Correctional Institutions," *Parks and Recreation* (April 1969), p. 31.

[17] Alfred H. Stanton, "Foreword," in John Cumming and Elaine Cumming, *Ego and Milieu: Theory and Practice of Environmental Therapy* (New York: Atherton Press, 1962).

[18] David M. Rioch and Alfred H. Stanton, "Milieu Therapy," *Psychiatry,* 16 (1953), pp. 65-72.

[19] Albert S. Norris, Anthony E. Raynes, and Robert L. Kelley, "Mental Hospitals," in *Handbook of Psychiatry* (2nd ed.), eds. Philip Solomong and Vernon D. Patch (Los Altos, Ca.: Lange Medical Publications, 1971), pp. 143-151.

[20] Morris S. Schwartz, "What is Therapeutic Milieu?" in *The Patient and the Mental Hospitals,* eds. Milton Greenblatt and other (Glencoe, Il.: Free Press, 1957), pp. 130-144.

21 William Cone, "The Therapeutic Community in Action: A St. Louis Experience," in *The Psychiatric Hospital as a Social System*, ed. Albert F. Wessen (Springfield, Il.: Charles C. Thomas Publishers, 1964), pp. 147–165.

22 M. Edelson, *Ego Psychology, Group Dynamics and the Therapeutic Community* (New York: Guno and Stratton, Inc., 1964), p. 93.

23 National Recreation Association, *Sheltered Workshop Project OVR 437* (New York: the Association, 1961).

24 Haun, *Recreation: A Medical Viewpoint*, pp. 22–32.

25 Elliott M. Avedon and Frances B. Arje, *Socio-Recreative Programming for the Retarded* (New York: Bureau of Publications, Teachers College, Columbia University, 1964), pp. 15–18.

26 Thomas A. Stein, "Recreation and Persons with Physical Disabilities," in *Recreation and Special Populations*, pp. 215–224.

27 Kraus, *Therapeutic Recreation Service*, p. 316.

28 Avedon, *Therapeutic Recreation Service*, pp. 100–103.

29 John A. Nesbitt, *New Concepts and New Processes in Special Education*, Report on the National Conference and National Institute on New Models of Community Based Recreation and Leisure Programs and Services for Handicapped Children and Youth, Institute Report 1 (Iowa City, Io.: Recreation Education Program, The University of Iowa, 1978), pp. 40–44.

30 David J. Szymanski and Tom Hoffman, "National Institute on New Models for Community Recreation and Leisure for Handicapped Children and Youth," in *Expanding Horizons in Therapeutic Recreation V*, ed. Gerald Hitzhusen (Columbia, Mo.: Department of Recreation and Park Administration, University of Missouri, 1978), pp. 47–54.

31 Nesbitt, *New Concepts and New Processes in Special Recreation*, p. v.

32 Stein, "Recreation and Persons with Physical Disabilities," p. 197.

33 James F. Murphy and others, *Leisure Service Delivery System: A Modern Perspective* (Philadelphia: Lee and Febiger, 1973), pp. 60–61.

34 It was presumed by Nesbitt that 10 percent of the total population of 10 million had disabling conditions; a total of one-million.

35 Nesbitt, *New Concepts and New Processes in Special Populations*, p. 110.

36 *Ibid.*

37 Donald D. Henkel and others, *Parks, Recreation, and Leisure Services Employment in the Public Sector: Status and Trends* (Arlington, Va.: National Recreation and Park Association, 1977), p. 67.

38 Stein, "Recreation and Persons with Physical Disabilities," p. 197.

39 For a discussion of the relationship between municipal recreators and therapeutic recreators see Kathleen Nolan, "A Comparison of Two Surveys Concerning Relationship Between the Therapeutic Recreator and the Community Recreator," *Therapeutic Recreation Journal*, 12:1 (1978), pp. 40–49.

[40] Fred Humphrey, "Therapeutic Recreation and the 1970's," *Therapeutic Recreation Annual,* 7 (1970), pp. 8–13.

[41] Gary M. Robb, "President Message," *Therapeutic Recreation Journal,* 12:2 (1978), pp. 3–4.

[42] See Gary M. Robb, "Letter to the Editor," *Therapeutic Recreation Journal,* 12:1 (1978), pp. 5–6.

[43] See Ann W. Rowthorn, "An Open Letter to Peter Witt: A Response to His Article, 'Therapeutic Recreation: The Outmoded Label,'" *Therapeutic Recreation Journal,* 12:1 (1978), pp. 7–9.

[44] See Peter A. Witt, "Therapeutic Recreation: The Outmoded Label," *Therapeutic Recreation Journal,* 11:2 (1977), pp. 39–41.

chapter eight—footnotes

[1] Doris Berryman, quoted in Frye and Peters, *Therapeutic Recreation,* p. 41.

[2] *Ibid.,* p. 42.

[3] Ball, "The Meaning of Therapeutic Recreation," pp. 17–18.

[4] *Ibid.,* p. 18.

[5] Frye and Peters, *Therapeutic Recreation,* p. 43.

[6] Gunn and Peterson, *Therapeutic Recreation Program Design,* pp. 59–72.

[7] 334S. *SUPP,* p. 341.

[8] David Mechanic, *Politics, Medicine, and Social Science* (New York: Wiley-Interscience Publishers, 1974), pp. 227–248.

[9] For a discussion about these procedures as they relate to reimbursement see Richard Patterson, "The Development of a Self-Sufficient Therapeutic Recreation Service," in *Expanding Horizons in Therapeutic Recreation III,* eds. Gary Robb and Gerald Hitzhusen (Columbia, Mo.: Department of Recreation and Park Administration, University of Missouri, 1975), pp. 49–52.

[10] Gerald S. O'Morrow, "Dynamic Alternates in Institutional Recreation Service to the Disabled," in *Therapeutic Recreation: Dynamic Alternates,* eds. Viki S. Annand, Andrea F. Morris, David C. Park, and Morris W. Stewart (Columbia, Mo.: Department of Recreation and Park Administration, 1979), pp. 2–21.

[11] Webster's *Third International Dictionary* (Boston: G. and C. Merriam Company, 1967).

[12] Thomas R. Collingwood, "Therapeutic Recreation Relevance to the Rehabilitation Process," *Therapeutic Recreation Annual,* 7 (1971), p. 31.

[13] Joanne Bridges, "Providing Therapeutic Recreation Services, the Two Way Stretch," *Therapeutic Recreation Annual,* 7 (1971), p. 16.

[14] Martha Peters and Peter J. Verhoven, Jr., "A Study of Therapeutic Recreation Services in Kentucky Nursing Homes," *Therapeutic Recreation Journal,* 4:4 (1970), pp. 19–22.

[15] Isaiah Ginsburg, "Therapeutic Recreation: A Modality for Rehabilitation of the Aged," *Therapeutic Recreation Journal,* 8:1 (1974), pp. 42–46.

[16] A partial listing of assessment instruments useful to therapeutic recreation specialists can be found in Gunn and Peterson, *Therapeutic Recreation Program Design,* pp. 332–335, and throughout various sections of AAHPER, *Physical Education and Recreation for Impaired, Disabled and Handicapped Individuals.*

[17] Julius Fast, *Body Language* (Philadelphia: J. G. Lippincott Co., 1970), p. 9.

[18] For a discussion about team practice and the role of the therapeutic recreation specialist see Gerald S. O'Morrow, "Team Practice and the Therapeutic Recreation Specialist," in *Expanding Horizons in Therapeutic Recreation II,* ed. Jerry Kelley (Champaign, Il.: Office of Recreation and Park Resources, University of Illinois, 1974), pp. 47–54.

[19] Frederick J. MacDonald, *Educational Psychology,* 2nd ed. (Belmont, Ca.: Wadsworth Publishing Company, Inc., 1969), p. 253.

[20] Maslow, *Motivation and Personality.*

[21] Erik H. Erikson, *Childhood and Society,* 2nd ed. (New York: W. W. Norton and Company, 1963), pp. 247–274.

[22] E. M. Duvall, *Family Development* (Philadelphia: J. B. Lippincott Co., 1971).

[23] Frye and Peters, *Therapeutic Recreation,* pp. 99–100.

[24] For additional help in writing objectives in behavioral terms see Robert F. Mager, *Preparing Instructional Objectives* (Palo Alto, Ca.: Feason Publishing Co., 1962).

[25] Dolores G. Musgrove, "The Application of System Analysis Theory to Therapeutic Recreation Service," *Therapeutic Recreation Journal,* 5:2 (1961), pp. 60–62.

[26] See NTRS, *Guidelines for Therapeutic Recreation Service in Clinical and Residential Facilities.*

[27] Frye and Peters, *Therapeutic Recreation,* pp. 165–166.

[28] See Suggested References at end of the chapter for various articles concerning evaluation tools.

[29] Anthony G. Linford, "A Criterion-Referenced Approach to Program Evaluation in Therapeutic Recreation Service," *Therapeutic Recreation Journal,* 5:2 (1971), pp. 54–56, 93.

[30] For a discussion of presently used evaluation instruments see Viki S. Annand, "A Review of Evaluation in Therapeutic Recreation," *Therapeutic Recreation Journal,* 11:2 (1977), pp. 42–47, and David M. Compton, "Evaluation," in *Therapeutic Recreation Management School: First Year Curriculum,* pp. 96–105.

chapter nine—footnotes

1 Adapted from American Association for Health, Physical Education, and Recreation, *Guidelines for Professional Preparation for Personnel Involved in Physical Education and Recreation for the Handicapped* (Washington, D.C.: the Association, 1973), pp. 31–43.
2 John Nesbitt, "The Mission of Therapeutic Recreation Specialist: To Help and To Champion the Handicapped," *Therapeutic Recreation Journal,* 4:4 (1970), pp. 2–4, 41–42.
3 Gerald S. O'Morrow, "The Consultant-Consultee Relationship," in *Consultation: Enhancing Leisure Service Delivery to Handicapped Children and Youth,* ed. Judith E. Goldstein (Arlington, Va.: National Recreation and Park Association, 1977), pp. 10–11.
4 Christopher R. Edginton and David M. Compton, "Consumerism and Advocacy: A Conceptual Framework for the Therapeutic Recreator," *Therapeutic Recreation Journal,* 9:1 (1975), p. 27.
5 These job classifications are found primarily in government agencies and are open to any number of specialists who meet the qualifications. More will be said about these titles below.
6 Many of these positions are not therapeutic recreation positions and do not require therapeutic recreation preparation. They are listed only because therapeutic recreation specialists are presently employed in such positions.

chapter ten—footnotes

1 Stephen C. Anderson and Morris W. Stewart, "Therapeutic Recreation Education: 1979 Survey," paper presented before the 1979 Congress for Recreation and Parks, New Orleans, Louisiana, October 29, 1979.
2 *Therapeutic Recreation Curriculum Development Conference.*
3 American Association for Health, Physical Education, and Recreation, *Guidelines for Professional Preparation for Personnel Involved in Physical Education and Recreation for the Handicapped.*
4 Donald Lindley, "Relative Importance of College Courses in Therapeutic Recreation," *Therapeutic Recreation Journal,* 4:2 (1970), pp. 8–12.
5 Edith L. Ball, "Academic Preparation for Therapeutic Recreation Personnel," *Therapeutic Recreation Journal,* 2:4 (1971), pp. 13–15.
6 Carol A. Peterson, "A Systems Approach to Curriculum Development," *Therapeutic Recreation Journal,* 8:3 (1974), pp. 129–137.
7 S. Harold Smith, "Practitioners' Evaluation of College Courses, Com-

petencies and Functions in Therapeutic Recreation," *Therapeutic Recreation Journal,* 10:4 (1976), pp. 152–156.

[8] Kelley and others, *Therapeutic Recreation Education: Guidelines for A Competency-Based Entry-Level Curriculum.*

[9] Jordan, Dayton, and Brill, *Theory and Design of Competency-Based Education in Therapeutic Recreation.*

[10] National Therapeutic Recreation Society, Minutes of the Mid-year Board of Directors Meeting, Champaign, Illinois, February 11 and 12, 1977.

[11] W. J. McGlothlin, *Patterns of Professional Education* (New York: Putnam, 1960), p. 7.

[12] National Recreation and Park Association, *Standards and Evaluative Criteria for Recreation, Leisure Services and Resources Curricula Baccalaureate and Masters Degree Programs* (Arlington, Va.: the Association, March 1977), pp.11–12.

[13] Bryne J. Horton, "The Professor," *Scientific Monthly,* 58:2 (1944), pp. 164–176.

[14] Park, "Professionalism in the '70's," p. 63.

[15] *Ibid.,* p. 64.

[16] "About the NRPA," *Communique,* 4:6 (1973), p. 21.

[17] Charter and By-Laws, National Therapeutic Recreation Society, 1974.

[18] Gary M. Robb, "Report to the Membership—National Therapeutic Recreation Society," Miami, Florida, October 1978.

[19] Robert A. Young, Secretary-Treasurer, The National Correctional Recreation Association, personal communication, October 6, 1974.

[20] William A. Hillman, Jr., "Development of Personnel Standards in Therapeutic Recreation," *Therapeutic Recreation Journal,* 2:4 (1968), pp. 20–22.

[21] William A. Hillman, Jr., personal communication, September 16, 1974.

chapter eleven—footnotes

[1] David C. Park, "The Effects of Future Shock on Our Profession," in *Expanding Horizons in Therapeutic Recreation III,* eds. Gary Robb and Gerald Hitzhusen (Columbia, Mo.: Department of Recreation and Park Administration, University of Missouri, 1976), p. 13.

[2] Personal copies of reports, October 1978.

index

A

Accreditation
 defined, 79
 types of, 80
Ackerman, Ora R., 128
Activity Analysis, defined, 148–51
Activity programming, see Therapeutic recreation service
Activity value references, 161–65
Acuff, Sidney H., 104, 106, 132
Addams, Jane, 93
Aide, defined, 70
Aids in Independent Living, 133
Alcoholism, see Special populations, conditions
Allied health discipline, defined, 67
American Alliance for Health, Physical Education, and Recreation, 104, 110
American Association for Health, Physical Education, and Recreation, 104, 100
 workshop on therapeutic recreation, 111
American Association for Leisure and Recreation Service, 80
American Association for the Advancement of Physical Education, 255
American Association of Homes for the Aged, 80
American Association on Mental Deficiency, 28, 29, 111
American Camping Association, 257
American Cancer Association, 39, 62
American Coalition of Citizens with Disabilities, 11
American Correctional Association, 63, 81 99
American Foundation for the Blind, 41, 62, 101, 111
American Heart Association, 62
American Justice Institute, 60
American Lung Association, 62
American Medical Association, 63, 82, 111
 acknowledgement of recreation, 111

American Nursing Association, 63
American Nursing Home Association, 81
American Occupational Therapy Association, 81
American Park and Recreation Society, 117
American Physical Education Association, 255
American Physical Therapy Association, 63
American Prison Association, 23
American Psychiatric Association, 111
American Red Cross, 62, 96, 97, 103
American Recreation Journal, 104
American Recreation Society, 104, 106, 245
American Standards Association, 133
Anderson, Stephen C., 244
Anti-Tuberculosis Society of Philadelphia, 62
Aristotle, 153
Association for the Aid of Crippled Children, 101
Association for the Blind of New York City, 101
Association of State Correctional Administrators, 12
Assessing, see Therapeutic recreation process
Augustus, John, 95
Avedon, Elliott M., 83, 124, 134, 149, 151, 157, 159, 206

B

Ball, Edith L., 104, 113, 187–88
Basic Concepts of Hospital Recreation, 104, 119
Berryman, Doris L., 148, 150, 187
Bockoven, Sanbourne J., 92
Branden, Nathaniel, 141
Bulletin, The, 104
Bureau of Census, U.S., 10, 51, 71
Bureau of Education for the Handicapped, U.S., 11, 112, 179, 245
Bureau of Narcotics, U.S., 50

Bureau of Prisons, U.S., 57, 77
Brush, Edward N., 93

C

Caldwell, Ronald G., 24
Carter, Rosalynn, 44
Challenge of Crime in a Free Society, The,
    60
Children's Bureau, U.S., 57, 71
Cincinnati Park and Recreation Department,
    102
Clinical Center, National Institutes of
    Health, 75
Collingwood, Thomas R., 161, 193
Cometrack, Inc., 109, 110
Commission on Accreditation of Rehabilita-
    tion Facilities, 81
Commonwealth Fund, 62
Community delivery system models, 179–80
Community Recreation Programming for
    Handicapped Children, 107
Communiqué, The, 107
Compton, David M., 232
Congress, 13th World Congress of Rehabili-
    tation International, 107
Corrections Magazine, 11
Correction process, 61
Correctional service personnel, defined,
    70–71
Correctional systems, administration of, 77
Council for the Advancement of Hospital
    Recreation, 105, 107
Council on Accreditation, NRPA, 80, 245,
    248
Council on Leisure for Special Populations,
    256
Cyclic nature of the therapeutic recreation
    process, *figure,* 173

D

Dain, Norman, 92
Decker, Larry E., 173
Departments, U.S.
    Defense, 57
    Health, Education, and Welfare, 112
    Justice, 57
    Labor, 15
    Treasury, 56
Deutsch, Albert, 172

Disabled, historical attitude toward, 14–19
Disability, defined, 21
Drug abuse, *see* Special populations, condi-
    tions
Drug therapy, 275–83
Dubos, René, 21
Duvall, E. M., 202

E

Eagleton, Thomas, 44
Edalson, M., 175
Edginton, Christopher R., 232
Education for All Handicapped Children Act
    (PL 94–142), 5, 9, 102, 108, 179, 183, 191,
    224, 255
Eisenhower, Dwight D., 56
Emotional disturbance, *see* Special popula-
    tions, conditions
Environmental Protection Agency, 57
Erikson, Erik M., 202
Evaluating, *see* Therapeutic recreation proc-
    ess

F

Facilities
    corrections
        organizational structure, 79
        types of, 76–79
    health
        organizational structure, 75–76
        types of, 72–75
Fain, Gerald S., 169
Fait, Hollis F., 125
Federal Bureau of Investigation, 57
Federal Communication Commission, 57
Federal Security Agency, 56
Federal Trade Commission, 57
Flint Community School, 101
Flynn, Edith E., 121
Ford Foundation, 12, 60, 62
Friends Asylum, 92
Fromm, Eric, 140
Frye, Virginia, 6, 83, 86, 113, 120, 122, 187,
    188, 203, 209

G

Gallaudet College, 91–2
Gallaudet, Thomas H., 92

Goodwill Industries, 101
Gunn, Scout L., 121, 125, 126, 187, 188
Gray, David E., 117
Gossman, Herbert, 29
Greater Kansas City Council on Recreation for the Handicapped, 101
Greenblatt, Milton, 172
Gymnastique Medicinale et Chirurgicale, 93

H

Halberg, Kathleen J., 173
Handicapped, defined, 117
Harrisburg State Hospital, 97
Haun, Paul, 120, 152, 169, 178
Hayes, Gene A., 148
Health, defined, 19
Health-disease, concept of, 8, 19–22
Health service personnel, defined, 67–70
Heber, R. F., 28
Hill, Beatrice, 110
Hippocrates, 36, 88, 89
Hormachea, Carroll, 100, 131
Horton, Bryne J., 250–51
Hospital Recreation, defined, 116
Hospital Recreation Section of the American Recreation Society, 104, 106, 119, 245, 254
Hoyman, Howard S., 20
Human needs, 139–42
Human service models
    community, 178–84
    custodial, 171–73
    education and training, 176–78
    medical-clinical, 169–71
    therapeutic community, 173–76
Human service teams, 71
Humphrey, Fred, 104, 106, 123, 132, 170, 182
Hutchison, Ira J., 100, 106

I

Illness, discussed, 22
Impact, 107
In-patient health facilities by types, *tables,* 74
Indiana State Prison for Adult Males, 256
Indiana Women's Prison, 76
Individual evaluation plan (IEP), 149, 191
Information and Research Utilization Center in Physical Education and Recreation for the Handicapped, 111

Institute of Physical Medicine and Rehabilitation, 119
Itard, Jean, 91

J

JeHarned, 266
Johnson, Lyndon B., 60
Job titles, *see* Therapeutic recreation specialist
Joint Commission on Hospital Accreditation, 81, 107, 190
    Accreditation Council for Facilities for the Mentally Retarded of, 157
Journal of Health, Physical Education, and Recreation, 105

K

Kellogg Foundation, 62
Kennedy, Edward, 32
Kennedy Foundation, 101, 112
Kerner Commission, 102
Klinger, Judith L., 133
Kraus, Richard G., 112, 125

L

Leadership, *see* Therapeutic recreation service
Leadership roles, *see* Therapeutic recreation specialist
Learning disabilities, *see* Special populations, conditions
Legislation, *see* Rehabilitation, legislation
Leisure counseling, 131–32
Leisure and Mental Health: A Psychiatric Viewpoint, 111
Licensure, defined, 79
Lincoln State School and Colony, 97
Lowan, Edward, 133

M

MacEachern, Malcolm T., 75
Hargalis, Joseph H., 6
Marine Hospital Service, 56
Marson, Ruth, 110
Martin, Alexander R., 135
Martin, Fred W., 127
Maslow, Abraham, 140, 141, 202
Materia Medica, 275

McAndrew, Jonh B., 131
McCall, Isabelle, 97
McDowell, Chester F., 132
McGee, Richard A., 95
McGlothlin, W.J., 245
Medical recreation, defined, 116
Medical terminology, 266–274
Medical World News, 49
Medicare, 52, 59, 148, 191
Menninger Clinic, 97
Menniger, William C., 4, 97, 119
Mental illness, *see* Special populations, emotional disturbances
Mental retardation, *see* Special populations, mental retardation
Meyer, Lee E., 117, 121
Meyer, Martin W., 105, 120
Meyerson, Lee, 16
Milwaukee Public Schools, 101
Moral treatment, 171–72
Morris, Andrea, 132
Mullen, Dorothy, 120
Muscular Dystrophy Association, 62, 101
Musgrove, Dolores G., 205
Muth, E. H., 12

N

National Arts Foundation, 11
National Association for Mental Health, 43, 44, 62, 111
National Association for Recreational Therapists, Inc., 105, 106
National Association for Retarded Citizens, 27, 62, 101, 110, 111
National Center for Health Statistics, 31, 44, 66
National Council on Aging, 102
National Correctional Recreation Association, 256
National Education Association, 256
National Forum on Meeting the Recreation and Park Needs of Handicapped People 6, 109, 179
National Health Council, 63
National Institute of Aging, 51
National Institute of New Models for Community and Leisure for Handicapped Children and Youth, 179, 180, 181
National Institute of Neurological Disease and Stroke, 34

National Multiple Sclerosis Association, 101
National Park Service, 31
National Police Academy, 57
National Recreation Association, 102, 109, 245, study of hospitals by, 109–10
National Recreation and Park Association, 6, 80, 106, 108, 109, 117, 133, 179, 181, 183, 239, 245, 254, 255, 258, manpower study, 66
National Rehabilitation Association, 63
National Therapeutic Recreation Society, 63 81, 96, 99, 106, 107, 108, 109, 111, 117, 245, 249, 254–55, 256, 258
National Voluntary Registration of Hospital Recreation Personnel, 105
Nesbitt, John A., 103, 106, 179, 180, 222
New York Auburn Prison, 94
New York Service for Orthopedically Handicapped, 101
New York Times, 11, 15
Nonsensory impairments, *see* Special populations, conditions
Norris, Albert S., 174
Notes on Nursing, 93
Nightingale, Florence, 93
Ninth Southern Regional Institute on Therapeutic Recreation, 113, 122

O

Occupational therapist, 69, 81, 97, 103, 136
Oregon State Division of Corrections, 173
Organization, serving special populations governmental, 56–61
nongovernmental, 61–63
need for, 63
Overs, Robert P., 132

P

Paré, Ambroise, 90
Park, David C., 102, 106, 107, 113, 251, 256
Parks and Recreation, 121
Patients Activity Center for Education, 150
Pennsylvania Hospital for the Insane, 91
Personality, defined, 3
Peters, Martha, 6, 122, 187, 188, 199, 203, 209
Peterson, Carol A., 121, 125, 126, 148, 149, 187, 188
Pharmacopea, 275
Physical Education and Recreation for Im-

paired, Disabled and Handicapped Individuals - Past, Present, and Future, 111
Physicans Desk Refernce, 275
Pinel, Phillippe, 91
Planning, *see* Therapeutic recreation process
Play, 2, 4, 5, 30
Playground Association of America, 100, 109
Pomery, Janet, 101
Prescription, written, 130
Presidential Commission on Assessment of Critical Issues, NTRS, 108, 255, 263
President's Commission on Law Enforcement and Administration of Justice, 11, 57, 99
President's Commission on Mental Health, 11
President's Committee on Employment of the Handicapped, 109, 179
President's Committee on Mental Retardation, 12, 26
President's Task Force on the Physically Handicapped, 30
Prison
  custodial, 23
  philosophies, 22–24
  progressive, 23
  punishment in, 22–24
  rehabilitation in, 22–24
  treatment in, 22–23
Proceedings of the Annual Congress of the American Correctional Association, 99
Professional organizations
  function of, 252
  meaning of, 249–52
  membership in, 63
  participation in, 257–58
  purpose of, 63
  structure of 252–54
Progress note terminology guide, 284–89
Public Health Service, U.S., 10, 56, 124
Punishment, defined, 22

R

Recreation, 110
Recreation
  activity values, 151–56
  activities, 5, 8, 84, 86, 87, 88, 90, 92–93, 97, 99, 101, 102, 151–56
  as an allied health field, 111
  contribution, 2–6
  implications, 6

philosophy of, 118
  value of, 2–6
Recreation Center for the Handicapped, 101
Recreation for special populations defined, 117
Recreation for the handicapped, defined, 117
Recreation for the Handicapped in the Community Setting, 110
Recreation for the Ill and Handicapped, 105
Recreation in Nursing Homes, 107
Recreation in Treatment Centers, 107
Recreation therapists, 104, 124
Recreation therapy, defined, 117
Recreation Therapy Section, AAHPER, 104, 256
Recreation Trends in North American Mental Institutes, 111
Recreative progression, *table,* 187
Registration, defined, 79
Rehabilitation
  Act of 1973, 58, 59, 179, 224
  correctional legislation 60
  correctional services, 65, 70–71
  facilities, 72–75
  health services, 64–66, 75
  historical development
    correctional, 94–95
    health, 84–94
  legislation, 50, 57–60, 66, 103
  organizations, 55–64
  personnel in, 66–71
Rehabilitation-punishment, concept of, 8, 19, 22–25
Rehabilitation Services Administration, 112
Reports and record keeping, 216
Research, *see* Therapeutic recreation service
Ridgway, R. F. L., 96
Robb, Gary M., 106, 108, 183
Roberts, Leigh M., 131
Rockefeller Foundation, 62
Rush, Benjamin, 92
Rusk, Howard A., 119, 132

S

St. Elizabeth's Hospital, 96
San Francisco Park and Recreation Department, 102
Schmas, Claire, 143
Schlotter, Bertha E., 97
Schwab, Lois, 11

Senior Centers, 102
Sensory impairments, *see* Special populations, conditions
Shivers, Jay S., 125
Social Security Administration, 10
Society of Park and Recreation Educators, 117
Soulek, Mariann, 16
Special populations
  attitude toward, 14–19
  conditions
    aging, 51–52
    alcoholism, 49–50
    drug abuse, 50
    emotional disturbance, 43–48
    learning disabilities, 29–30
    mental retardation, 26–30
    nonsensory impairments, 30–41
    sensory impairments, 40–43
    speech defects, 43
  defined, 8
  premises about, 194–95
  prevalence of, 8, 9–14
Specifications for Making Buildings and Facilities Accessible to and Usable by the Physically Handicapped, 133
Speech defects, *see* Special populations, conditions
Starting a Recreation Program in a Civilian Hospital, 110
Statistical Abstracts of the United States, 11
Stein, Thomas A., 112, 181
Stewart, Morris W., 244
Supreme Court, U.S., 189
Svendsen, Margaret, 97
System of Practical Therapeutics, 93

T

Technician, defined, 70
Tissot, Clement-Joseph, 93
Therapeutic Recreation Annual, 107
Therapeutic Recreation
  activities, 142–48
  as a system, 126, 188
  behavioral objectives, 205
  challenge of, 6–7
  clinical affiliation, 134–35
  concept of, 118–22
  competencies, 248–49
  curricula in, 244–46
  curriculum development, 108, 112

  defined, 121
  future of, 261–65
  general education in, 246–47
  historical development, 95–103
  in communities, 100–03, 178–84
  in human service models, 168–184
  in hospitals, 96–98, 169–70, 172–73, 175, 177
  in prisons, 99–100, 173
  job titles, 235–36
  leadership in, 156–61
  occupational opportunities, 236–37
  organizations, 254–57
  personal philosophy, 258–59
  plan, 207–09, 211–12
  professional development, 103–13
  professional education, 108, 112–13, 247–49
  program planning, 209–11
  registration, 81, 107
  research in, 226–27
    need for, 264
  service development in, 96–103
  specialist, *see* Therapeutic recreation specialist
  statements about, 119–21
  training program, 750-hour, 108
Therapeutic Recreation: Its Theory, Philosophy, and Practice, 6, 120
Therapeutic Recreation Journal, 106, 225
Therapeutic Recreation Management School, 108
Therapeutic recreation process
  activities in, 206–07
  activity analysis, 148–51, 206
  assessing in, 192, 195–204
  behavioral objectives in, 205
  benefits of, 186
  components in, 192–216
  concept of, 122–24
  evaluating in, 192, 208–11, 213–15
  failure of, 215–16
  goals in, 191–92, 204–06
  implementing in, 192, 211–13
  instruments used in, 199–201
  judgement in, 203–04
  models, 186–88
  problem identification in, 201–03
  rationship and models, 217
  rationale for, 188–91
  results of, 214–15
  techniques used in, 198–99

Therapeutic Recreation Program Design: Principles and Procedures, 121
Therapeutic recreation service
  activity programming, 129–31
  administration, 133
  competencies needed, 248–49
  concept of, 126
  defined, 124–27
  early models, 127–28
  education and training, 134–35
  employment opportunities, 233–35
  facilities, 133
  leadership in, 131, 156–61
  range of, 128–36
  research in, 135–36
Therapeutic recreation specialist
  attitude of, 198–99
  career as, 220
  intervention of, 124
  job titles, 235–36
  leadership roles, 221–29
  occupational opportunities, 234–35, 236–37
  personal and professional relationships, 229–233
  professional education, 244–49
  selection of a position, 238–241
Therapeutic Recreation: State of the Art, 107
Treatment
  plan, 148, 190–91, 207–08
  team, 201, 208, 215
Trends, 133

U

Unit system, 76
United Cerebral Palsy Association, 62, 101
UNited Nations, 99

V

Verhoven, Peter, 199
Veterans Administration, 98, 104, 174
Veterans Bureau, U.S., 96
Voluntary registration standards, NTRS, 290–92
Volunteers, 135, 147

W

Walnut Street Jail, 76
Whole-person, concept of, 3, 134, 151, 169
Wiener, Daniel, 151
Witt, Peter A., 121
Wolffe, J. B., 120
World War I, 57, 58, 97, 103
World War II, 60, 97, 98, 104, 109
Wyatt vs Stickney, 189

Y

Yearbook, NTRS, 107

Z

Zilboorg, Gregory, 92